LECTURES IN APPLIED MATHEMATICS

Proceedings of the Summer Seminar, Boulder, Colorado, 1960

VOLUME I

LECTURES IN STATISTICAL MECHANICS

By G. E. Uhlenbeck and G. W. Ford with E. W. Montroll

VOLUME II

MATHEMATICAL PROBLEMS OF RELATIVISTIC PHYSICS

By I. E. Segal with G. W. Mackey

VOLUME III

PERTURBATION OF SPECTRA IN HILBERT SPACE

By K. O. Friedrichs

VOLUME IV

THE GENERAL THEORY OF QUANTIZED FIELDS

By Res Jost

LECTURES IN APPLIED MATHEMATICS

Proceedings of the Summer Seminar, Boulder, Colorado, 1960

VOLUME IV

by

RES JOST

MARC KAC, *Editor*

The Rockefeller Institute

The General Theory of Quantized Fields

by

RES JOST

EIDGENÖSSISCHE TECHNISCHE HOCHSCHULE
ZÜRICH, SWITZERLAND

1965
AMERICAN MATHEMATICAL SOCIETY
PROVIDENCE, RHODE ISLAND

The Summer Seminar was conducted, and the proceedings prepared in part, by the American Mathematical Society under the following contracts and grants:

Grant NSF-G12432 from the National Science Foundation.

Contract No. AT(30-1)-2482 with the United States Atomic Energy Commission.

Contract Nonr-3081(00) with the Office of Naval Research.

Contract DA-19-020-ORD-5086 with the Office of Ordnance Research.

Library of Congress Catalog Card Number 64-18129

Printed in the United States of America

Foreword

This is the fourth of a series of four volumes which are to contain the Proceedings of the Summer Seminar on Applied Mathematics, arranged by the American Mathematical Society and held at the University of Colorado for the period July 24 through August 19, 1960. The Seminar was under the sponsorship of the National Science Foundation, Office of Naval Research, Atomic Energy Commission, and the Office of Ordnance Research.

For many years there was an increasing barrier between mathematics and modern physics. The separation of these two fields was regrettable from the point of view of each—physical theories were largely isolated from the newer advances in mathematics, and mathematics itself lacked contact with one of the most stimulating intellectual developments of our times. During recent years, however, mathematicians and physicists have displayed alacrity for mutual exchange. This Seminar was designed to enlarge the much-needed contact which has begun to develop.

The purpose of the Seminar was primarily instructional, with emphasis on basic courses in classical quantum theory, quantum theory of fields and elementary particles, and statistical physics, supplemented by lectures specially planned to complement them. The publication of these volumes is intended to extend the same information presented at the Seminar to a much wider public than was privileged to actually attend, while at the same time serving as a permanent reference for those who did attend.

Following are members of a committee who organized the program of the Seminar:

Kurt O. Friedrichs, Chairman
Mark Kac
Menahem M. Schiffer
George E. Uhlenbeck
Eugene P. Wigner

Local arrangements, including the social and recreational program, were organized by a committee from the University of Colorado, as follows:

Charles A. Hutchinson
Robert W. Ellingwood

The enduring vitality and enthusiasm of the chairmen, and the cooperation of other members of the university staff, made the stay of the participants extremely pleasant; and the four agencies which supplied financial support, as acknowledged on the copyright page, together with the Admissions Committee, consisting of Bernard Friedman, Wilfred Kaplan, and Kurt O. Friedrichs, Chairman, also contributed immeasurably to the successful execution of the plans for the Seminar.

The Seminar opened with an address given by Professor Mark Kac, Department of Mathematics, Cornell University, on the subject "A Mathematician's Look at Physics: What Sets us Apart and What May Bring us Together." Afternoons were purposely kept free to give participants a chance to engage in informal seminars and discussions among themselves and with the distinguished speakers on the program.

Editorial Committee
V. BARGMANN
G. UHLENBECK
M. KAC, CHAIRMAN

Contents

Vorrede

Seit meinen Vorlesungen in Boulder Col. im Jahr 1960 stand ich unter der Verpflichtung, den nun vorliegenden Bericht zu schreiben. Ich versuchte dieser Verpflichtung in den folgenden Jahren, trotz erheblicher anderweitiger Belastung, so gut als möglich nachzukommen. So ist denn das vorliegende Buch in relativ kurzen, weitauseinanderliegenden, Zeitabschnitten entstanden. Die dadurch verursachte Inhomogenität wird auch dem flüchtigen Leser sogleich in die Augen springen. Sie betrifft Uneinheitlichkeiten in der Bezeichnung und äussert sich in Wiederholungen. Ich bitte den Leser für diese und andere Mängel um Nachsicht.

Das Manuskript war zu Ende des Jahres 1962 im wesentlichen abgeschlossen. Spätere Ergebnisse wurden nicht mehr berücksichtigt. Eine popularisierende Uebersicht über neuere Tendenzen der Forschung findet der Leser in einem Referat des Autors über Axiomatic Fieldtheory in Rendiconti della Conferenza internationale di Siena sulle particelle elementari, Società Italiana di Fisica, Bologna 1964, Vol. II, p. 140–144. Mit Nachdruck aber muss hier auf das, nach dieser Zeit erschienene, Buch von R. F. Streater und A. S. Wightman über PCT, *Spin & Statistics, and all that*, W. A. Benjamin, New York 1964, hingewiesen werden. Der Leser wird durch den Vergleich mit diesem Werk erkennen, wie die Gegenstände dieses Buches hätten behandelt werden *sollen*.

Zum Schluss bleibt mir die angenehme Pflicht, den Mitgliedern des Seminars für Theoretische Physik an der ETH für ihre mannigfache Hilfe während der Abfassung des vorliegenden Berichtes herzlich zu danken. Besondern Dank schuldet der Verfasser den Drs. Othmar Steinmann und David Ruelle und schliesslich seinem Assistenten Dr. Klaus Hepp, ohne dessen hingebungsvolle Mitarbeit dieses Buch nie entstanden wäre. Die Gefühle des Autors lassen sich am besten in die Aussage fassen: "Was gut ist an dem Buch stammt von seinen jüngeren Freunden, das Schlechte hat er selbst dazu getan".[1]

September 1964

[1] Vergleiche den Zusatz der Mutter im Brief Nr. 2 von Jacob Burckhardt, Jacob Burckhardt, Briefe Bd. I, Benno Schwabe, Basel 1949.

Introduction

1. In recent years,[1] a new way of looking at the old problems of quantum field theory has developed. This new theory analyzes the notions which are at the basis of all previously analyzed specific models. It can at most give a framework for a concrete theory of existing particles and their corresponding fields. Hence we shall refer to it as the *general theory of quantized fields*, a name we find preferable to the usual one of *axiomatic field theory*.

2. This new theory is necessarily rather abstract. It is, in addition, mathematical to such a degree that one wonders whether it may not exist simply because a few physicists would like to have somewhere a field to practice their limited mathematical skill. We do not think that this is the full reason for its existence and would like to justify this belief.

3. A justification is only possible if one knows something about the classical theory of quantized fields, its history, its failures and successes. Since we are not going to present the classical theory in the main body of the text, we shall in this Introduction give an outline of the historical development of the most important specific model, quantum electrodynamics.

4. The theory of quantized fields has its historical roots at the beginning of quantum theory itself. The black body radiation which led Planck [Pl 1] to the introduction of a universal quantum of action belongs above all to the theory of the electromagnetic field. It is true that Planck himself introduced his revolutionary postulate for a material oscillator in interaction with the electromagnetic field. But a few years later Ehrenfest and Debye applied the quantum postulate directly to the field oscillators, i.e., the Fourier components of the transverse electromagnetic field.[2]

5. As nonrelativistic quantum theory developed to its final form, it was immediately realized by Heisenberg, Born and Jordan [Bn 1] that the reinterpretation of physical observables could not be stopped at the purely mechanical quantities, such as position and momentum of a point electron, but had to include the electromagnetic field too. How this had to be done

[1] See for instance, A. S. Wightman, *Les problèmes mathématiques de la théorie quantique des champs*, [Wi 2].

[2] [Db 1] As to Debye's reluctance to interpret the light quanta as a property of the ether, see [Db 1, p. 1434].

for the field operators was clear by the Ehrenfest-Debye analogy (which goes historically back to Jeans) between field oscillators and material oscillators.

6. It was Dirac [Di 1] who in the memorable year 1927 treated for the first time the quantized electromagnetic field in interaction with material systems. Success and failure were immediate. The success: Dirac was able to derive and therefore to understand rationally the already familiar rules describing the emission and absorption of light. The failure: P. Ehrenfest [Pa 1] immediately pointed out that the theory had to lead to infinities because it contained as an essential quantity the value of the vector potential at the position of the point-electron.

7. Dirac's method of treating the interaction between the electromagnetic field and the atom was perturbation theory, i.e., the expansion of the relevant quantities in a power series in the charge of the electron (or equivalently the fine structure constant 1/137). The first nonvanishing term of such an expansion is, as we know today, in excellent agreement with experiment [He 2*]. In the higher orders, however, Ehrenfest's prediction became true. They are all infinite[3] or at least, as one today says euphemistically, they are indeterminate. The theory did not seem to have any content at all besides the "first order of perturbation theory", and this perturbation theory was the only tool which allowed the extraction of sensible results. The last statement is still essentially true today.

8. But the theory was beset by other difficulties. Dirac's theory of the electron was part of it. It had its own troubles: the states of negative energy. How seriously these were taken is best illustrated by Pauli's corresponding remarks in his truly marvellous article in the Handbuch der Physik, Vol. 24.1: "Ein Versuch, die Theorie in ihrer bisherigen Form zu retten, scheint angesichts dieser Folgerungen" (transitions to states with negative energy) "von vorneherein aussichtslos; · · · ."[4] The theory was, however, brilliantly saved by Dirac's hole theory and the prediction and discovery of the positron [Di 2].

9. Another difficulty arose from observations on the penetrating component of cosmic radiation. These were taken as indicating a breakdown of the first approximation of perturbation theory at energies which, in the laboratory system, were conveniently put at 137 times the mass of the electron, until one discovered that this penetrating component was composed of mesons and not of electrons.

10. It is clear that, while the situation was that unclear, quantum electrodynamics was a happy playground where all sorts of general ideas

[3] See for instance for the self-energy of the electron [Pa 1*, p. 270].

[4] [Pa 1*, p. 245]. For the general situation in quantum electrodynamics see pp. 269 ff.

were produced and at times very impressive and nontrivial mathematical methods could be invented to remedy the situation. Many of the more general and philosophical proposals have survived to this day and are still praised as medicine against all sorts of ills. In the meantime the theory of interaction of electrons with the Maxwell field developed rather slowly until after the Second World War.

11. At that time the idea of renormalization, which has its roots in papers by Heisenberg [Hei 4], Dirac and Weisskopf [Wei 1] from the mid thirties, was vigorously pursued and proved to be effective in bringing order into the disturbing abundance of infinities. It turned out that these could be completely absorbed into three renormalization constants [Kä 1*] of which one could be fixed by convention and the two others by the substitution of the known value of the electron mass and the experimental value of the dimensionless fine structure constant. This very great progress leads to a new, renormalized, perturbation series of which every single term is well defined but of which the convergence properties are unknown.[5] The first few terms of this (formal) power series in the fine structure constant, however, agree with experiment, in all cases checked, to an astonishing and heretofore unknown degree. Renormalized quantum electrodynamics is by far the most successful theory we have today [Pe 1].

12. This very impressive fact, however, does not make the whole situation less strange. We start out from equations which do not make sense. We apply certain prescriptions to their solutions and end up with a power series of which we do not know that it makes sense. The first few terms of this series, however, give the best predictions we know. Things do not become more understandable by the fact that the success of quantum electrodynamics is completely singular. Mathematically it is possible to write down other renormalizable theories. If nature has made use of these it has chosen the coupling constants so big that the renormalized perturbation series is necessarily useless. There are on the other hand very weak interactions in nature, but these seem to correspond to nonrenormalizable theories.

13. The most impressive feature of the development of quantum electrodynamics is the astonishing ability of the theory to survive. Exactly from what this faculty derives is unknown. The analysis of other models can hardly shed light on this circle of problems. It seems to be a pressing task, however, to analyze the general notions which underlie all relativistic quantum field theories. The *general theory of quantized fields* sets itself this task. It does not solve it, however.

[5] See for instance [Kä 1*].

14. The main problem, namely the question of whether the fundamental postulates are only compatible together with a trivial S-matrix (namely $S = I$) and are thus physically inadmissible, seems so difficult that most workers in the field find it hopeless. It was possible to ignore this question till now, because sufficiently many nontrivial and solvable problems could be treated.

15. The structure of the theory is axiomatic; it is founded on a set of basic postulates which are in part highly technical and abstract. This and the fact that intuition hardly can guide us, forces us to use standards of rigor usually frowned upon in theoretical physics.

16. We have to point out, however, that the axioms as they stand are described in this work in a special case, exclude quantum electrodynamics because of the conditions on the energy-momentum spectrum.[6] It is thought that despite this fact they define an interesting structure. The above-mentioned singular character of quantum electrodynamics, however, does not exactly support such a hope.

17. We shall not say anything about possible successes of this new approach, since the reader should be able to form his own opinion after having studied those aspects of the theory which are presented in this volume.

18. A last word may be in order comparing the axiomatic approach of the general theory of quantized fields with other axiomatic enterprises.

A. It is quite clear that this attempt has little in common with ordinary axiomatization in classical mathematics or mathematical physics. It has therefore nothing to do with the sixth problem of David Hilbert [Hi 1*, p. 306] and with the *Grundlagen der Geometrie* of the same author. In all these cases axiomatization formed the keystone of a well-founded building. Here we have to do with the nonexisting foundations of a building which may never be constructed.

B. The axiomatization under discussion could be called a "last resort axiomatization". It could, if one absolutely wants to have a parallel, at most be compared with the axiomatization of set theory. This also was an attempt to separate sense from nonsense. We feel, however, that this comparison is also very much out of balance. It seems to us that the ratio between sense and nonsense favors naïve set theory.

C. Recently other attempts to axiomatize theories of as yet unknown physical significance have been made. The quotation of one of the proposed postulates will suffice to show that they have little in common with the work presented here.

---

[6] See, however, [Wi 3].

"F. *Physical connection.* Physically interpretable functions obtained by analytic continuation from functions describing physical phenomena also describe physical phenomena; they are not mere mathematical chimeras. Specifically, the M functions at all physical-type points of a physical sheet correspond to processes actually occurring in nature. Regarding interpretation, if a simple connection can be set up permitting a consistent interpretation of the quantities appearing in the theory, and also those that could be obtained by analytic continuation, then this interpretation accords uniformly to reality if it accords at all."[7]

19. This book is based on a series of lectures which the author gave in a Summer Seminar of the American Mathematical Society in 1960. Its content is not identical with the content of the Seminar lectures. It has, however, the character of lectures in the following sense:

(a) The material presented is a selection.

(b) We have been rather careless in quoting literature. We connect no scholarly ambition with this work.

(c) The style is determined by our ability or inability to use the English language. It is a mixture of broken English and colloquialism. It may be nerve-wracking for the reader. It was for the author. We hope it is understandable.

[7] Henry P. Stapp [Sta 1, p. 2141]. In all fairness to the author one has to point out that "the mathematical forms" (of the postulates) "will be introduced as they are needed in the proofs". We feel that this is, depending on the standpoint, a rather dangerous or an extremely economical procedure: economical in the sense that you quote things exactly where you need them, and there they mean what they need to mean, neither more nor less.

Chapter I

Mathematical Tools; Space-Time, Spinor Calculus

The mathematical tools necessary for the understanding of the *general theory of quantized fields* differ considerably from the standard equipment of the workshop of classical mathematical physics. They are more abstract, more modern, and simpler. We found it advisable to devote a section to a quick review of the main ideas. No proofs are given. References to the literature are, however, frequent and detailed.

The rest of this introductory chapter deals with the structure of space-time and related problems.

1. **The mathematical tools.**

A. The function spaces [Kö 1*, Sw 2*]. Almost all mathematical tools necessary for the understanding of the later parts of the book are connected with topological linear spaces. Many of these spaces are function spaces. We describe here the more important such spaces.

We are exclusively dealing with spaces of functions over a real finite-dimensional linear space R^N (real affine space). Since the infinite-dimensional spaces are generalizations of R^N, let us briefly recapitulate the main properties of R^N. The elements of R^N are N-tuples of real numbers $x = (x^1, x^2, \cdots, x^N)$. Addition and scalar multiplication are defined as usual. R^N is invariant under nonsingular linear inhomogeneous transformations ($x' = Mx + a$, M nonsingular). These form the automorphisms of R^N. R^N becomes a topological space if we introduce a *basis of neighborhoods* to every point in R^N [Kö 1*, p. 3]. It is even sufficient to introduce such a basis for *one* vector, e.g. $x = 0$, and to define the neighborhoods in any other point by translation ($x' = x + a$ is a translation).

We introduce a basis of neighborhoods of 0 with help of the *norm* [Kö 1*, p. 127]

$$\|x\| = \left(\sum_{k=1}^{N} (x^k)^2\right)^{1/2}. \tag{1}$$

The spheres $\{x \mid \|x\| < \rho\}$ of positive radius ρ then form our basis of neighborhoods. The norm (1) is clearly not invariant under *homogeneous* nonsingular linear transformations ($x' = Mx$). The topology introduced by it, however, is invariant under all automorphisms of R^N [Kö 1*, p. 129].

A set $S \subset R^N$ is *bounded*, if the supremum of $\|x\|$ for $x \in S$ is finite:

(2) $$\sup_{x \in S} \|x\| < \infty.$$

A bounded set is always contained in a sufficiently large sphere. Let ρ be larger than the supremum (2), then $S \subset \{x \mid \|x\| < \rho\}$. We assume the reader is familiar with the notions of *open* and *closed* sets. A *bounded* and *closed* set $S \subset R^N$ is *compact*.

We pass now to complex-valued functions φ over R^N. φ is a mapping of R^N into the complex numbers **C**. **C** is a complex one-dimensional topological linear space. The topology is introduced by the usual norm: the absolute value of the complex numbers. φ is *bounded*, if the image $\varphi(R^N)$ is bounded, that is, if

(3) $$\sup |\varphi(x)| < \infty.$$

The *support* of φ is the smallest closed set in R^N outside of which φ vanishes. We denote it by supp φ. We can formally describe supp φ by

(4) $$\operatorname{supp} \varphi = \overline{R^N - \varphi^{-1}\{0\}},$$

where the bar means closure in R^N. If supp φ is compact then φ vanishes outside a suitable sphere and vice versa.

Again we do not define continuity and differentiability of a function: But we need some simple tools. Let $m = (m_1, m_2, \cdots, m_N)$ be a set of N natural numbers. Then we define

(5) $$D^m = \frac{\partial^{|m|}}{(\partial x^1)^{m_1}(\partial x^2)^{m_2} \cdots (\partial x^N)^{m_N}},$$

where $|m| = \sum_{k=1}^N m_k$ is the order of the differential monomial D^m. Similarly we define

(6) $$x^m = (x^1)^{m_1}(x^2)^{m_2} \cdots (x^N)^{m_N},$$

$|m|$ then is the degree of the monomial x^m.

A function φ is said to be C_α if all its derivatives $D^m\varphi$ for $|m| \leqq \alpha$ exist and are continuous. C_0 contains all continuous functions. We shall sometimes write C for C_0. If, for all m, $D^m\varphi$ exists and is continuous we say that φ is C_∞.

We are now ready to introduce a simple topological linear function space. Let B contain all bounded C functions. We introduce a norm in B by the definition

(7) $$\|\varphi\| = \sup |\varphi|.$$

Now we proceed exactly as in R^N. A basis of neighborhoods of 0 is given by the spheres $\{\varphi \mid \|\varphi\| < \rho\}$, a basis of neighborhoods around a point ψ is obtained by translation $\{\varphi \mid \|\varphi - \psi\| < \rho\}$. Convergence in this topology means uniform convergence in R^N. B is complete: every Cauchy sequence converges to an element in B. Thus B is a *complete linear normed* space. Such a space is a *Banach*-space (B-space) [Kö 1*, Chapter 3].

A set $S \subset B$ is *bounded* if

$$\sup_{\varphi \in S} \|\varphi\| < \infty. \tag{8}$$

This is completely analogous to the definition (2). It is clear what a closed set is. In contrast to the space R^N, a closed bounded set is *not necessarily compact*. Such a set may contain an infinite class $\{A_\alpha\}$ of closed subsets such that any finite subclass $\{A_{\alpha_k}\}$, $k = 1, 2, \cdots, s$, contains common points [Kö 1*, §3.1, (2)]: $\bigcap A_{\alpha_k} \neq \emptyset$ but such that the intersection $\bigcap A_\alpha$ is empty. As an example take the closed unit sphere $\{\varphi \mid \|\varphi\| = 1\}$ and choose for A_α ($\alpha = 1, 2, 3, \cdots$) the sets

$$A_\alpha = \{\varphi \mid \|\varphi\| = 1, \operatorname{supp} \varphi \subset \{x \mid \|x\| \geqq \alpha\}\}. \tag{9}$$

Of some importance to us is a *closed* (linear) *subspace* B_0 of B. B_0 is defined by

$$B_0 = \{\varphi \mid \varphi \in B;\ \lim_{\|x\| \to \infty} \varphi(x) = 0\}. \tag{10}$$

Thus B_0 is again a B-space with the same norm (7).

The notion of B-space is very flexible, and therefore useful. Here is another example. Take all C_l functions for which

$$\|\varphi\| = \max_{|m| \leqq l} \sup (1 + \|x\|^2)^{k/2}\, |D^m \varphi| < \infty. \tag{11}$$

They form again a B-space $B^{k,l}$.

There are, however, other kinds of topological linear spaces with which we have to concern ourselves. Take the intersection $\mathscr{S}$ [Sw 2*, p. 91] of all the spaces $B^{k,l}$. $\mathscr{S}$ is for us the most important topological linear space. It contains all C_∞ functions for which all the expressions

$$p_\kappa(\varphi) = \max_{k + |m| \leqq \kappa} \sup |(1 + \|x\|^2)^{k/2} D^m \varphi|, \qquad \kappa = 0, 1, 2, \cdots, \tag{12}$$

are finite. The expressions $p_\kappa(\varphi)$ are norms and therefore seminorms [Kö 1*, §14.1]. The geometry in $\mathscr{S}$, however, can only be described by the infinite set of seminorms (12). It is impossible to replace these seminorms by one single norm. To replace them, as one might try, by $\sup_\kappa p_\kappa(\varphi)$ is clearly nonsensical, because $\sup_\kappa p_\kappa(\varphi) < \infty$ implies $\varphi = 0$. Thus we have to adjust our notions to this new situation. This is quite simple. We define a basis of neighborhoods $N(\kappa, \epsilon)$ of $\varphi = 0$ by

$$N(\kappa, \epsilon) = \{\varphi \mid p_\kappa(\varphi) < \epsilon\}. \tag{13}$$

It is easy to verify that these neighborhoods (and the ones obtained by translation) define a topology in $\mathcal{S}$ and that $\mathcal{S}$ is complete. From the fact that p_κ is a norm, it follows that the neighborhood $N(\kappa, \epsilon)$ is absolutely convex [Kö 1*, p. 164]. Thus $\mathcal{S}$ is a locally convex complete topological linear space with a countable basis of neighborhoods of 0. Such a space is called a *Fréchet*-space (F-space) because it is metrizable [Kö 1*, §18.2].

Whereas in a B-space we could choose a basis of *bounded* neighborhoods of 0, this is not possible in $\mathcal{S}$. A useful definition of a *bounded* set $S \subset \mathcal{S}$ is the following: S is bounded, if *for all* κ

$$\sup_{\varphi \in S} p_\kappa(\varphi) < \infty. \tag{14}$$

And now we refer to the simple but remarkable fact, that the *closed bounded* sets in $\mathcal{S}$ are *compact* [Sw 2*, p. 91]. This is in marked contrast to the situation in the space B and is also true in R^N. In this respect $\mathcal{S}$ behaves more like a finite-dimensional vector space than B. A space in which the bounded closed sets are compact is called a *Montel*-space (M-space). Thus $\mathcal{S}$ is an FM-space [Kö 1*, §27.2].

Every convergent sequence $\{\varphi_k \mid k = 1, 2, 3, \cdots\}$, is clearly bounded, because $\varphi_k \to \varphi$ implies $p_\kappa(\varphi - \varphi_k) \to 0$ for all κ and therefore $p_\kappa(\varphi_k) \leqq p_\kappa(\varphi - \varphi_k) + p_\kappa(\varphi)$ stays bounded.

Let us summarize what we have said so far about $\mathcal{S}$: $\mathcal{S}$ contains all C_∞ functions which, together with their derivatives, *decrease fast* (namely, faster than $(1 + \|x\|^2)^{-k/2}$ for any k). A sequence of elements $\varphi_k \in \mathcal{S}$ converges in $\mathcal{S}$ to φ if for any m and k, $(1 + \|x\|^2)^{k/2} D^m(\varphi_k - \varphi) \to 0$ uniformly in R^N.

More complicated topological linear spaces than $\mathcal{S}$ will play only a minor role later. Let us mention two: $\mathcal{D}$ and $\mathcal{E}$. $\mathcal{D}$ is a subset of $\mathcal{S}$ and contains all the functions from $\mathcal{S}$ with *compact support* [Sw 1*]. A sequence φ_k converges in $\mathcal{D}$ if for all k supp φ_k is contained in a compact set, independent of k, and if for any m, $D^m\varphi_k$ converges uniformly in R^N. It is easy to characterize the topology in $\mathcal{D}$ by a *noncountable* set of seminorms. $\mathcal{D}$ is not an F-space but is still an M-space [Sw 1*, Chapter III].

$\mathscr{E}$ contains $\mathscr{S}$. The elements of $\mathscr{E}$ are all the C_∞ functions. A sequence $\varphi_k \to \varphi$ in $\mathscr{E}$ if, for any m, $D^m\varphi_k \to D^m\varphi$ uniformly on compact sets. A sequence of seminorms is given by

$$p_{\kappa,K}(\varphi) = \max_{|m|\leq\kappa} \sup_{\|x\|\leq K} |D^m\varphi| \tag{15}$$

for natural numbers κ and K. $\mathscr{E}$ is again an FM-space [Sw 1*, p. 88].

$\mathscr{D}$ is the smallest of the three spaces. $\mathscr{D}$ is, however, *dense* in $\mathscr{S}$ and $\mathscr{E}$ (in their respective topologies). $\mathscr{D}$ is also dense in B_0 introduced earlier.

All these spaces are *separable*: they contain countable dense subsets. For $\mathscr{S}$, $\mathscr{E}$, and B_0 the linear combinations with rational coefficients of the functions

$$x^m \exp(-\tfrac{1}{2}\|x\|^2) \tag{16}$$

form a dense set.

As a tool for later we want to discuss briefly the *tensor product* of function spaces. This *tensor product* is a purely algebraic construction and has nothing or little to do with the topology of the spaces involved [Sw 1*, Chapter IV].

Let R^{N_1} and R^{N_2} be two affine spaces with elements x and y, respectively. Their direct sum $R^{N_1+N_2}$ has as elements the ordered pairs (x, y) and an obvious definition of addition and scalar multiplication. Let $\mathscr{S}_x$, $\mathscr{S}_y$, $\mathscr{S}_{xy}$ be the function spaces over R^{N_1}, R^{N_2} and $R^{N_1+N_2}$. Pairs of functions $\varphi_x \in \mathscr{S}_x$, $\varphi_y \in \mathscr{S}_y$ are then mapped into $\mathscr{S}_{xy}$ by

$$(\varphi_x \otimes \varphi_y)(x, y) = \varphi_x(x) \cdot \varphi_y(y). \tag{17}$$

$\varphi_x \otimes \varphi_y$ is continuous in both factors. The finite linear combination of functions of the form (17) form a linear set in $\mathscr{S}_{xy}$ which is denoted by $\mathscr{S}_x \otimes \mathscr{S}_y$. $\mathscr{S}_x \otimes \mathscr{S}_y$ is *dense* in $\mathscr{S}_{xy}$. This follows from the density of the set described by (16). Similarly $\mathscr{D}_x \otimes \mathscr{D}_y$ is dense in $\mathscr{D}_{xy}$, $\mathscr{S}_{xy}$, $\mathscr{E}_{xy}$ and B_{0xy}.

The notion of *direct sum* of a finite number of topological linear spaces is evident. For later purposes we have to discuss a certain infinite direct sum. Let $\{R^{4n}\}$, $n = 0, 1, 2, \cdots$, be a sequence of real affine spaces, R^0 being the 0-dimensional space containing the vector 0 only. Let $\mathscr{S}_n$ be the $\mathscr{S}$-space corresponding to R^{4n}, $\mathscr{S}_0 = \mathbf{C}$. Let $\underline{\varphi} = (\varphi_0, \varphi_1, \varphi_2, \cdots)$ be a sequence of elements $\varphi_n \in \mathscr{S}_n$, but such that *all but a finite number of components* φ_k *equal zero*. These "finite" sequences form, with a natural definition of linear operations, a linear space

$$\underline{\mathscr{S}} = \bigoplus_{n=0}^{\infty} \mathscr{S}_n. \tag{18}$$

Now we introduce the following notion of convergence into $\underline{\mathscr{S}}$. A sequence $\{\underline{\varphi}^l\}$, $l = 1, 2, 3 \cdots$, converges in $\underline{\mathscr{S}}$, if (a) there is an integer K such that $\varphi^l_k = 0$ for all $k > K$ and if (b) each component φ^l_k converges to φ_k as $l \to \infty$ in the topology of $\mathscr{S}_k$.

It is not hard to characterize a topology in $\underline{\mathscr{S}}$ by a noncountable number of seminorms. $\underline{\mathscr{S}}$ then becomes again a locally convex topological linear space. From the above definition of convergence it is, however, already clear that $\underline{\mathscr{S}}$ is *separable* [Kö 1*, §18.5].

It is interesting, though almost trivial, that $\underline{\mathscr{S}}$ is not only a vector space but also a *topological algebra*. The multiplication is defined by

$$(19) \qquad (\underline{\varphi} \otimes \underline{\psi})_n = \sum_{k=0}^{n} \varphi_{n-k} \otimes \psi_k$$

and is continuous in both factors. This algebra will play some role later.

B. The dual spaces. A continuous linear mapping of a complex (real) topological linear space into $\mathbf{C}(R)$ is called a *functional*. Functionals themselves form a linear space (if addition and scalar multiplication are defined according to common sense). This linear space is the *dual space* of the original space.

The dual space of R^N (with elements x) consists of the linear functions $(p, x) = \sum_{k=1}^{N} p_k x^k$. Its elements are uniquely characterized by the real N-tuples $p = (p_1, \cdots, p_N)$. The dual space of R^N, $(R^N)'$, is again a (real) N-dimensional vector space.

Let us discuss the dual of B_0. A functional μ is continuous if and only if μ is bounded on the unit sphere $\|\varphi\| = 1$ [Kö 1*, §14.6]. We define

$$(20) \qquad \sup_{\|\varphi\|=1} |\mu(\varphi)| = \|\mu\|.$$

The quantity $\|\mu\|$ has all the properties of a norm in the dual space B_0'. B_0' is complete with respect to this norm. Thus B_0' is a B-space. B_0' contains more than the zero element. In fact for any fixed $a \in R^N$

$$(21) \qquad \mu_a(\varphi) = \varphi(a)$$

is a functional. From (20) we conclude that the functionals *separate* B_0: if $\varphi \neq \psi$, then there exists a point a such that $\varphi(a) \neq \psi(a)$ and thus a functional μ, namely the one defined by (21), such that

$$(22) \qquad \mu_a(\varphi) \neq \mu_a(\psi).$$

The functionals μ_a all satisfy $\|\mu_a\| = 1$ and for $a \neq b$, $\|\mu_a - \mu_b\| = 2$. Thus B_0' is not separable, since R^N is not countable.

It can be shown that the general functional in B_0' is uniquely represented by a Stieltjes integral

$$\mu(\varphi) = \int \varphi(x)\, d\mu(x), \tag{23}$$

where $\mu(x)$ is a bounded, complex-valued measure.

The dual of B_0', B_0'' is *not equal* to B_0. B_0 is not a *reflexive space.*

Let us pass to a more important case and discuss the dual of $\mathscr{S}$, $\mathscr{S}'$ [Sw 2*, VII, §4]. The elements of $\mathscr{S}'$ are the *tempered distributions T.* $\mathscr{S}'$ contains clearly nontrivial elements, e.g.,

$$T(\varphi) = (D^m\varphi)(a) \tag{24}$$

for fixed m and a. In a similar fashion to the case above, the elements of $\mathscr{S}'$ separate the elements of $\mathscr{S}$. A distribution $T(\varphi)$ is continuous in φ. This implies that $|T(\varphi)| < 1$ for a suitable neighborhood $N(\kappa, \epsilon)$ defined by (13). Therefore a κ_0 exists such that

$$|T(\varphi)| < 1 \quad \text{if } |p_{\kappa_0}(\varphi)| < K. \tag{25}$$

The value of κ_0 of course depends on T. This in effect means that every tempered distribution T is in the dual of one of the B-spaces characterized by the norms $p_\kappa(\varphi)$. The smallest value of κ_0 could be called the *order of the distribution T.* It follows from this argument that every distribution is bounded on bounded sets $S \subset \mathscr{S}$ (see (14)). Conversely, every linear mapping of $\mathscr{S}$ into **C** bounded on bounded sets is a tempered distribution. This fact suggests the introduction of a topology in $\mathscr{S}'$, defined by the (noncountable) set of seminorms

$$p_S'(T) = \sup_{\varphi \in S} |T(\varphi)| \qquad S \text{ bounded in } \mathscr{S}. \tag{26}$$

With this topology, $\mathscr{S}'$ is complete. Since the topology in $\mathscr{S}'$ is determined by a set of seminorms, $\mathscr{S}'$ is again a locally convex topological linear space. Its dual is $\mathscr{S}$, thus $\mathscr{S}$ is reflexive. A set $S' \subset \mathscr{S}'$ is bounded, if for all bounded sets S

$$\sup_{T \in S'} p_S'(T) < \infty. \tag{27}$$

Bounded sets are relatively compact; thus $\mathscr{S}'$ is an M-space. A set S' is bounded if and only if the orders of the distributions in S' are bounded by κ_0 and if in addition

$$\sup_{p_{\kappa_0}(\varphi) \leq 1,\, T \in S'} |T(\varphi)| < \infty. \tag{28}$$

A set $S' \subset \mathscr{S}'$ is therefore bounded if all its elements are in the dual space of one of the B-spaces characterized by the norms $p_\kappa(\varphi)$ and if they, in addition, form a bounded set in this dual space. Besides the *strong topology* in $\mathscr{S}'$ we can also introduce a *weak topology* defined by the seminorms

(29) $$p''_\varphi(T) = |T(\varphi)|.$$

Correspondingly, a weakly bounded set S' is defined by

(30) $$\sup_{T \in S'} p''_\varphi(T) < \infty \quad \text{for all } \varphi.$$

It is a remarkable (and very general) fact that the *weakly bounded* and the *strongly bounded* sets are *identical* (Mackey's Theorem [Kö 1*, §20, 11.(7)]).

The reason why the strong topology plays a relatively minor role in the actual applications of distributions lies in the following

THEOREM [Sw 1*, p. 74, Theorem XIII]. *Let* $\{T_k\}$, $k = 1, \frac{1}{2}, \frac{1}{3}, \cdots$, *be a sequence of tempered distributions and assume that for every* φ

(31) $$\lim_{k\to 0} T_k(\varphi) = T(\varphi)$$

exists. Then $T(\varphi)$ *is also a tempered distribution and* $T_k \to T$ *in the strong topology. The same holds if the index k varies in a finite-dimensional linear space.*

Thus weak and strong convergence coincide for sequences and for those distributions which are functions of a finite number of continuous parameters.

The continuous functions f which are bounded by a polynomial are elements of $\mathscr{S}'$ in the following sense:

(32) $$T_f(\varphi) = \int f(x)\varphi(x)\, d\underline{x}.$$

Every distribution of the form T_f is called a continuous function. Thus $\mathscr{S}$ is a subset of $\mathscr{S}'$, as are B_0 and $\mathscr{D}$. It is useful to know that $\mathscr{D}$ is *dense* in $\mathscr{S}'$ (in the topology of $\mathscr{S}'$). Since the topology induced on $\mathscr{D}$ by the topology of $\mathscr{S}'$ is weaker than the topology of $\mathscr{D}$, and since $\mathscr{D}$ is separable, we find that $\mathscr{S}'$ is *separable*.

In view of (32) we can interpret distributions as generalized functions and write formally

(33) $$T(\varphi) = \int T(x)\varphi(x)\, d\underline{x}.$$

Another notation frequently used is the scalar product

(34) $$\langle T, \varphi\rangle = T(\varphi).$$

In this notation the duality of $\mathscr{S}$ and $\mathscr{S}'$ is exhibited.

Before we close this subsection we want to introduce the notion of *support of a distribution* $T \in \mathscr{S}'$. We say that T vanishes in an open subset $\mathfrak{B}$ of R^N, if $T(\varphi) = 0$ whenever $\operatorname{supp} \varphi \subset \mathfrak{B}$. The support of T is defined as the smallest set outside of which T vanishes; for this set, which carries T, we write supp T.

Let us briefly mention the duals of the spaces $\mathscr{E}$ and $\mathscr{D}$. We clearly have $\mathscr{E}' \subset \mathscr{S}' \subset \mathscr{D}'$. $\mathscr{E}'$ contains all distributions with *compact support*. The relation of the distributions in $\mathscr{D}'$ to the tempered distributions is slightly more involved. We saw (see (32)) that all continuous functions bounded by const. $\times (1 + \|x\|^2)^{k/2}$ for some value of k are elements from $\mathscr{S}'$. It follows from the definition of $\mathscr{D}$, that *all continuous functions*, irrespective of their growth at $\|x\| = \infty$ are elements from $\mathscr{D}'$. This situation is typical. The tempered distributions are elements from $\mathscr{D}'$ which increase slowly at infinity [Sw 1*, 2*].

A last incoherent remark. A distribution T is *positive* if $T(\varphi) \geqq 0$ for *test functions* φ which satisfy $\varphi(x) \geqq 0$. Positive distributions are *positive measures*, restricted, of course, to the relevant test function space. If they are elements from $\mathscr{E}'$, their support is compact; if they are in $\mathscr{S}'$ then $\mu/(1 + \|x\|^2)^{k/2}$ is bounded for some value of k. Measures from $\mathscr{D}'$ are not restricted [Sw 1*, p. 29].

C. OPERATIONS ON DISTRIBUTIONS. The linear operations on distributions are related to linear mappings of the *test function spaces* $\mathscr{S}$. We therefore begin with a discussion of these mappings. Let $\mathscr{S}_1$ and $\mathscr{S}_2$ be two test function spaces (over two affine spaces R^{N_1} and R^{N_2}) and let A be a linear continuous mapping of $\mathscr{S}_2$ into $\mathscr{S}_1$. As one easily convinces oneself, such a mapping transforms bounded sets in $\mathscr{S}_2$ into bounded sets in $\mathscr{S}_1$. On the other hand, a linear transformation transforming bounded sets into bounded sets is continuous. We have already encountered a special case of this for distributions themselves. This is the case where R^{N_1} is zero-dimensional ($N_1 = 0$) and $\mathscr{S}_1 = \mathbf{C}$.

Now A defines an *adjoint* mapping of $\mathscr{S}'_1$ into $\mathscr{S}'_2$ by the following formula:

$$\langle A'T_1, \varphi_2 \rangle = \langle T_1, A\varphi_2 \rangle, \tag{35}$$

where $T_1 \in \mathscr{S}'_1$ and $\varphi_2 \in \mathscr{S}_2$. One verifies easily that

(a) the left-hand side of (35) defines a distribution in $\mathscr{S}'_2$ or in other words $A'T_1 \in \mathscr{S}'_2$;

(b) the linear mapping of $\mathscr{S}'_1 \xrightarrow{A'} \mathscr{S}'_2$ is continuous;

(c) A' maps bounded sets in $\mathscr{S}'_1$ into bounded sets in $\mathscr{S}'_2$.

The linear continuous mappings from $\mathscr{S}_2$ into $\mathscr{S}_1$ (and from $\mathscr{S}'_1$ into $\mathscr{S}'_2$) again form a linear space. In this linear space one can (in a canonical way), again introduce a locally convex topology. We shall not do this. We shall replace topological considerations, if necessary, by the following theorem of Banach-Steinhaus.

THEOREM [Kö 1*, §15, 13(3)]. *Let* $\{A_n \mid n = 1, 2, 3, \cdots\}$, *be a sequence of linear continuous mappings from* $\mathscr{S}_2$ *into* $\mathscr{S}_1$. *If for all* $\varphi_2 \in \mathscr{S}_2$ *the sequence* $A_n\varphi_2$ *converges, then* $\lim_{n\to\infty} A_n\varphi_2 = A\varphi_2$ *again defines a linear continuous mapping of* $\mathscr{S}_2$ *into* $\mathscr{S}_1$.

REMARKS. 1. Under the conditions of the theorem it follows from (35) that

$$\lim_{n\to\infty} A'_n T_1 = A'T_1.$$

2. The theorem holds mutatis mutandis for a set of mappings which depend on a finite number of continuous parameters.

3. A special case ($\mathscr{S}_1 = \mathbf{C}$) of the Banach-Steinhaus theorem was encountered in subsection B.

EXAMPLES.

1. *Multiplication of a distribution* [Sw 2*, p. 99]. Let $\mathscr{O}_M$ be the space of C_∞ functions which, together with all their derivatives, are bounded by polynomials. Let $\alpha \in \mathscr{O}_M$ and

$$(\alpha\varphi)(x) = \alpha(x)\varphi(x). \tag{36}$$

The mapping $\varphi \to \alpha\varphi$ is linear and continuous from $\mathscr{S}$ into $\mathscr{S}$. Accordingly

$$\langle \alpha T, \varphi\rangle = \langle T, \alpha\varphi\rangle \tag{37}$$

defines a linear continuous mapping from $\mathscr{S}'$ into $\mathscr{S}'$. Formally we write $(\alpha T)(x) = \alpha(x)T(x)$.

2. *Differentiation of a distribution* [Sw 1*, p. 80]. The linear mapping

$$\varphi \to (-1)^{|m|} D^m\varphi \tag{38}$$

is clearly continuous from $\mathscr{S}$ into $\mathscr{S}$. The adjoint mapping

$$\langle D^m T, \varphi\rangle = \langle T, (-1)^{|m|} D^m\varphi\rangle \tag{39}$$

defines the differentiation of a distribution. It follows from the continuity of $D^m T$ that a convergent series of distributions $\sum_{n=1}^{\infty} T_n$ can be differentiated term by term.

As we saw earlier, continuous functions bounded by polynomials form a subset of $\mathscr{S}'$. Now we see that all their derivatives are in $\mathscr{S}'$. The following theorem states that all elements of $\mathscr{S}'$ are obtained in this way.

THEOREM [Sw 2*, p. 95, Theorem VI]. *To every distribution $T \in \mathscr{S}'$ there is an m and a continuous, polynomially bounded function f, such that*

$$T = D^m f.$$

3. *Automorphisms of R^N.* Let $x' = Mx + a$ be a nonsingular mapping of R^N into R^N. This mapping defines a continuous mapping of $\mathscr{S}$ into itself by

$$\varphi_{(a,M)}(x) = \varphi(M^{-1}(x - a)). \tag{40}$$

The adjoint mapping

$$\langle T_{(a,M)}, \varphi\rangle = \langle T, \varphi_{(a,M)}\rangle \tag{41}$$

defines a linear continuous mapping of $\mathscr{S}'$ into itself. All these mappings are homeomorphisms. For (41) we also write $T_{(a,M)}(x) = T(Mx + a)$.

Let $(a(\tau), M(\tau))$ be an analytic one-parameter subgroup and define $\varphi_\tau = \varphi_{(a(\tau),M(\tau))}$. Then

$$\lim_{\tau\to 0} \tau^{-1}(\varphi_\tau - \varphi_0) = \frac{d}{d\tau}\varphi_\tau\Big|_{\tau=0} \tag{42}$$

converges in the topology of $\mathscr{S}$ for every φ and defines therefore a continuous mapping of $\mathscr{S}$ into itself. Thus

$$\lim_{\tau\to 0} \tau^{-1}(T_\tau - T_0) = \frac{d}{d\tau} T_\tau\Big|_{\tau=0} \tag{43}$$

exists too. If the one parameter group is a translation, then (43) defines the first order differentiation in $\mathscr{S}'$.

4. *Fourier transformation* [Sw 2*, Chapter VII]. The Fourier decomposition

$$\varphi(x^1, \cdots, x^N) = (2\pi)^{-N}\int \exp[-i \textstyle\sum p_k x^k]\tilde{\varphi}(p_1, \cdots, p_N)\, d\underline{p} \tag{44}$$

transforms the space $\tilde{\mathscr{S}}$ of fast decreasing C_∞ functions over the dual space $(R^N)'$ of R^N linearly and continuously onto $\mathscr{S}$. We write (44)

$$\varphi = \mathscr{F}\tilde{\varphi} \tag{45}$$

and define the Fourier transform of a distribution by

$$\langle \tilde{T}, \tilde{\varphi}\rangle = \langle \mathscr{F}'T, \tilde{\varphi}\rangle = \langle T, \mathscr{F}\tilde{\varphi}\rangle = \langle T, \varphi\rangle. \tag{46}$$

Formally we find

$$\tilde{T}(p) = (2n)^{-N}\int e^{-i(p,x)}T(x)\, d\underline{x} \tag{47}$$

and

$$T(x) = \int e^{i(p,x)}\tilde{T}(p)\, d\underline{p}, \tag{48}$$

since the Fourier transformation clearly has an inverse.

We discussed in Example 1 the multiplicators of $\mathscr{S}$ and found them to be in $\mathcal{O}_M$. Similarly the multiplicators of $\tilde{\mathscr{S}}$ are in $\mathcal{O}_M$. To the continuous mapping $\tilde{\varphi} \to \alpha\tilde{\varphi}$ with $\alpha \in \mathcal{O}_M$ corresponds, by Fourier transformation, a mapping which we write $\varphi \to S * \varphi$ in $\mathscr{S}$. It is easy to see that this mapping takes the form

$$(S * \varphi)(x) = \int S(y - x)\varphi(y)\, d\underline{y}, \tag{49}$$

where

$$S(x) = (2\pi)^{-N} \int e^{i(p,x)} \cdot \alpha(p)\, d\underline{p}, \qquad \alpha \in \mathcal{O}_M, \tag{50}$$

is a *special* distribution. Let us elaborate slightly more on this point. (49) makes sense for an *arbitrary* distribution $S \in \mathscr{S}'$ and clearly results in a C_∞ function. This C_∞ function and all its derivatives are bounded by polynomials [Sw 2*, p. 95, Theorem VI]. Thus in general $(S * \varphi) \in \mathcal{O}_M$. For the special distributions (50) [where $\alpha \in \mathcal{O}_M$], however, $S * \varphi$ is a continuous mapping of $\mathscr{S}$ into itself. Thus clearly $S * \varphi \in \mathscr{S}$. On the other hand it can be shown that a distribution which has the property that for any $\varphi \in \mathscr{S}$, $S * \varphi \in \mathscr{S}$ defines a continuous mapping of $\mathscr{S}$ into itself, is of the form (50) [Sw 2*, p. 124, Theorem XV; p. 100, Theorem IX]. The special distributions (50) form a linear space $\mathcal{O}'_C$, the space of *rapidly decreasing distributions.* The adjoint mapping to $\varphi \to S * \varphi$ is given by

$$\langle S * T, \varphi\rangle = \langle T, S * \varphi\rangle \tag{51}$$

and can formally be written

$$(S * T)(x) = \int S(x - y)T(y)\, d\underline{y}, \qquad S \in \mathcal{O}'_C. \tag{52}$$

We shall later need the following representation theorem.

THEOREM [Sw 2*, p. 100, Theorem IX]. *A necessary and sufficient condition for $T \in \mathcal{O}'_C$ is that, for any natural number k, T is a finite sum of derivatives of continuous functions each of which stays bounded after multiplication by* $(1 + \|x\|^2)^{k/2}$.

The convolution product $S * T$ defined by (49)–(52) is intimately related to the *regularization* of a distribution. Clearly, all continuous functions which decrease fast for $\|x\| \to \infty$ belong to $\mathcal{O}'_C$ (however, $\exp i\,\|x\|^2$ is also in $\mathcal{O}'_C$). Thus $\mathscr{S}$ and $\mathscr{D}$ are contained in $\mathcal{O}'_C$. Let us choose $\alpha \in \mathscr{D}$. Then

$$(\alpha * T)(x) = \int \alpha(x - y)T(y)\, d\underline{y} \tag{53}$$

is a C_∞ function. According to the comment above $(\alpha * T) \in \mathcal{O}_M$. $(\alpha * T)$ is obtained by *regularization* of T by α. supp$(\alpha * T)$ lies in a certain neighborhood of supp T, which depends on supp α. If we choose now a sequence $\alpha_k \in \mathscr{D}$ such that, in the topology of $\mathscr{S}'$, $\alpha_k(x) \to \delta(x)$ [the Dirac δ-function]. Then $\alpha_k * \varphi \to \varphi$ for all $\varphi \in \mathscr{S}$ and thus $\alpha_k * T \to T$ for all $T \in \mathscr{S}'$. Every distribution from $\mathscr{S}'$ thus appears explicitly as a limit of functions from $\mathcal{O}_M$. Thus $\mathcal{O}_M$ is dense in $\mathscr{S}'$ [Sw 2*, pp. 21 ff.].

D. THE TENSOR PRODUCT OF DISTRIBUTIONS AND RELATED PROBLEMS "THÉORÈME NUCLÉAIRE". In subsection A we introduced the tensor product $\mathscr{S}_x \otimes \mathscr{S}_y$ of two test function spaces. We also remarked that $\mathscr{S}_x \otimes \mathscr{S}_y$ is dense in $\mathscr{S}_{xy}$, the test function space over $R_x \otimes R_y$. Now we want to introduce the tensor product $\mathscr{S}'_x \otimes \mathscr{S}'_y$. Let $T_x \in \mathscr{S}'_x$ and $S_y \in \mathscr{S}'_y$. Then we define $T_x \otimes S_y$ first on $\mathscr{S}_x \otimes \mathscr{S}_y$ by linear extension of

$$(T_x \otimes S_y)(\varphi_x \otimes \psi_y) = T_x(\varphi_x)S_y(\psi_y). \tag{54}$$

A distribution $Q \in \mathscr{S}'_{xy}$ which agrees on $\mathscr{S}_x \otimes \mathscr{S}_y$ with $T_x \otimes S_y$ is clearly uniquely determined, since $\mathscr{S}_x \otimes \mathscr{S}_y$ is dense in $\mathscr{S}_{xy}$. We shall then write $T_x \otimes S_y = Q$.

It is not hard to see that such an extension always exists. Let $\chi \in \mathscr{S}_{xy}$; then

$$\langle T_x, \chi\rangle(y) = \int T(x)\chi(x, y)\, d\underline{x} \in \mathscr{S}_y.$$

Thus $\langle S_y, \langle T_x, \chi\rangle\rangle$ exists and can be shown to be continuous. The distribution so defined agrees on $\mathscr{S}_x \otimes \mathscr{S}_y$ with the values obtained from (54). Thus we find

$$\langle S_y, \langle T_x, \chi\rangle\rangle = \langle T_x, \langle S_y, \chi\rangle\rangle = (T_x \otimes S_y)(\chi). \tag{55}$$

Now we define $\mathscr{S}'_x \otimes \mathscr{S}'_y$ as the finite linear combinations of distributions of the form $T_x \otimes S_y$. It is trivial that $\mathscr{S}'_x \otimes \mathscr{S}'_y$ is dense in $\mathscr{S}'_{xy}$. Already $\mathscr{S}_x \otimes \mathscr{S}_y$ is dense in $\mathscr{S}'_{xy}$ [Sw 1*, Chapter IV].

A much deeper problem is connected with the *multilinear* forms. Let $R^N = \bigoplus_{k=1}^r R^{N_k}$, r finite. Let $\varphi_k \in \mathscr{S}_k$ and let $\mathscr{S}_k$ be the test function space over R^{N_k}. Finally, let $L(\varphi_1, \varphi_2, \cdots, \varphi_r)$ be linear and continuous in each argument φ_k separately. Clearly $L(\varphi_1, \varphi_2, \cdots, \varphi_r)$ can, by linearity, be extended into $\mathscr{S}_1 \otimes \mathscr{S}_2 \otimes \cdots \otimes \mathscr{S}_r$. Again the question arises whether a distribution T in $\mathscr{S}'_{x_1,\cdots,x_r}$ exists which satisfies

$$T(\varphi_1 \otimes \varphi_2 \otimes \cdots \otimes \varphi_r) = L(\varphi_1, \varphi_2, \cdots, \varphi_r). \tag{56}$$

The "théorème nucléaire" of L. Schwartz [Sw 1; Gå 3] guarantees the existence of such a distribution T. Its uniqueness is again trivial.

Finally we want to discuss the dual space to $\underline{\mathscr{S}}$, introduced by (18). $\underline{\mathscr{S}}'$ consists of *all* the sequences $\underline{T} = (T_0, T_1, T_2, \cdots)$, $T_k \in \mathscr{S}'_k$. The scalar product is defined by

$$\langle \underline{T}, \underline{\varphi} \rangle = \sum_k \langle T_k, \varphi_k \rangle. \tag{57}$$

Clearly $\langle \underline{T}, \underline{\varphi} \rangle \to 0$ as $\underline{\varphi} \to 0$ with the notion of convergence defined earlier. $\underline{\mathscr{S}}'$ again forms an algebra if the multiplication is defined by

$$(\underline{S} \otimes \underline{T})_n = \sum_{k=0}^{n} S_{n-k} \otimes T_k. \tag{58}$$

This algebra however will play no role for us later.

E. The Hilbert space [Ac 1*; RN 1*]. The only abstract space we shall encounter is the infinite-dimensional separable Hilbert space $\mathfrak{H}$.

The elementary theory of $\mathfrak{H}$ is so well known that we shall not discuss it here in any detail. We restrict ourselves to reminding the reader of some facts about *unbounded operators* and the spectral resolution of continuous *abelian groups of unitary operators*.

The elements of $\mathfrak{H}$ are denoted by $\Phi, \Psi, \cdots$; the positive symmetric scalar product (linear in the *second* factor) by (Φ, Ψ). $\|\Phi\| = (\Phi, \Phi)^{1/2}$ is the norm in $\mathfrak{H}$.

The functionals (continuous linear forms) in $\mathfrak{H}$ are exactly the scalar products $l(\Phi) = (\Psi, \Phi)$. Thus $\mathfrak{H}$ is equal to its dual space $\mathfrak{H}'$.

In $\mathfrak{H}$ we have again a *weak topology* defined by the seminorms $p_\Psi(\Phi) = |(\Psi, \Phi)|$. A set S is *weakly bounded*, if $\sup_{\Phi \in S} |(\Psi, \Phi)| < \infty$ for all Ψ; S is *strongly bounded*, if $\sup_{\Phi \in S} \|\Phi\| < \infty$. Again we have *equality of weakly bounded and strongly bounded sets.*

Every *continuous operator* A (continuous linear mapping of $\mathfrak{H}$ into $\mathfrak{H}$) defines uniquely an *adjoint operator* A^* by

$$(\Phi, A\Psi) = (A^*\Phi, \Psi). \tag{59}$$

A is *selfadjoint*, if $A^* = A$. An operator U is unitary if $U^{-1} = U^*$.

An operator A is bounded, if $\sup_{\|\Phi\|=1} \|A(\Phi)\| = \|A\| < \infty$. Bounded operators and continuous operators are identical. A sequence A_k of operators converges strongly to an operator A if $A_k\Phi \to A\Phi$ in the strong topology of $\mathfrak{H}$, for all $\Phi \in \mathfrak{H}$. The set of bounded operators is closed with respect to strong convergence.

The following theorem contains the "basic fact of life" about *unbounded* (discontinuous) operators.

THEOREM (HELLINGER-TOEPLITZ) [Ac 1*, p. 51]. *If a pair of operators A and B, defined for every vector in $\mathfrak{H}$, satisfies*

$$(\Phi, A\Psi) = (B\Phi, \Psi) \tag{60}$$

for all $\Phi, \Psi \in \mathfrak{H}$, then A and B are bounded and $B = A^*$.

PROOF. We show that the image of the unit sphere $\|\Phi\| = 1$ is strongly bounded. Now

$$|(\Psi, A\Phi)| = p_\Psi(A\Phi) = |(B\Psi, \Phi)| \leqq \|B\Psi\| \, \|\Phi\| = \|B\Psi\|.$$

$\{A\Phi \mid \|\Phi\| = 1\}$ is therefore weakly bounded. But every weakly bounded set is also strongly bounded. Therefore

$$\sup_{\|\Phi\|=1} \|A\Phi\| = \|A\| \tag{61}$$

exists and A is bounded. Clearly then $B = A^*$.

The Hellinger-Toeplitz theorem implies that *unbounded selfadjoint* operators cannot be defined in all of $\mathfrak{H}$. We therefore have to associate with every unbounded operator A its *domain* of definition D_A and its *range* $AD_A = \Delta_A$. We can always assume that D_A is linearly closed and it is reasonable to restrict ourselves to dense domains D_A.

If D_A is dense, then A defines uniquely an adjoint operator by

$$(\Phi, A\Psi) = (A^*\Phi, \Psi). \tag{62}$$

The domain of A^*, D_{A^*}, contains exactly the vectors Φ for which $(\Phi, A\Psi)$ is *bounded* in Ψ and thus defines uniquely a continuous linear form on $\mathfrak{H}$. D_{A^*} may contain only the zero vector. If, however, D_{A^*} is again dense in $\mathfrak{H}$, then A^{**} can be defined. A^{**} is an *extension* of A: $D_{A^{**}} \supset D_A$ and on D_A both operators agree. A^{**} has the remarkable property of being *closed*. This means that $\Phi_k \to \Phi$ and $A^{**}\Phi_k \to \Psi$ for $\Phi_k \in D_{A^{**}}$ imply that $\Phi \in D_{A^{**}}$ and $A^{**}\Phi = \Psi$. A^{**} is the smallest closed extension of A. $A^{***} = A^*$; thus A^* is also closed.

We shall only deal with operators A for which D_{A^*} is dense. Thus all our operators will allow closed extensions. The operators with which we shall have to work have even the additional property that $D_A \cap D_{A^*}$ is dense in $\mathfrak{H}$.

An operator A is *symmetric*, if for all $\Phi, \Psi \in D_A$

$$(\Phi, A\Psi) = (A\Phi, \Psi). \tag{63}$$

For a symmetric operator, A^* is an extension of A. Thus A^{**} exists. We have $A \subset A^{**} \subset A^*$. If $A = A^*$ then A is *selfadjoint*. If $A^* = A^{**}$ then A is *essentially selfadjoint* because A has a unique selfadjoint extension. Not every symmetric operator allows a selfadjoint extension. The following is a necessary and sufficient condition for a symmetric A to have a selfadjoint extension

$$m_+ = \dim[(A + iI)D_A]^\perp = \dim[(A - iI)D_A]^\perp = m_-. \tag{64}$$

If A is essentially selfadjoint then $m_+ = m_- = 0$ and conversely. m_+ and m_- are the *defect indices* of A.

A selfadjoint operator has a unique spectral representation

$$A = \int_{-\infty}^{\infty} \lambda \, dE(\lambda), \tag{65}$$

where $E(\lambda)$ is a *spectral measure* on the real line R. Conversely, every operator of the form (65), where $E(\lambda)$ is a spectral measure on the real line is a selfadjoint operator, D_A being defined by

$$D_A = \left\{\Phi \,\middle|\, \int \lambda^2 \, d(\Phi, E(\lambda)\Phi) < \infty\right\}. \tag{66}$$

A *unitary operator* U has a unique spectral representation

$$U = \int_{-0}^{2\pi} e^{i\varphi} \, dE(\varphi),$$

where $E(\varphi)$ is a *spectral measure* "on the unit circle".

A weakly continuous one-parameter group of unitary operators $U(\tau)$ is defined by

$$\begin{aligned} &U(\tau_1 + \tau_2) = U(\tau_1)U(\tau_2), \qquad -\infty < \tau_{1,2} < +\infty, \\ &U^{-1}(\tau) = U^*(\tau), \\ &(\Phi, U(\tau)\Psi) \text{ continuous in } \tau \text{ for all } \Phi, \Psi \in \mathfrak{H}. \end{aligned} \tag{67}$$

Such a group has a unique spectral representation of the form

$$U(\tau) = \int_{-\infty}^{\infty} e^{i\lambda\tau} \, dE(\lambda), \tag{68}$$

where $E(\lambda)$ is again a spectral measure on R. Conversely, the operators of the form (68) form a strongly continuous one-parameter group of unitary operators. The selfadjoint operator

$$A = \int_{-\infty}^{\infty} \lambda \, dE(\lambda) = \lim_{\tau \to 0} \tau^{-1}[U(\tau) - U(0)] \tag{69}$$

is the infinitesimal generator of $U(\tau)$. We write

$$U(\tau) = e^{i\tau A}. \tag{70}$$

These statements form the content of a theorem by Stone. We need an almost immediate generalization of this theorem.

THEOREM [RN 1*, p. 387 for a much more general theorem]. *Let $U(x)$, $x \in R^N$, be a weakly continuous unitary representation of the vector addition on R^N:*

$$U(x_1 + x_2) = U(x_1)U(x_2),$$
$$U^{-1}(x) = U^*(x), \tag{71}$$
$$(\Phi, U(x)\Psi) \text{ continuous in } x \text{ for all } \Phi \text{ and } \Psi \text{ in } \mathfrak{H}.$$

$U(x)$ then determines uniquely a projection-valued measure $E(p)$ in the dual space $(R^N)'$ such that

$$\int_{(R^N)'} dE(p) = I$$

and

$$U(x) = \int e^{i(p,x)}\, dE(p). \tag{72}$$

Conversely, every projection-valued measure $E(p)$ for which $\int_{(R^N)'} dE(p) = I$ determines by (72) *a strongly continuous representation $U(x)$ of the group of vector addition in R^N. The selfadjoint "vector operator"*

$$P = \int p \cdot dE(p) \tag{73}$$

is the infinitesimal generator of $U(x)$ and we write

$$U(x) = e^{i(P,x)}. \tag{74}$$

Finally we mention that very often the following generalization of the notion of distribution will occur: Let $\mathcal{S}$ be a space of test functions and Φ a continuous linear mapping of $\mathcal{S}$ into $\mathfrak{H}$. Then we shall call Φ a vector-valued distribution. Similarly, a weakly continuous mapping A of $\mathcal{S}$ into operators over $\mathfrak{H}$ will be called an operator-valued distribution. This last notion will be further discussed at the appropriate place.

2. **The structure of space-time.** The structure of space-time which underlies the general theory of quantized fields is the flat Minkowski space. We shall always neglect gravitational effects which would show themselves in a curvature of space-time.

The structure of space-time is so important to us that we devote a section to it despite the fact that we say nothing new or unfamiliar. In order to compensate for this last circumstance we choose a slightly unconventional procedure which stresses the difference between space-time and ordinary euclidean space.

The number of dimensions N of space-time is for the present discussion immaterial, provided $N \geqq 3$. The case $N = 2$ requires minor modifications. Of course, only $N = 4$ is of direct physical significance.

Flat space-time is a real affine space R^N of N dimensions ($N \geqq 3$) which carries a metric structure through a nonsingular symmetric bilinear scalar product $(\xi_1, \xi_2) = (\xi_2, \xi_1)$, where $\xi_k = x_k - x_0$, $k = 1, 2$, are difference vectors between x_1, x_2 and an arbitrary fixed point x_0. The difference vectors $\xi = x - x_0$ form a vector space $\mathfrak{V}$, the structure of which is independent of x_0.

If $(y - x, y - x) = 0$ then x and y can be joined by a light signal.

A *linear subspace* of R^N (or $\mathfrak{V}$) is *isotropic* [At 1*] if every pair of points can be joined by a light signal. Mathematically expressed, if its metric structure is completely degenerate: the scalar product restricted to the subspace vanishes identically. The principal property of R^N is expressed by the following postulate.

POSTULATE. One-dimensional isotropic subspaces exist. There are no isotropic subspaces of more than one dimension. The isotropic subspaces of R^N are the *light rays*.

With this postulate we normalize the metric in $\mathfrak{V}$ as follows. Choose $\alpha \neq 0$ from an isotropic subspace. Then the space orthogonal to α: $\mathfrak{U}_\alpha = \{\xi \mid (\alpha, \xi) = 0\}$ contains $\langle\alpha\rangle$, the span generated by α, but no other isotropic space. The metric in $\mathfrak{U}_\alpha$ is therefore semi-definite. The sign of the metric does not depend on the specific choice of α because the intersection $\mathfrak{U}_\alpha \cap \mathfrak{U}_{\alpha'}$ is at least $(N - 2)$-dimensional. Now we *choose* the sign of the metric in $\mathfrak{U}_\alpha$ to be *negative*. Every vector ξ with a negative square $(\xi, \xi) < 0$ belongs to a certain $\mathfrak{U}_\alpha$. Otherwise the orthogonal complement $\xi^\perp$ would not contain any zero vectors, the metric in $\mathfrak{V}$ would be negative-definite and $\mathfrak{V}$ euclidean.

DEFINITION.

$$\xi \neq 0 \text{ is } \left.\begin{matrix}\text{space-}\\ \text{light-}\\ \text{time-}\end{matrix}\right\} \text{like if and only if } (\xi, \xi) \begin{matrix}<\\=\\>\end{matrix} 0.$$

All space-like vectors form a connected cone, the *side cone*. The *light cone N* contains all light-like (null-) vectors. It decomposes into two disjoint cones. Let $\alpha \in N$ and denote by N_α all the null-vectors β, for which $(\alpha, \beta) > 0$ together with the half line $\{\lambda\alpha\}$, $\lambda > 0$. Then

$N_\alpha \cap N_{-\alpha} = \emptyset$. By choosing a time direction we distinguish these two cones as the forward light cone N_+ and the backward light cone N_-.

The convex cone $\bar{V}_+$ generated by the vectors of N_+ is the closed forward cone. Similarly $\bar{V}_-$, the convex hull of N_-, is the closed backward cone. The open forward V_+ and backward V_- cones are defined by

$$V_\pm \equiv \{\xi \mid \xi \in \bar{V}_\pm, (\xi, \xi) > 0\}. \tag{1}$$

$V_+ \cup V_-$ contains all the time-like vectors. $V_+ \cap V_- = \emptyset$. $\mathfrak{B}$ is the union of V_+, V_-, N_+, N_-, the side cone and $\{\xi = 0\}$. V_+ (V_-) is convex and therefore connected. One verifies easily that $\xi, \eta \in V_+$ implies $(\xi, \eta)^2 \geqq (\xi, \xi)(\eta, \eta)$.

Finally, we note that in a suitable orthonormal coordinate system we have

$$(\xi, \xi) = \xi^0\xi^0 - \sum_{k=1}^{N-1} \xi^k\xi^k = \xi^T G \xi \tag{2}$$

and

$$V_\pm = \{\xi \mid (\xi, \xi) > 0, \ \xi^0 \gtrless 0\}. \tag{3}$$

The dual space to R^N is the momentum space $(R^N)'$. All the elements of $(R^N)'$ are of the form $(p, x) = \sum_{k=0}^{N} p_k x^k = p^0x^0 - \sum_{k=1}^{N-1} p^k x^k$.

The weak topology in R^N, the topology for which $x_k \to x$ if for every p, $(p, x_n) \to (p, x)$ is equivalent to the euclidean topology defined by the distance

$$\|x - y\| = \left(\sum_{k=0}^{N-1} (x^k - y^k)^2\right)^{1/2}. \tag{4}$$

This distance itself has of course no invariant meaning, but the corresponding topology has, as was already stated in 1A.

3. The inhomogeneous Lorentz group. The symmetries of space-time consist[1] of the real, nonsingular, inhomogeneous linear transformations $\tilde{x} = \Lambda x + a$, for which $(\Lambda\xi, \Lambda\eta) = (\xi, \eta)$. We denote such a transformation by (a, Λ) and note the following multiplication law $(a_1, \Lambda_1)(a_2, \Lambda_2) = (a_1 + \Lambda_1 a_2, \Lambda_1\Lambda_2)$ together with $(a, \Lambda)^{-1} = (-\Lambda^{-1}a, \Lambda^{-1})$. If we express the above linear transformation in an orthonormal coordinate system, Λ will become a matrix which satisfies $\Lambda^{-1} = G\Lambda^T G$, from which it follows that $(\text{Det } \Lambda)^2 = 1$. Both signs for Det Λ actually occur. We note the following homomorphisms of the inhomogeneous Lorentz group:

(I) $(a, \Lambda) \to \Lambda$.

The corresponding normal subgroup (kernel) is $\{(a, I)\}$, the group of

[1] See for instance [Jo 5; Wi 5].

translations. The factor will be denoted by $L = \{\Lambda\}$ and is the homogeneous Lorentz group.

(II) $\Lambda \to \operatorname{Det} \Lambda$.
The corresponding normal subgroup is $L_+ = \{\Lambda\colon\ \operatorname{Det} \Lambda = +1\}$, the proper Lorentz group.

(III) $\Lambda \in L_+$ leaves V_+ either invariant or permutes V_+ and V_-. This permutation actually occurs in L_+. L_+ is therefore homomorphic to the permutation group of $\{V_+, V_-\}$. The corresponding normal subgroup is $L_+^\uparrow$, the *restricted Lorentz group.*

For even dimensions we can write the decomposition of L with respect to $L_+^\uparrow$ as follows:

$$L = \underbrace{L_+^\uparrow + PTL_+^\uparrow}_{L_+} + \underbrace{PL_+^\uparrow + TL_+^\uparrow}_{TL_+},$$

where

$$PT\xi = -\xi, \qquad P\xi^0 = \xi^0, \qquad T\xi^0 = -\xi^0,$$
$$P\xi^k = -\xi^k, \qquad T\xi^k = \xi^k, \qquad k = 1, 2, 3, \cdots, N-1.$$

In Appendix I we show that $L_+^\uparrow$ is connected and simple. It has therefore only trivial homomorphisms.

4. Spinor calculus for the physical case $N = 4$**.** Let

$$\sigma_0 = \begin{pmatrix} 1 & 0 \\ 0 & 1 \end{pmatrix}, \quad \sigma_1 = \begin{pmatrix} 0 & 1 \\ 1 & 0 \end{pmatrix}, \quad \sigma_2 = \begin{pmatrix} 0 & -i \\ i & 0 \end{pmatrix}, \quad \sigma_3 = \begin{pmatrix} 1 & 0 \\ 0 & -1 \end{pmatrix}$$

be the Pauli spin matrices completed by the unit matrix.

$$(\xi^0, \xi^1, \xi^2, \xi^3) \leftrightarrow X = \sum_{k=0}^{3} \xi^k \sigma_k \tag{1}$$

gives a one-to-one correspondence between vectors of $\mathfrak{V}$ and hermitian 2×2 matrices [Wae 1*]. Furthermore,

$$\operatorname{Det} X = \xi^0\xi^0 - \sum_{r=1}^{3} \xi^r\xi^r = (\xi, \xi). \tag{2}$$

The linear transformation of X:

$$\tilde{X} = AXA^* \quad \text{with } \operatorname{Det} A = 1 \tag{3}$$

corresponds to a real Lorentz transformation $\tilde{\xi} = \Lambda(A)\xi$. Since $\Lambda(A_1)\Lambda(A_2) = \Lambda(A_1A_2)$, the group of Lorentz transformations appears as a representation of $SL_2(C)$, the gróup of unimodular complex 2×2 matrices A. The representation is not faithful since $\Lambda(-A) = \Lambda(A)$. As is easily seen this is the only degeneracy: $\Lambda(A) = \Lambda(B)$ implies $B = \pm A$. The kernel of the representation is therefore $\{E, -E\}$. The transformations $\Lambda(A)$ are all orthochronous (do not permute V_+ and V_-). To see this note that generally $2\xi^0 = \operatorname{Tr} X$ and therefore $2\xi^0 = \operatorname{Tr} AXA^*$; now specialize to $X = 1$, corresponding to $\xi = (1, 0, 0, 0)$. Then $2\xi^0 = \operatorname{Tr} AA^* > 0$, therefore $\xi \in V_+$. Finally $\Lambda(A)$ is never a reflection, since $\sigma_0 = A\sigma_0 A^*$, $-\sigma_k = A\sigma_k A^*$, $k = 1, 2, 3$, would imply $A^* = A^{-1}$ and therefore $-\sigma_k = A\sigma_k A^{-1}$. But this cannot be true, since $\sigma_1\sigma_2 = i\sigma_3$, so we have shown that $\Lambda(A) \in L_+^\uparrow$. It is easily seen that every $\Lambda \in L_+^\uparrow$ occurs in this way.

$SL_2(C)/\{E, -E\}$ is isomorphic to $L_+^\uparrow$.

Since $SL_2(C)$ is simply connected, it is the universal covering group of $L_+^\uparrow$. $SL_2(C)$ acts naturally on a two-dimensional complex vector space V with elements $u = \binom{u_1}{u_2}$: $u' = Au$. Besides V we shall have to consider a second vector space $\dot{V}$ with elements $\dot{u} = \binom{\dot{u}_1}{\dot{u}_2}$ on which A acts according to $\dot{u}' = \bar{A}\dot{u}$. $\bar{A} = A^{*T}$ is the conjugate complex matrix to A.

The fact that all elements of $SL_2(C)$ have determinant 1 reflects itself in the symplectic structure of V and $\dot{V}$: $(u, v) = u_1v_2 - u_2v_2 = \epsilon^{\alpha\beta}u_\alpha v_\beta$ and $(\dot{u}, \dot{v}) = \dot{u}_1\dot{v}_2 - \dot{u}_2\dot{v}_1 = \epsilon^{\dot{\alpha}\dot{\beta}}\dot{u}_{\dot{\alpha}}\dot{v}_{\dot{\beta}}$ are invariant skew symmetric scalar products. The existence of these allows the definition of contravariant components of a vector u defined by $u^\alpha = \epsilon^{\alpha\beta}u_\beta$ and correspondingly for $\dot{u}$.

A general spinor of rank (k, l) is simultaneously a tensor of rank k over V and of rank l over $\dot{V}$. Its components are given by $u_{\alpha_1\cdots\alpha_k,\, \dot{\beta}_1\cdots\dot{\beta}_l}$.

A spinor of rank (k, l) which is symmetric in the k undotted and the l dotted arguments is irreducible. The linear space of such spinors is $((k + 1)(l + 1))$-dimensional and carries an irreducible representation of $SL_2(C)$. All finite-dimensional irreducible representations are obtained in this way [Wae 1*]. A nonsymmetric spinor can be split into symmetric spinors by contraction with the universal spinors ϵ and $\dot{\epsilon}$ and symmetrization over the remaining dotted and undotted indices separately. Similarly, every finite-dimensional continuous representation of $L_+^\uparrow$ is completely reducible into irreducible representations.

A representation of rank (k, l) of $SL_2(C)$ is a (one-valued) representation of $L_+^\uparrow$ if and only if $-E \in SL_2(C)$ is represented by the identity. This happens when $k + l$ is even. All other representations are two-valued over $L_+^\uparrow$ (or ray representations). The representation (1, 1) was our starting point and is equivalent to the original representation of $L_+^\uparrow$ in $\mathfrak{V}_4$. There is a one-to-one correspondence between spinors of rank (1, 1) and ordinary vectors which is given by $u_{\alpha\dot{\beta}} = \sum_k \xi^k \sigma_{k,\alpha\dot{\beta}}$ and is identical with (3.1). Similarly, if $k + l$ is even then the spinor corresponds uniquely to a tensor over $\mathfrak{V}_4$.

A further classification of spinors (and representations) beyond the parity of $k + l$ is given by the sign pair $((-1)^k, (-1)^l) = (\rho_1, \rho_2)$ [Pa 4] (Pauli Character).

(ρ_1, ρ_2)	Correspondence	Representation of $L_+^\uparrow$
(1, 1)	Tensor of even rank	one-valued
(−1, −1)	Tensor of odd rank	one-valued
(+1, −1)	Undors	two-valued
(−1, +1)	Undors	two-valued

To the product of two spinors (the Kronecker product of two representations) belonging to (ρ_1, ρ_2) and (ρ_1', ρ_2') corresponds to sign pair $(\rho_1\rho_1', \rho_2\rho_2')$.

IRREDUCIBLE REPRESENTATIONS AND SPINORS

k	l	Dimension $(k+1)(l+1)$	Name	Valuedness
0	0	1	scalar	one
1	0	2	spinor	two
0	1	2	spinor	two
1	1	4	vector	one
0	2	3	antisymmetric, self-dual tensor of rank 2	one
2	0	3	anti-self-dual tensor of rank 2	one
2	1	6	"undor"	two
1	2	6	"undor"	two
2	2	9	symmetric tensor of rank 2 with trace zero	one

Finally, we note the following identities involving $u_{\alpha\beta} = \sum_k \xi^k \sigma_{k,\alpha\beta}$, $w_{\alpha\beta} = \sum_k \eta^k \sigma_{k,\alpha\beta}$:

$$\begin{Vmatrix} u_{1\dot{1}} & u_{1\dot{2}} \\ u_{2\dot{1}} & u_{2\dot{2}} \end{Vmatrix} = \xi^0\sigma_0 + \sum_{r=1}^{3} \xi^r\sigma_r = \xi_0\sigma_0 - \sum_{r=1}^{3} \xi_r\sigma_r \tag{4}$$

$$\begin{Vmatrix} w^{1\dot{1}} & w^{2\dot{1}} \\ w^{1\dot{2}} & w^{2\dot{2}} \end{Vmatrix} = \eta^0\sigma_0 - \sum_{r=1}^{3} \eta^r\sigma_r = \eta_0\sigma_0 + \sum_{r=1}^{3} \eta_r\sigma_r \tag{5}$$

from which we have, e.g.: $u_{\alpha\beta}u^{\gamma\beta} = \delta_\alpha^\gamma(\xi, \xi)$.

5. **The simplest linear covariant differential equations.**[2] In this section we encounter for the first time the notion of a field and we start with the simplest case, that of a *scalar field*.

A complex (real) scalar field is a complex- (real-) valued function $\psi(x)$ in space-time, which transforms under a coordinate transformation $\tilde{x} = \Lambda x + a$ according to $\tilde{\psi}(\tilde{x}) = \psi(x)$. The simplest nontrivial linear differential equation to which we can subject such a field is evidently $\Box\psi + m^2\psi = 0$, $\Box = g^{kl}\partial_k\partial_l$. Here $\partial_k = \partial/\partial x^k$ and m is a constant of the dimension of a reciprocal length. We shall discuss the above equation and its quantization in great detail later. Right now, however, we want to take it as a model for generalizations. Before we go to the next simplest case of a spinor field we introduce the spinor representation corresponding to the differential operator ∂_k:

(1) $$\partial_{\alpha\beta} = g^{kl}\,\partial_k \sigma_{l,\alpha\beta}$$

and notice that

(2) $$\begin{Vmatrix} \partial_{1\dot{1}} & \partial_{1\dot{2}} \\ \partial_{2\dot{1}} & \partial_{2\dot{2}} \end{Vmatrix} = \sigma_0\partial_0 - \sum_{r=1}^{3} \sigma_r\partial_r$$

and

(3) $$\begin{Vmatrix} \partial^{1\dot{1}} & \partial^{2\dot{1}} \\ \partial^{1\dot{2}} & \partial^{2\dot{2}} \end{Vmatrix} = \sigma_0\partial_0 + \sum_{r=1}^{3} \sigma_r\partial_r.$$

A spinor field with the components $\psi_\alpha(x)$ transforms under the coordinate transformation $\tilde{x} = \Lambda x + a$, where $\Lambda = \Lambda(A)$, as follows: $\tilde{\psi}(\tilde{x}) = A\psi(x)$.

The simplest covariant equation is evidently

(4) $$\partial^{\alpha\beta}\psi_\alpha = 0 \quad \text{or} \quad \left(\sigma_0\partial_0 + \sum_{r=1}^{3} \sigma_r\partial_r\right)\psi = 0.$$

Since $\partial_{\gamma\beta}\partial^{\alpha\beta} = \delta^\alpha_\gamma\Box$ it has as consequence that $\Box\psi_\alpha = 0$. ψ satisfies the wave equation and propagates with the velocity of light. It describes, after quantization, particles of spin $\frac{1}{2}$, which also propagate with light velocity and therefore are of mass zero. The equation (4) is used to describe neutrinos. It was first proposed by H. Weyl [Pa 1*, p. 149].

If we want ψ to satisfy the Klein-Gordon equation (1) instead of the wave equation, we have to remember that $\bar{\psi}$ transforms as $\bar{\psi}^{\sim}(\tilde{x}) = \bar{A}\bar{\psi}(x)$ and therefore represents a spinor $\chi_{\dot{\alpha}} = \bar{\psi}_\alpha$. This allows us to generalize equation (4) to

(5) $$\partial^{\alpha\beta}\psi_\alpha = m\chi^\beta$$

[2] In this section we use the summation convention.

and

$$\partial^{\alpha\beta}\chi_\beta = m\psi^\alpha \tag{5$'$}$$

or equivalently

$$\partial_{\alpha\beta}\chi^\beta = -m\psi_\alpha \tag{5$''$}$$

from which it follows that

$$\Box\psi_\alpha = -m^2\psi_\alpha, \qquad \Box\chi_{\dot\alpha} = -m^2\chi_{\dot\alpha}. \tag{6}$$

These new equations are the Dirac equation supplemented by the Majorana reality condition [Maj 1] $\chi_{\dot\alpha} = \bar\psi_\alpha$. If we forget this last condition and make $\chi_{\dot\alpha}$ an independent field we have the ordinary Dirac equation. The Dirac field (ψ, χ) corresponds therefore to the sum of the two irreducible representations (1, 0) and (0, 1).

Finally, we want to transform the field equations into a more familiar form. Simultaneously we want to keep the Majorana condition as simple as possible. In order to do this we write (5) and (5$'$) in matrix form:

$$\Big(\sigma_0\partial_0 + \sum_r \sigma_r\partial_r\Big)\psi = m\epsilon\chi, \tag{7}$$

$$\Big(\sigma_0\partial_0 + \sum_r \sigma_r^T\partial_r\Big)\chi = m\epsilon\psi \tag{8}$$

with the reality condition $\chi = \bar\psi$. Notice also that $\sigma_r^T = \bar\sigma_r$. Now we introduce $\psi_1 = (\psi + \chi)/2$ and $\psi_2 = (\psi - \chi)/2i$ as new vectors and form the 4 component spinor $\binom{\psi_1}{\psi_2} = \varphi$.

We find:

$$(\gamma^k\partial_k + m)\varphi = 0, \tag{9}$$

where

$$\gamma^0 = \left(\begin{array}{cc|cc} 0 & 1 & & \\ -1 & 0 & & \\ \hline & & 0 & -1 \\ & & 1 & 0 \end{array}\right), \qquad \gamma^1 = \left(\begin{array}{cc|cc} 1 & 0 & & \\ 0 & -1 & & \\ \hline & & -1 & 0 \\ & & 0 & 1 \end{array}\right)$$

(10)

$$\gamma^2 = \left(\begin{array}{cc|cc} & & -1 & 0 \\ & & 0 & -1 \\ \hline -1 & 0 & & \\ 0 & -1 & & \end{array}\right), \qquad \gamma^3 = \left(\begin{array}{cc|cc} 0 & -1 & & \\ -1 & 0 & & \\ \hline & & 0 & 1 \\ & & 1 & 0 \end{array}\right)$$

satisfy the famous relations:

$$\gamma^k\gamma^l + \gamma^l\gamma^k = -2g^{kl}. \tag{11}$$

In this special representation the Majorana condition simply expresses the reality of φ. If we let φ be complex we have the usual Dirac equation. Note the special property of $C = i\gamma^0 = C^* = C^{-1} = -C^T$:

$$C^{-1}\gamma^k C = -\gamma^{kT}. \tag{12}$$

Whereas the existence of such a matrix C follows from general arguments [Pa 1, 2], to which we shall come later, the fact that $C = i\gamma^0$ is dependent on our special representation of the γ-matrices.

We leave further discussions of the Dirac equation to a later section. We shall, however, not touch the subject of field equations for more complicated fields and the interested reader is referred to the literature [Fi 1; Um 1*].

CHAPTER II

Classical Field Theory. The Quantization of Free Fields

1. **Introductory remarks.** This chapter starts with the *Lagrangian theory of classical fields* [We 1*]. This theory and its further development into a Hamiltonian theory plays an essential rôle in the conventional quantization procedure [We 1*; Hei 1, 2]. Important as this procedure is for the discussion of special models and theories, e.g. quantum electrodynamics of Dirac electrons, we shall not treat it here. Our aim is first to prepare the ground for the discussion of free fields and secondly to illustrate the fundamental connection between symmetries and conservation laws, a connection which stays intact also in the quantized theories.

Next we treat the simplest free fields both classical and quantized. These are the free real (and complex classical) scalar field and the Dirac field. The first field will be the model from which we later abstract the axioms of a general real scalar field.

These two fields, the scalar field and the Dirac field, show a very important difference even before quantization.

(a) In the case of the complex (or real) scalar field the energy density and therefore also the *total energy* is *positive-definite* (except in the trivial case where the field vanishes). The "charge density" s_0 contained in (3.9), as well as its space-integral, the "total charge" (3.11), is *indefinite*. This behavior is typical for free fields belonging to a one-valued representation of the Lorentz group (tensor fields) [Fi 1; Pa 6].

(b) For the unquantized Dirac field the charge density and therefore the *total charge* is *positive-definite*. It was therefore at first wrongly interpreted as a probability density. The energy density and the *total energy* are *indefinite*. This behavior is typical of free fields belonging to a two-valued representation of the Lorentz group (spinor fields) [Fi 1; Pa 6].

There is an intimate relation between these facts and the possible modes of quantization. A free scalar field can be quantized so that the corresponding field-quanta (particles) obey Bose-Einstein statistics; a free Dirac field cannot be quantized in this way; its field-quanta (particles) have to obey Fermi-Dirac statistics. This important connection between the geometric character of a field and its possible mode of quantization will be systematically explored later within the framework of the general theory of quantized fields.

Finally, as a transition to the mathematically more ambitious main part of the book, a rather detailed description of the generalized free scalar field is presented.

2. **The variational principle and the conservation laws.** Let $\psi_\sigma(x)$ be the fields appearing in our field equations. The index σ distinguishes different components of one field and simultaneously different fields. Each single field transforms under the restricted inhomogeneous Lorentz transformation (a, Λ) according to a finite-dimensional irreducible representation of $L_+^\uparrow$ (or its covering group $SL_2(C)$). We know all these representations from Chapter I, §3. All the fields $\psi_\sigma(x)$ together therefore transform under the coordinate transformation $\tilde{x} = \Lambda x + a$ as[1]

(1) $$\tilde{\psi}_\sigma(\tilde{x}) = S_\sigma^{\sigma'}(\Lambda)\psi_{\sigma'}(x),$$

where $S(\Lambda)$ is a finite-dimensional, possibly two-valued, representation of $L_+^\uparrow$. We shall often abbreviate the above equation to

(2) $$\tilde{\psi}(\tilde{x}) = S(\Lambda)\psi(x).$$

If we choose Λ infinitesimal and write

(3) $$\Lambda = I + r, \qquad \delta\xi = \tilde{\xi} - \xi = r\xi,$$

then $S(\Lambda)$ will also be infinitesimal and its deviation from unity is linear in r:

(4) $$S = I + r \cdot \tau \quad \text{and} \quad \delta\psi = \tilde{\psi}(\tilde{x}) - \psi(x) = r \cdot \tau\psi.$$

By differentiating $\tilde{\psi}(\tilde{x}) = \psi(\tilde{x} - r\tilde{x}) + r \cdot \tau\psi(\tilde{x})$ with respect to $\tilde{x}^k$ we find

(5) $$\delta\psi_{,k} = \tilde{\psi}_{,\tilde{x}^k}(\tilde{x}) - \psi_{,x^k}(x) = r\tau\psi_{,k} - \psi_{,x}(rx)_{,x^k}.$$

After these preliminaries we are ready to discuss the field equations. Since we want to stay as close as possible to the canonical formalism of classical mechanics[2] we begin with the remark that in all important cases the classical equations of motion are equivalent to the Euler-Lagrange equations of a variational principle, the Hamilton principle:

(6) $$\delta \int_{P_0}^{P_1} L(q_1, \cdots, q_f, \dot{q}_1, \cdots, \dot{q}_f)\, dt = 0$$

---

[1]With summation over repeated indices.
[2]See for instance [La 1*].

under the condition $\delta q_k = 0$ at the end-points P_0 and P_1. The equations of motion are therefore

$$L_{,q_k} = \partial_t L_{,\dot{q}_k}. \tag{7}$$

L is the Lagrangian of the mechanical system.

In complete analogy we require (and again we shall cover all interesting cases) the field equations to be derivable from a variational principle

$$\delta \int_{C_4} L(\psi, \psi_{,k})\, d^4x = 0 \tag{8}$$

under the condition $\delta\psi = 0$ on ∂C_4, the boundary of the domain C_4. $L(\psi, \psi_{,k})$ will be called the Lagrangian density of the field theory. The field equations are

$$L_{,\psi_\sigma} = \partial_k L_{,\psi_{\sigma,k}}. \tag{9}$$

The variational principle is only of significance in as far as it is equivalent to the above differential equations.

The principal restriction to be imposed on the field equation is their covariance. This is guaranteed if $L(\psi(x), \psi_{,k}(x))$ transforms like a scalar field:

$$L(\tilde{\psi}(\tilde{x}), \tilde{\psi}_{,k}(\tilde{x})) = L(\psi(x), \psi_{,k}(x)) \tag{10}$$

under the coordinate transformation (a, Λ).

The well-known connection between symmetry properties and conservation laws [Noe 1] is as valid here as in the case of classical mechanics. The translation group $\{(a, 1)\}$ leads to energy momentum conservation: it is equivalent to the property of L that it depends on x only through the fields and not explicitly. We have therefore

$$L_{,\psi} \cdot \psi_{,k} + L_{,\psi_{,l}} \cdot \psi_{,lk} - \partial_k L = 0 \tag{11}$$

which, under the assumption that we substitute a solution ψ of the field equations, can also be written as

$$\partial_l L_{,\psi_{,l}} \cdot \psi_{,k} - \partial_k L = 0 \tag{12}$$

or

$$T^l{}_{k,l} = 0, \tag{13}$$

where

$$T^l{}_k = L_{,\psi_{,l}} \cdot \psi_{,k} - \delta^l{}_k L. \tag{14}$$

A simple argument shows that (under the assumption of a sufficiently fast decrease of $T^l{}_k$ at infinity)

(15) $$P_k = \int_{x^0=t} T^0{}_k \, d^3x$$

are the components of a time-independent four-vector. From the connection with the translation group these conservation laws have to be interpreted as energy momentum conservation. $T^l{}_k$ is the canonical energy momentum tensor.

In a similar way the homogeneous Lorentz group is connected to the conservation of angular momentum: L does not vary if we subject the fields to the variations (4) and (5). We therefore have

(16) $$L_{,\psi} r\tau\psi + L_{,\psi_{,k}} r\tau\psi_{,k} - L_{,\psi_{,k}} \cdot \psi_{,x}(rx)_{,x^k} = 0$$

which, after making use of the field equation (and the corresponding assumption of substituting a solution into (16)) leads to

(17) $$\partial_k(L_{,\psi_{,k}} r\tau\psi) - \partial_k(L_{,\psi_{,k}} \psi_{,x} rx) + L_{,\psi}\psi_{,x} rx + L_{,\psi_{,k}} \psi_{,k,x}(rx) = 0$$

and finally to

(18) $$\partial_k(L_{,\psi_{,k}} r\tau\psi - L_{,\psi_{,k}} \cdot \psi_{,x} rx + L(rx)^k) = 0,$$

where $(rx)^k$ is the k-component of $r \cdot x$. Notice that $(rx)^k{}_{,k} = 0$. Writing $(rx)^k = r^{kl}x_l$, where $r^{kl} + r^{lk} = 0$, and $r\tau = r^{kl}\tau_{kl}$, where τ_{kl} is still a linear operation on the fields, we have

(19) $$r^{lm}\partial_k\{2L_{,\psi_{,k}}\tau_{lm}\psi - L_{,\psi_{,k}}\psi_{,l}x_m + L_{,\psi_{,k}}\psi_{,m}x_l + L(\delta^k_l x_m - \delta^k_m x_l)\} = 0$$

which, since r^{lm} is arbitrary, leads to the conservation laws

(20) $$M^k{}_{lm,k} = 0,$$

(21) $$M^k{}_{lm} = T^k{}_l x_m - T^k{}_m x_l - 2L_{,\psi_{,k}}\tau_{lm}\psi.$$

It might help to write the last term out in complete detail:

(22) $$-2L_{,\psi_{\sigma,k}}\tau_{lm;\sigma}{}^{\eta}\psi_\eta$$

and to point out that $\tau_{lm} + \tau_{ml} = 0$ has been assumed.

Under suitable conditions about the asymptotic behavior of $M^k{}_{lm}$, it follows from (20) that

(23) $$P_{lm} = \int_{x^0=t} M^0{}_{lm} \, d^3x$$

are the six components of a skew-symmetric, t-independent tensor. Its derivation gives it the meaning of angular momentum.

We want to make an application of angular momentum conservation. We first observe that in general the canonical energy momentum tensor T_{kl} is unsymmetric. This is unaesthetic, and it is a handicap if we want to use this tensor as the source of a symmetric tensor field of rank 2 or to incorporate it into a theory of gravitation. It is therefore gratifying [Pa 5] that the conservation of P_{lm} allows us to construct a symmetric energy momentum tensor θ_{kl} without changing the canonical energy momentum vector P_k.

We start with the decomposition of $M^k{}_{lm}$ into

(24) $$M^k{}_{lm} = {}^0M^k{}_{lm} + {}^1M^k{}_{lm},$$

(25) $${}^0M^k{}_{lm} = T^k{}_l x_m - T^k{}_m x_l.$$

Evidently we have

(26) $${}^1M^k{}_{lm} + {}^1M^k{}_{ml} = 0$$

and

(27) $${}^1M^k{}_{lm,k} = T_{lm} - T_{ml}.$$

We introduce

(28) $$f_{klm} = \tfrac{1}{2}({}^1M_{klm} - {}^1M_{lmk} + {}^1M_{mlk}),$$

which satisfies

(29) $$f_{klm} + f_{kml} = 0,$$

and define

(30) $$\theta_{kl} = T_{kl} - f_{lk}{}^m{}_{,m}.$$

This tensor is symmetric, because

(31) $$\theta_{kl} - \theta_{lk} = T_{kl} - T_{lk} - f_{lk}{}^m{}_{,m} + f_{kl}{}^m{}_{,m}$$

but $f_{lk}{}^m - f_{kl}{}^m = -{}^1M^m{}_{lk}$ and from (27) the right-hand side vanishes. The antisymmetry of $f_l{}^{km}$ in the last two indices guarantees

(32) $$\theta^k{}_{l,k} = T^k{}_{l,k} = 0.$$

Finally

(33) $$\int \theta^0{}_k \, d^3x = P_k - \int \left(\sum_{r=1}^{3} f_k{}^{0r}{}_{,r} \right) d^3x = P_k$$

under the usual conditions of sufficiently fast decrease at infinity.

These few derivations should illustrate the fact that classical field theory is a rather straightforward generalization of classical mechanics. This is also true of the methods. In particular, we find in field theory the same intimate connection between symmetries of a theory and conservation laws we are already familiar with in classical mechanics.

It is possible to follow this parallelism between field theory and classical mechanics still further by the introduction of canonical momenta $L_{,\psi_{,0}} = \pi$ and canonical equations of motion derived from a Hamiltonian. Finally one can apply the well-known rules of quantization to this Hamiltonian formulation of field theory [Hei 1, 2; We 1*]. There are limitations to such a procedure (it always leads to Bose-Einstein statistics). There is, however, also a serious formal disadvantage connected with it, the Lorentz invariance is not at all evident and has to be proved by rather lengthy arguments [Hei 1, 2].

In the case of free fields, to which we now turn, we shall introduce quantization in a different and evidently covariant fashion.

3. **The classical free scalar field.** Let us illustrate in part the formal developments of the last section by a simple (in fact essentially the simplest) example, the case of a free complex scalar field $\psi(x)$. For the Lagrangian density we take [Pa 7; We 1*]:

(1) $$L = g^{kl}\bar{\psi}_{,k}\psi_{,l} - m^2\bar{\psi}\psi,$$

where ψ and $\bar{\psi}$ are varied independently. The equations of motion are familiar to us from Chapter I, §4. They read

(2) $$(\Box + m^2)\psi = 0 \quad \text{and} \quad (\Box + m^2)\bar{\psi} = 0.$$

The energy momentum tensor is symmetric and given by

(3) $$T_{kl} = \bar{\psi}_{,k}\psi_{,l} + \bar{\psi}_{,l}\psi_{,k} - g_{kl}L,$$

the angular momentum tensor by

(4) $$M^k{}_{lm} = T^k{}_l x_m - T^k{}_m x_l.$$

We notice especially the fact that the energy density

(5) $$T_{00} = |\psi_{,0}|^2 + \sum_{r=1}^{3} |\psi_{,r}|^2 + m^2 |\psi|^2 \geqq 0$$

is nonnegative and vanishes only for the trivial field $\psi = 0$. This has an important consequence for the energy momentum vector

(6) $$P_k = \int_{x^0=t} T_{0k}\, d^3x = \int_{x^0=t} T^0{}_k\, d^3x$$

which is either zero or (if $\psi \neq 0$) has a positive 0-component, $P_0 > 0$. Since it is evident that the possible P-vectors form an invariant cone, this cone can only be a forward cone supplemented by the vector $P = 0$. A simple argument shows that

$$\{P\} = V_+ \cup \{0\} \equiv \underset{\circ}{V}. \tag{7}$$

The possible P-vectors therefore are in V_+ with the single exception of $P = 0$ which belongs to $\psi = 0$. This state $\psi = 0$ is reasonably called the vacuum. Our Lagrange density allows an additional symmetry, the "gauge group"

$$\psi \to e^{i\alpha}\psi, \qquad \bar{\psi} \to e^{-i\alpha}\bar{\psi}. \tag{8}$$

The corresponding conservation law is $s^k{}_{,k} = 0$, where

$$s_k = -i(\bar{\psi}_{,k}\psi - \bar{\psi}\psi_{,k}) \equiv i\bar{\psi}\overleftrightarrow{\partial}_k\psi. \tag{9}$$

The operator $\overleftrightarrow{\partial}$ is defined as

$$f\overleftrightarrow{\partial}_k g = fg_{,k} - f_{,k}g. \tag{10}$$

Alternatively

$$\int_{x^0=t} s^0\, d^3x = \int_{x^0=t} s_0\, d^3x = i\int_{x^0=t} \bar{\psi}\overleftrightarrow{\partial}_0\psi\, d^3x \equiv (\psi, \psi) \tag{11}$$

is (if it exists) independent of t. The usual argument then shows that the same is true for

$$(\psi, \varphi) = i\int_{x^0=t} \bar{\psi}\overleftrightarrow{\partial}_0\varphi\, d^3x. \tag{12}$$

This "scalar product" (ψ, φ) has all the properties of a (symmetric) scalar product except positivity. In fact, if $(\psi, \psi) > 0$ then $(\varphi, \varphi) < 0$ for $\varphi(x) = \bar{\psi}(x)$ and $(\psi, \psi) = 0$ for real ψ.

In order to get away from these purely formal discussions, we have to introduce the Fourier transform of a solution ψ: $\tilde{\psi}(p) = (2\pi)^{-4}\int e^{i(p,x)}\psi(x)\, d^4x$. It is evident from the differential equation that the support of $\tilde{\psi}(p)$ is on $\{(p, p) = m^2\}$. This hyperboloid decomposes into two shells, depending on the sign of p_0. These two shells play an essentially different part in all future developments. We shall therefore write

$$\tilde{\psi}(p) = (2\pi)^{-3/2}\,\delta(p^2 - m^2)[\theta(p)a(p) + \theta(-p)\bar{b}(-p)] \tag{13}$$

giving

$$\begin{aligned} \psi(x) &= (2\pi)^{-3/2}\int e^{-i(p,x)}\,\delta(p^2 - m^2)\theta(p)a(p)\, d^4p \\ &\quad + (2\pi)^{-3/2}\int e^{i(p\,x)}\,\delta(p^2 - m^2)\theta(p)\bar{b}(p)\, d^4p \\ &\equiv \psi_+(x) + \psi_-(x). \end{aligned} \tag{14}$$

This splitting up of ψ into a "positive frequency part" ψ_+ and a "negative frequency part" ψ_- (the names are conventional, and strange) is $L^{\uparrow}$-invariant. The scalar product (ψ, ψ) becomes

$$(\psi, \psi) = \|\psi_+\|^2 - \|\psi_-\|^2 \tag{15}$$

with

$$\|\psi_+\|^2 = \int d^4p\theta(p)\delta(p^2 - m^2)|a(p)|^2 \tag{16}$$

and

$$\|\psi_-\|^2 = \int d^4p\theta(p)\delta(p^2 - m^2)|b(p)|^2. \tag{17}$$

These scalar products define two Hilbert spaces (L_2-spaces with respect to the measure $\theta(p)\ \delta(p^2 - m^2)$) and we shall take pairs of elements ψ_+, ψ_- in these spaces as suitable definitions for our solutions of (2).

For the energy momentum vector we find

$$P_k = \int d^4p\delta(p^2 - m^2)\theta(p)(|a(p)|^2 + |b(p)|^2)p_k. \tag{18}$$

Finally, we note that whereas (ψ, ψ) appears as the integral over a local density in x-space, this is not the case for either $\|\psi_+\|^2$ or $\|\psi_-\|^2$. Both the solutions ψ_+ and ψ_- form an irreducible representation of the inhomogeneous Lorentz group. We remember [Wig 1*] that such a representation is uniquely characterized by its mass, which, in our case is m, and (provided m is real and different from zero) its spin, which in our case equals zero.

Let us introduce an orthonormal basis $\{f_\alpha\}$ for the space of positive frequency solutions. Then $\{\bar{f}_\alpha\}$ is a basis in the space of negative frequency solutions. The orthonormality relations read

$$(f_\alpha, f_\beta) = -(\bar{f}_\alpha, \bar{f}_\beta) = \delta_{\alpha\beta} \tag{19}$$

and the completeness relation

$$\sum_\alpha f_\alpha(x)\bar{f}_\alpha(x') = i\Delta_+(x - x'), \tag{20}$$

where $\Delta_+(\xi)$ is the following distribution:

$$\Delta_+(\xi) = -i(2\pi)^{-3}\int d^4p\delta(p^2 - m^2)\theta(p)e^{-i(p,\xi)}. \tag{21}$$

$\Delta_+(\xi)$ satisfies $(\Box + m^2)\,\Delta_+ = 0$, has only positive frequencies and is $L_+^{\uparrow}$-invariant. These conditions characterize $\Delta_+(\xi)$ up to a constant factor.

An arbitrary solution can be expanded

$$\psi = \sum_\alpha (f_\alpha, \psi)f_\alpha - \sum_\alpha (\bar{f}_\alpha, \psi)\bar{f}_\alpha. \tag{22}$$

The first term represents ψ_+, the second term ψ_-. We find an explicit representation for these "half-fields":

(23) $$\psi_+ = -\int_{x'_0=t'} \Delta_+(x - x')\overleftrightarrow{\partial}_{0'}\psi(x')\, d^3x',$$

(24) $$\psi_- = -\int_{x'_0=t'} \psi(x')\,\overleftrightarrow{\partial}_{0'}\, \Delta_+(x - x')\, d^3x'$$

and, by addition, the solution of the initial value problem

(25) $$\psi(x) = -i\int_{x'_0=t'} \Delta(x - x')\overleftrightarrow{\partial}_{0'}\psi(x')\, d^3x',$$

where

(26) $$\Delta(\xi) = \Delta_+(\xi) - \Delta_+(-\xi) = 2 \operatorname{Re} \Delta_+(\xi)$$

(for explicit expressions see for instance [Bog 1*]).

The two last equations lead immediately to the following characteristic properties of $\Delta(\xi)$:

(27a) $$(\Box + m^2)\,\Delta(\xi) = 0,$$

(27b) $$\Delta(\Lambda\xi) = \Delta(\xi), \qquad \Lambda \in L_+^\uparrow,$$

(27c) $$\Delta(-\xi) = -\Delta(\xi),$$

(27d) $$\Delta(0, \vec{\xi}) = 0,$$

$$\left(\frac{\partial}{\partial\xi^0}\Delta\right)(0, \vec{\xi}) = -\delta(\vec{\xi}).$$

From (b) and (c) alone we have the important property that $\Delta(\xi) = 0$ for $(\xi, \xi) < 0$. This is so because any two vectors ξ, η for which $(\xi, \xi) = (\eta, \eta) < 0$ are equivalent under $L_+^\uparrow$.

4. The quantization of the free real scalar field. We shall restrict the further discussion to the *real* scalar field $A(x)$. The corresponding Lagrangian density [We 1*] is

(1) $$L = \tfrac{1}{2}[g^{kl}A_{,k}A_{,l} - m^2A^2]$$

and $A(x)$ is of course real-valued. Again

(2) $$(\Box + m^2)A(x) = 0$$

and in addition

(3) $$T_{ik} = A_{,i}A_{,k} - g_{ik}L,$$

(4) $$T_{00} = \frac{1}{2}\left[(A_{,0})^2 + \sum_{r=1}^{3}(A_{,r})^2 + m^2A^2\right] \geqq 0$$

and

(5) $$M^k{}_{lm} = T^k{}_l x_m - T^k{}_m x_l.$$

It follows from the above equations that $P \in V_+$ unless $A = 0$. P is again the vector (P_0, P_1, P_2, P_3): $P_k = \int T^0{}_k \, d^3x$. The Fourier decomposition of $A(x)$ is given by

$$A(x) = A_+(x) + A_-(x)$$

(6)[3] $$= (2\pi)^{-3/2} \int d^4p \, \delta(p^2 - m^2)[\theta(p)a(p)e^{-i(p,x)} + \theta(-p)a^*(-p)e^{-i(p,x)}].$$

As before, we restrict ourselves to the Hilbert space characterized by

(7) $$\|A_+\|^2 = \int |a(p)|^2 \, \theta(p) \, \delta(p^2 - m^2) \, d^4p < \infty.$$

Finally, we note that

(8) $$P_k = \int d^4p \, \delta(p^2 - m^2)\theta(p)p_k a^*(p)a(p).$$

In terms of our basis $\{f_\alpha\}$, $A(x)$ has the decomposition

(9) $$A = \sum_\alpha (A_\alpha f_\alpha + A_\alpha^* \bar{f}_\alpha),$$

where

(10) $$A_\alpha = (f_\alpha, A), \qquad A_\alpha^* = -(\bar{f}_\alpha, A) = (A, f_\alpha).$$

The quantization will transform A_α and A_α^* into operators acting on a Hilbert space $\mathfrak{H}$. A_α^* will be the adjoint operator to A_α.

We postulate the following commutation relations:

(11) $$A_\alpha A_\beta^* - A_\beta^* A_\alpha \equiv [A_\alpha, A_\beta^*] = \delta_{\alpha\beta},$$

(12) $$[A_\alpha, A_\beta] = [A_\alpha^*, A_\beta^*] = 0.$$

These commutation relations do not depend on the particular orthonormal basis $\{f_\alpha\}$, i.e., they are invariant under unitary transformations. The inhomogeneous (restricted) Lorentz transformations induce just such unitary transformations on the basis $\{f_\alpha\}$ that our commutation relations are Lorentz invariant. This can be explicitly verified by computing the commutator of the field A with itself. One finds

(13) $$[A(x), A(y)] = i\Delta(x - y).$$

For the Fourier components $a(p)$ we get commutation relations

(14) $$[a(p), a^*(p')] = 2\omega(p) \, \delta(\vec{p} - \vec{p}{}') \qquad (\omega(p) = +\sqrt{(m^2 + \vec{p}^2)})$$

and

(15) $$[a(p), a(p')] = [a^*(p), a^*(p')] = 0.$$

---

[3]In view of our quantization we use here, for the moment, the notation a^* for the complex conjugate of a. Later * will denote the adjoint.

The following consequences of our commutation relations are as essential as Lorentz invariance and related to it:

$$(16) \qquad i[P_k, A] = A_{,k}.$$

They show that the energy momentum vector becomes the operator of infinitesimal translations.

Similarly

$$(17) \qquad i[P_{lm}, A] = A_{,l}x_m - A_{,m}x_l,$$

where

$$(18) \qquad P_{lm} = \int M^0{}_{lm}\, d^3x.$$

The components of the angular momentum thus become infinitesimal homogeneous Lorentz transformations. The commutation relations between P_k and P_{lm} (this follows already from the verifications just made) are the familiar commutation relations between the infinitesimal generators of the inhomogeneous Lorentz group.

Hence, through our process of quantization, we gain (at least formally) a representation of the inhomogeneous Lorentz group, which, as it will turn out shortly, is very much reducible [Wi 5]. But we still have to lay some solid foundation for these purely formal reasonings and to do this we shall specify a representation of the commutation relations (11), (12). These commutation relations have a great number of inequivalent representations [Fr 1*; Gå 2], among which there is one of special importance for us. To construct it we begin by postulating the existence of a state $\Omega \in \mathfrak{H}$ (later to be identified with the vacuum state) having the property $A_\alpha\Omega = 0$ for all α and $(\Omega, \Omega) = 1$. Given now a nonnegative integer-valued function $n(\alpha)$ with $\sum_\alpha n(\alpha) < \infty$, it is then easy to see that from the commutation relations

$$(19) \qquad \Phi^{(n)} = \prod_\alpha \frac{1}{\sqrt{(n(\alpha)!)}} A_\alpha^{*n(\alpha)}\Omega$$

is normalized. If we identify $\Phi^{(0)}$ with Ω, we have

$$(20) \qquad (\Phi^{(n)}, \Phi^{(m)}) = \delta(n, m) \equiv \prod_\alpha \delta_{n(\alpha), m(\alpha)}.$$

We take $\{\Phi^{(n)}\}$ as a basis for our Hilbert space $\mathfrak{H}$. The basis vectors are eigenvectors of $N_\alpha = A_\alpha^* A_\alpha$:

$$(21) \qquad N_\alpha\Phi^{(n)} = n(\alpha)\Phi^{(n)}$$

and of $N = \sum_\alpha N_\alpha$

$$(22) \qquad N\Phi^{(n)} = \sum_\alpha n(\alpha)\Phi^{(n)}.$$

The matrix elements of A_β and A_β^* are given by

(23)
$$A_\beta \Phi^{(n)} = \sqrt{(n(\alpha))}\Phi^{(n-e_\beta)},$$
$$A_\beta^* \Phi^{(n)} = \sqrt{(n(\alpha)+1)}\Phi^{(n-e_\beta)},$$

where

$$e_\beta(\alpha) = \delta_{\alpha\beta}.$$

N_α is the "number of particles" in the state α and N the "total number of particles". These "particles" evidently satisfy Bose statistics: the state is uniquely characterized by the number of particles in every state and this number itself is an arbitrary integer. To a given particle number $n = \sum_\alpha n(\alpha)$ there is a subspace $\mathfrak{H}_n$. Of special importance are the trivial space $\mathfrak{H}_0 = \langle\Omega\rangle$ and the space $\mathfrak{H}_1$, which allows a natural mapping onto the space of positive frequency solutions of $(\square + m^2)\psi = 0$:

$$\Phi^{(e_\beta)} \to f_\beta.$$

This space does not depend on the special choice of the basis $\{f_\alpha\}$ and it is, as well as $\mathfrak{H}_0$, Lorentz invariant. $\mathfrak{H}$ itself is the Fock space [Fo 1; Co 1; Ka 1, 2; Wi 3] constructed over $\mathfrak{H}_1$:

(24)
$$\mathfrak{H} = \mathfrak{H}_0 \oplus \mathfrak{H}_1 \oplus (\mathfrak{H}_1 \circledS \mathfrak{H}_1) \oplus (\mathfrak{H}_1 \circledS \mathfrak{H}_1 \circledS \mathfrak{H}_1) \oplus \cdots,$$

where $\mathfrak{H}_1 \circledS \cdots \circledS \mathfrak{H}_1$ is the symmetric tensor product of n factors $\mathfrak{H}_1$. The operators N_α and N are, to begin with, only defined on the basis (19), but linear extension and closure leads to selfadjoint operators ([Co 1] and §6).

The field operator $A(x)$ becomes an operator-valued distribution, as is already evident from (13). To every real testing function φ from the space $\mathscr{S}$ [Sw 2*] of testing functions corresponds an operator

(25)
$$A(\varphi) = \int A(x)\varphi(x)\, d^4x,$$

defined on the manifold D of states having only a finite number of non-vanishing components in the decomposition of $\mathfrak{H}$ into a direct sum (24). It is essentially selfadjoint on D [Wi 3], as we shall see in §6.

$\mathfrak{H}_0$ is Lorentz invariant and carries the trivial representation of the inhomogeneous Lorentz group. $\mathfrak{H}_1$ carries an irreducible, unitary, continuous representation of this group. This representation induces (reducible) representations in each space $\mathfrak{H}^{\circledS n}$. Thus the total $\mathfrak{H}$ itself carries a unitary continuous representation $U(a, \Lambda)$, which, from (9), (19), and (23), satisfies

(26)
$$U(a, \Lambda)A(x)U^{-1}(a, \Lambda) = A(\Lambda x + a).$$

The infinitesimal generators of $U(a, \Lambda)$ are the selfadjoint operators P_k and P_{lm}, which satisfy (16) and (17). The spectrum of P is found, except for an isolated eigenvalue $\{p = 0\}$ corresponding to $\Omega = \Phi^{(0)}$, to lie in the forward light-cone V_+.

5. **The free Dirac field.** We are already familiar with the Dirac equation

$$(\gamma^k \partial_k + m)\psi = 0, \tag{1}$$

where γ^k are 4×4 matrices satisfying $\gamma^k\gamma^l + \gamma^l\gamma^k = -2g^{kl}$ and we know its Lorentz covariance. γ^0 can be chosen antihermitian and γ^r $(r = 1, 2, 3)$ hermitian, and we keep to this choice. It is not hard to see that the algebra of the γ-matrices has exactly one irreducible representation [Pa 1*, p. 220]. If we define $\psi^+ = i\psi^*\gamma^0$ then

$$\partial_k\psi^+\gamma^k - m\psi^+ = 0 \tag{2}$$

is a consequence of (1). The transpose of the last equation is

$$-\gamma^{k^T}\partial_k\psi^{+^T} + m\psi^{+^T} = 0, \tag{3}$$

but $-\gamma^{k^T}$ satisfy the same algebraic relations as γ^k and there must exist a matrix $C = (C^*)^{-1}$ such that $C^{-1}\gamma^k C = -\gamma^{k^T}$. Then

$$\psi^c = C\psi^{+^T} \tag{4}$$

satisfies

$$(\gamma^k\partial_k + m)\psi^c = 0. \tag{5}$$

In the special representation of Chapter I, §5, we had $\psi^c = \bar{\psi}$ and $C = -i\gamma^0 = C^*, C^T = -C$. The antisymmetry of C is independent of the representation and $C^* = C$ can always be achieved (for a hermitian representation of γ^r $(1 \leqq r \leqq 4)$) [Pa 3, 4]. Of special importance is a conservation law connected with the gauge invariance of the Dirac equation: it easily follows from (1) and (2) that $s^k_{,k} = 0$, where

$$s^k = i\psi^+\gamma^k\psi. \tag{6}$$

This allows us to define an invariant, time-independent scalar product of two solutions ψ and χ of the Dirac equation:

$$(\psi, \chi) = i\int_{x^0=t} \psi^+\gamma^0\chi\, d^3x \tag{7}$$

which upon substitution of ψ^+ takes the simple form of

$$(\psi, \chi) = \int_{x^0=t} \psi^*\chi\, d^3x. \tag{8}$$

In marked contrast to the situation for the complex scalar field, the scalar product for the Dirac field is positive-definite. This important fact was originally taken as an indication that s^0 should be interpreted as a probability density [Pa 1*]. However, this interpretation could only be kept at a completely untenable price: no lower bound for the energy and therefore instability and rapid decay of all matter. *The unquantized Dirac field has therefore no useful physical interpretation.* We remark that

(9) $$(\psi^c, \chi^c) = (\psi, \chi)^* = (\chi, \psi).$$

Next we want to express this scalar product in terms of the Fourier transforms of the fields ψ and ψ^c. In order to prepare this, we first remark that ψ satisfies the Klein-Gordon equation $(\Box + m^2)\psi = 0$. The support of the Fourier transform is again a hyperboloid of which one shell corresponds to "positive" and the other to "negative" frequencies. If ψ belongs to positive frequencies then ψ^c belongs to negative frequencies. It is therefore sufficient to discuss the plane wave solutions for positive frequencies:

(10) $$\psi = u(p)e^{-i(p,x)}, \qquad p_0 = +\sqrt{(m^2 + \vec{p}^2)} = \omega(p).$$

The Dirac equation claims $(-i\gamma^k p_k + m)u(p) = 0$ or, after multiplication by $i\gamma^0$: $(-p_0 + \sum_r \alpha^r p_r + m\beta)u(p) = 0$, where $\alpha^r = \gamma^0\gamma^r$ and $\beta = i\gamma^0$. α^r and β satisfy the relations

(11) $$\alpha^r\alpha^s + \alpha^s\alpha^r = 2\delta_{rs}, \qquad \alpha^r\beta + \beta\alpha^r = 0, \qquad \beta\beta = 1$$

and they are hermitian. For $u(p)$ we have therefore a hermitian eigenvalue problem and we know the eigenvalue of interest: $p_0 = \omega(p)$. Let u_1, u_2 form an orthonormal basis:

(12) $$u_\sigma^*(p)u_{\sigma'}(p) = 2\omega(p)\delta_{\sigma\sigma'}.$$

Finally we write for the C-conjugate solution to $\psi = u_\sigma(p)e^{-i(p,x)}$:

(13) $$\psi^c = iC\gamma^{0T}\psi^{*T} = v_\sigma(+p)e^{i(p,x)}.$$

Now we are ready to give the Fourier decomposition of ψ:

(14)
$$\psi = (2\pi)^{-3/2}\int d^4p\delta(p^2 - m^2)\theta(p) \times \sum_{\sigma=1}^{2} [e^{-i(p,x)}a^\sigma(p)u_\sigma(p) + e^{i(p,x)}b^{\sigma*}(p)v_\sigma(p)],$$
$$\psi^c = (2\pi)^{-3/2}\int d^4p\delta(p^2 - m^2)\theta(p) \times \sum_{\sigma=1}^{2} [e^{-i(p,x)}b^\sigma(p)u_\sigma(p) + e^{i(p,x)}a^{\sigma*}(p)v_\sigma(p)].$$

For the scalar product we have the expression

$$(15)\quad (\psi, \psi) = \int d^4p\delta(p^2 - m^2)\theta(p) \times \sum_{\sigma=1}^{2} [a^{\sigma*}(p)a^{\sigma}(p) + b^{\sigma}(p)b^{\sigma*}(p)].$$

The Majorana reality condition amounts to the identification of $a^{\sigma}(p)$ with $b^{\sigma}(p)$.

Again we identify the solutions of the Dirac equation with the elements of the two Hilbert spaces $b^{\sigma} = 0$ and $a^{\sigma} = 0$ and defined by the scalar product (15). Each of these Hilbert spaces is invariant under the restricted, inhomogeneous Lorentz transformations and therefore gives rise to a unitary representation of this group. These representations belong to mass m and spin $\frac{1}{2}$. This last fact can easily be seen by observing the transformations induced by space rotations on the components $a^1(m, 0, 0, 0)$ and $a^2(m, 0, 0, 0)$. These transformations are described by SU_2.

Before we discuss the quantization of the Dirac field, we have to sketch how the free field theory fits into the general scheme of classical theory. As Lagrangian density we can, for example, take (other more elegant choices are also possible [Kä 1*])

$$(16)\quad L = -\psi^{+}(\gamma^k\partial_k + m)\psi,$$

where ψ and ψ^{+} have to be varied independently.

This leads to a nonsymmetric canonical energy momentum tensor

$$(17)\quad T^k{}_l = -\psi^{+}\gamma^k\psi_{,l} - \delta^k{}_l L.$$

The $\delta^k{}_l L$-term can be ignored if ψ is a solution of the Dirac equation. In this case, the energy momentum vector takes the form

$$(18)\quad P_k = i\int_{x^0=t} \psi^*\psi_{,k}\, d^3x$$

or, expressed in the Fourier transforms

$$(19)\quad P_k = \int d^4p\delta(p^2 - m^2)\theta(p)p_k \sum_{\sigma=1}^{2} [a^{\sigma*}(p)a^{\sigma}(p) - b^{\sigma}(p)b^{\sigma*}(p)].$$

We therefore find, again in marked difference to the case of the scalar field, that

$$(20)\quad P_0 = \int d^4p\delta(p^2 - m^2)\theta(p)\omega(p) \sum_{\sigma=1}^{2} [a^{\sigma*}(p)a^{\sigma}(p) - b^{\sigma}(p)b^{\sigma*}(p)]$$

is indefinite, a fact anticipated earlier.

The only way to remedy this catastrophic situation of an indefinite energy is quantization according to Fermi-Dirac statistics. The commutation rules are then as follows:

$$\begin{aligned}[a^{\sigma *}(p), a^{\sigma'}(p')]_+ &\equiv a^{\sigma *}(p)a^{\sigma'}(p') + a^{\sigma'}(p')a^{\sigma *}(p) \\ &= 2\omega(p)\delta(\vec{p} - \vec{p}\,')\delta_{\sigma\sigma'},\end{aligned} \tag{21}$$

$$[b^{\sigma *}(p), b^{\sigma'}(p')]_+ = 2\omega(p)\delta(\vec{p} - \vec{p}\,')\delta_{\sigma\sigma'} \tag{22}$$

and all other anticommutators ($[\ ]_+$ brackets) vanishing.

Now P_k can also be written as

$$P_k = \int d^4p\delta(p^2 - m^2)\theta(p)p_k \sum_{\sigma=1}^{2} [a^{\sigma *}(p)a^{\sigma}(p) + b^{\sigma *}(p)b^{\sigma}(p)] + P_k^0, \tag{23}$$

where P_k^0 is an undetermined, undefined and possibly infinite constant, which seems to be a comparatively minor obstacle, can be eliminated and will be ignored in what follows. After this correction of our bad fortunes we deal with a positive-definite energy

$$P_0 = \int d^4p\delta(p^2 - m^2)\theta(p)\omega(p) \sum_{\sigma=1}^{2} [a^{\sigma *}(p)a^{\sigma}(p) + b^{\sigma *}(p)b^{\sigma}(p)] \tag{24}$$

but our original scalar product

$$\begin{aligned}(\psi, \psi) = &\int d^4p\delta(p^2 - m^2)\theta(p) \sum_{\sigma=1}^{2} [a^{\sigma *}(p)a^{\sigma}(p) - b^{\sigma *}(p)b^{\sigma}(p)] \\ &+ 2\int d^4p\delta(p^2 - m^2)\theta(p)\end{aligned} \tag{25}$$

now becomes indefinite under the same (in part avoidable) manipulation of ignoring the last term. It is in fact, after multiplication by the elementary electric charge, the charge operator and the corresponding density $\epsilon(\psi^*\psi - \psi^{c*}\psi^c)/2$ is the source of the electrostatic field. The complete vector

$$s^k = \frac{i\epsilon}{2} [\psi^+\gamma^k\psi - \psi^{c+}\gamma^k\psi^c] \tag{26}$$

is the source of the electromagnetic field (as far as this source is carried by the spinor field ψ). The above "charge symmetric" form of s^k contains the subtraction indicated above and can serve as a model of how this subtraction can be effected in a natural and elegant way in more general situations (e.g. in the tensor $T^k{}_l$ or in the Lagrangian density). We note however that this is only possible after quantization. If we substitute in the above expression the c-number field we get s^k identically zero. For the anticommutation relations of the field ψ with itself and with ψ^+ one finds after some manipulations

$$(27)\quad \begin{aligned}[\psi_\alpha(x), \psi_\beta(y)]_+ &= [\psi^+_\alpha(x), \psi^+_\beta(y)]_+ = [\psi^c_\alpha(x), \psi^c_\beta(y)]_+ \\ &= [\psi^{c+}_\alpha(x), \psi^{c+}_\beta(y)]_+ = 0\end{aligned}$$

and

$$(28)\quad [\psi_\alpha(x), \psi^+_\beta(y)]_+ = -iS_{\alpha\beta}(x - y) = [\psi^c_\alpha(x), \psi^{c+}_\beta(y)]_+,$$

where

$$(29)\quad S(\xi) = (\gamma^k \partial_k - m)\,\Delta(\xi).$$

The main identities used to derive this result are

$$(30)\quad \sum_{\sigma=1}^{2} u_{\sigma,\alpha}(p) u^+_{\sigma,\beta}(p) = -[-i\gamma^k p_k - m]_{\alpha\beta}$$

and

$$(31)\quad \sum_{\sigma=1}^{2} v_{\sigma,\alpha}(p) v^+_{\sigma,\beta}(p) = +[i\gamma^k p_k - m]_{\alpha\beta}.$$

Before we discuss the connection between statistics and the "quantization by anticommutators", we want to point out two important facts.

1. A simple verification proves that

$$(32)\quad i[P_k, \psi] = \psi_{,k}, \qquad i[P_k, \psi^+] = \psi^+_{,k};$$

and therefore P_k becomes the infinitesimal translation operator. A similar result would be true for the angular momentum operator P_{kl}, derivable by the general formalism, but not derived here. Here too P_k and P_{kl} form a (highly reducible) representation of the infinitesimal Lorentz transformations.

2. $\psi(x)$ anticommutes with $\psi^+(y)$ at space-like separation. This has the important consequence, that *local*, *bilinear* expressions of ψ and ψ^+ commute at space-like separation. This is e.g. true for the current-density

$$(33)\quad s^k(x) = \frac{i\epsilon}{2}[\psi^+(x)\gamma^k\psi(x) - \psi^{c+}(x)\gamma^k\psi^c(x)]$$

for which one finds

$$(34)\quad [s^k(x), s^l(y)] = 0$$

for $(x - y)^2 < 0$. This fact is evidently of the greatest importance if we really couple the electromagnetic field F_{kl} to s^k by equations of the sort

$$(35)\quad F^k_{l,k} = s_l.$$

Now $F_{kl}(x)$ commutes with $F_{mn}(y)$ at space-like separation. This is the result of the usual canonical quantization, which leads to Bose-Einstein statistics for photons (and to the correct formula for black-body radiation). But this commutability is also strongly suggested by the local measurability, not of the electromagnetic field itself, but of mean values $F(\varphi) = \int F_{kl}\varphi^{kl}\, d^4x$ over test functions φ^{kl} with arbitrary small support.[4] Two such measurements of $F(\varphi_1)$ and $F(\varphi_2)$ will certainly disturb one another if the operators $F(\varphi_1)$ and $F(\varphi_2)$ do not commute. But we have no reason to expect such a disturbance for the case that every point in the support of φ_1 has a space-like separation from every point in the support of φ_2. In this case no action taking place in the support of φ_1 can propagate to any point in the support of φ_2 nor vice versa.

This principle of locality forces the commutator $[s^k(x), s^l(y)]$ to vanish for $(x - y)^2 < 0$ and this is satisfied for our commutation relations.

The Dirac field $\psi(x)$ itself is not measurable, even if we do not (as in the case of a Majorana field) impose any gauge group (stating that only quantities invariant under $\psi \to e^{i\alpha}\psi$ are measurable), because $\psi(x)$ belongs to a two-valued representation of $L_+^\uparrow$ and changes sign under a 360° rotation. We have therefore no reason to require commutability of $\psi(x)$ with $\psi^+(y)$ for space-like separation.

Finally, we discuss the representation of the commutation relations (21), (22). To do this, we introduce an orthonormal basis of *positive frequency* solutions:

(36) $$(\gamma^k\partial_k + m)u_\alpha = 0, \qquad (u_\alpha, u_\beta) = \delta_{\alpha\beta}$$

and the corresponding charge conjugate solutions $v_\alpha = u_\alpha^c = iC\gamma_0^T u_\alpha^{*T}$. The field ψ is then expanded:

(37) $$\psi = \sum_\alpha (A_\alpha u_\alpha + B_\alpha^* v_\alpha),$$

where

(38) $$A_\alpha = (u_\alpha, \psi), \qquad B_\alpha^* = (v_\alpha, \psi).$$

The charge conjugate field is given by

(39) $$\psi^c = \sum_\alpha (A_\alpha^* v_\alpha + B_\alpha u_\alpha).$$

The commutation relations (21), (22) are equivalent to the relations

(40) $$[A_\alpha, A_\beta^*]_+ = [B_\alpha, B_\beta^*]_+ = \delta_{\alpha\beta},$$

(41) $$[A_\alpha, B_\beta]_+ = [A_\alpha, B_\beta^*]_+ = 0.$$

---

[4]See [BR 1, 2; Cor 1; Hei 3].

As in the corresponding case of commutation relations, these anticommutation relations have many unitarily inequivalent representations (see e.g. [Gå 2]).

There is one which for us is of principal importance. As before, it is characterized by the existence of a "vacuum state" Ω with the property $A_\alpha\Omega = B_\alpha\Omega = 0$. To construct a basis for the Hilbert space, let $n^+(\alpha)$ and $n^-(\alpha)$ be two functions with range 0 and 1 satisfying $\sum_\alpha n^+(\alpha) < \infty$ and $\sum_\alpha n^-(\alpha) < \infty$. Again it is easy to verify that

$$\Phi^{(n^+,n^-)} = \prod_\alpha A_\alpha^{*\,n^+(\alpha)} \prod_\alpha B_\alpha^{*\,n^-(\alpha)}\Omega \tag{42}$$

(where a fixed though arbitrary sequence of the factors in the formally infinite products is observed) satisfy, from the anticommutation relations,

$$(\Phi^{(n^+,n^-)}, \Phi^{(m^+,m^-)}) = \delta(n^+, m^+)\delta(n^-, m^-). \tag{43}$$

Obviously (43) stays true after the definition

$$\Phi^{(0,0)} \equiv \Omega. \tag{44}$$

These vectors span a Hilbert space $\mathfrak{H}$. The vectors $\Phi^{(n^+,m^-)}$, which belong to a fixed sum $\sum_\alpha (n^+(\alpha) + n^-(\alpha)) = n$ span a subspace $\mathfrak{H}_n$. $\mathfrak{H}_0$ is one-dimensional and Lorentz invariant. $\mathfrak{H}_1$ is in a natural way mapped on the Hilbert space of the positive frequency solutions of the Dirac equation. Under the action of the inhomogeneous Lorentz group it decomposes into two irreducible spaces which carry the same representation of mass m and spin $\frac{1}{2}$. $\mathfrak{H}_n$ is the antisymmetric direct product of n factors $\mathfrak{H}_1$:

$$\mathfrak{H}_n = \mathfrak{H}_1 \,@\, \cdots \,@\, \mathfrak{H}_1. \tag{45}$$

It carries a uniquely determined unitary continuous representation of the universal covering group of the inhomogeneous Lorentz group, as well as the total Hilbert space $\mathfrak{H}$ which is given by

$$\mathfrak{H} = \bigoplus_{n=0}^{\infty} \mathfrak{H}_n. \tag{46}$$

Again, it was first introduced in this way by Fock [Fo 1; Ka 1, 2; Co 1].

The operators $N_\alpha^+ = A_\alpha^* A_\alpha$ and $N_\alpha^- = B_\alpha^* B_\alpha$ are defined by

$$N_\alpha^\pm \Phi^{(n^+,n^-)} = n^\pm(\alpha)\Phi^{(n^+,n^-)}. \tag{47}$$

They are bounded and selfadjoint. The operators $N^\pm = \sum_\alpha N_\alpha^\pm$, which are defined on the dense set of finite linear combinations of the basis vectors (42), have a unique selfadjoint extension.

$N_\alpha^\pm$ are the operators for the numbers of particles in the states u_α and v_α, respectively, and $N_\alpha^\pm$ for the total number of particles in all the states $\{u_\alpha\}$

and $\{v_\alpha\}$. We are clearly dealing with Fermi-Dirac statistics, since the occupation numbers $n^\pm(\alpha)$ are restricted to the eigenvalues 0 and 1.

As in §4 the fields $\psi(x)$ and $\psi^+(x)$ are only meaningful if averaged over suitable testing functions:

$$\psi(\varphi) = \int \psi(x)\varphi(x)\, d^4x. \tag{48}$$

Under the unitary representation $U(a, \Lambda')$ of the universal covering group $\{(a, \Lambda')\}$ of the inhomogeneous Lorentz group the fields transform covariantly:

$$U(a, \Lambda')\psi(x)U^{-1}(a, \Lambda') = S(\Lambda'^{-1})\psi(\Lambda x + a), \tag{49}$$

where $\Lambda(\Lambda')$ is the Lorentz transformation corresponding to Λ' and $S(\Lambda')$ the representation of $SL_2(C)$ to which the Dirac spinor ψ belongs according to Chapter I, §§4, 5.

6. **The generalized free real scalar fields.** The free fields will serve as models from which we shall abstract the Wightman axioms. This is the reason why we discuss here a mathematically more satisfactory approach to the free real scalar field. All other free fields can be treated in a very similar way. Our model will actually be slightly more general. The *generalized free fields* to be discussed played some role in recent investigations of the Wightman axioms.

All ideas which underlie the construction are essentially due to V. Fock [Fo 1].

The construction will be done in the following way. First we construct the Hilbert space $\mathfrak{H}$. Then follows the "smeared out" field operator $\tilde{A}(\tilde{\varphi})$ in momentum space. Finally, after a few mathematical steps, we arrive at the field operator $A(x)$ in x-space. A unitary continuous representation of the inhomogeneous Lorentz group will appear during the construction of $\mathfrak{H}$.

A. The Hilbert space. We start with a positive, $L_+^\uparrow$-invariant measure $d\rho$ from $\tilde{\mathscr{S}}'$, the space of the tempered distributions over the momentum space. $d\rho$ is from $\tilde{\mathscr{S}}'$ if, for some $k > 0$, $d\rho/(1 + \|p\|^2)^{k/2}$ is bounded. We require further that supp $d\rho \subset V_+$.

Let $\mathfrak{H}_1$ be the Hilbert space of the $d\rho$-measurable, square integrable functions ψ_1,

$$\|\psi_1\|^2 = \int |\psi_1(p)|^2\, d\rho(p) < \infty. \tag{1}$$

Functions ψ_1 which differ on a $d\rho$-null set are identified as usual. Thus two functions which differ only outside V_+ are equal as elements of $\mathfrak{H}_1$.

We want to construct the *Fock space* over $\mathfrak{H}_1$. In order to do this, we first introduce the symmetric tensor product $\mathfrak{H}_n$ of n spaces $\mathfrak{H}_1$. $\mathfrak{H}_n$ contains all $(d\rho)^{\times n}$ square integrable functions $\psi_n(p_1, p_2, \cdots, p_n)$ symmetric in the n vector variables $p_1, p_2, \cdots, p_n$. We write

$$\|\psi_n\|^2 = \int |\psi_n(p_1, p_2, \cdots, p_n)|^2 \, d\rho(p_1) d\rho(p_2) \cdots d\rho(p_n). \tag{2}$$

Finally we introduce $\mathfrak{H}_0$, the *vacuum space*, as a one-dimensional Hilbert space. The state generating $\mathfrak{H}_0$ is denoted by Ω.

The Fock space $\mathfrak{H}$ is defined as the direct sum

$$\mathfrak{H} = \bigoplus_{n=0}^{\infty} \mathfrak{H}_n. \tag{3}$$

Its elements are therefore sequences $\Psi = (\psi_0, \psi_1, \cdots)$, $\psi_n \in \mathfrak{H}_n$ and the norm is defined by

$$\|\Psi\|^2 = \sum_{n=0}^{\infty} \|\psi_n\|^2. \tag{4}$$

$\mathfrak{H}$ is clearly a separable Hilbert space. It carries a unitary, continuous representation of the inhomogeneous Lorentz group, given by

$$(U(a, \Lambda)\Psi)_n(p_1 \cdots p_n) = e^{i(a, \Sigma p_k)} \psi_n(\Lambda^{-1}p_1, \cdots, \Lambda^{-1}p_n). \tag{5}$$

The $L_+^\uparrow$ invariance of $d\rho$ guarantees that

$$\|U(a, \Lambda)\Psi\|^2 = \|\Psi\|^2. \tag{6}$$

The translation operator $T(a) = U(a, I)$ has the spectral decomposition

$$T(a) = \int e^{i(p,a)} \, dE(p) \tag{7}$$

and $dE(p)$ is defined by the formula

$$\left(\int f(p) \, dE(p)\Psi\right)_n (p_1 \cdots p_n) = f(p_1 + p_2 + \cdots + p_n)\psi_n(p_1, p_2, \cdots, p_n), \tag{8}$$

which holds for any bounded measurable function f.

The spectrum of the infinitesimal generators

$$P = \int p \, dE(p) \tag{9}$$

of $T(a)$ (which have to be interpreted as the components of the energy momentum vector) is the support of $dE(p)$. This is given by

$$\text{supp } dE(p) = \{0\} \cup \bigcup_{n=1}^{\infty} n \cdot \text{supp } d\rho, \tag{10}$$

where $n \cdot \operatorname{supp} d\rho = \{p | p = p_1 + p_2 + \cdots + p_n;\ p_k \in \operatorname{supp} d\rho\}$. It contains the discrete eigenvalue $p = 0$, corresponding to the vacuum $\mathfrak{H}_0$ and is, for the rest, contained in V_+.

B. The field operator in momentum space. We now introduce the "smeared out" field operator $\int \tilde{A}(p)\tilde{\varphi}(p)\, d^4p$ in momentum space. As a preliminary step we characterize the space of the "smearing functions" $\tilde{\varphi}$. The largest space that can be allowed is again an L_2-space, namely, $L_2(\rho_1)$ when the measure $d\rho_1$ is defined by

$$d\rho_1(p) = d\rho(p) + d\rho(-p). \tag{11}$$

The norm in $L_2(\rho_1)$ is given by the usual expression

$$\|\tilde{\varphi}\|^2 = \int |\tilde{\varphi}(p)|^2\, d\rho_1(p) = \int [|\tilde{\varphi}(p)|^2 + |\tilde{\varphi}(-p)|^2]\, d\rho(p). \tag{12}$$

Now the operator $\tilde{A}(\tilde{\varphi})$ is defined by

$$\begin{aligned}(\tilde{A}(\tilde{\varphi})\Psi)_n(p_1 \cdots p_n) = {} & \frac{1}{\sqrt{n}} \sum_{k=1}^{n} \tilde{\varphi}(p_k)\psi_{n-1}(p_1 \cdots \check{p}_k \cdots p_n) \\ & + \sqrt{(n+1)} \int \tilde{\varphi}(-p)\psi_{n+1}(p, p_1 \cdots p_n)\, d\rho(p),\end{aligned} \tag{13}$$

where $\check{p}_k$ means that the variable p_k has to be left out.

Since $\tilde{A}(\tilde{\varphi})$ is in all interesting cases an unbounded operator, we have to specify its domain. The expression (13) defines a vector in $\mathfrak{H}$, if Ψ has only a finite number of nonvanishing components. This domain, which we shall call D_2, is common to all $\tilde{A}(\tilde{\varphi})$. If P_N is the projection which annihilates the components of a vector of index greater than N, then D_2 is defined by

$$D_2 = \bigcup_{N=0}^{\infty} P_N \mathfrak{H}. \tag{14}$$

Let us denote the restriction of $\tilde{A}(\tilde{\varphi})$ to D_2 by $\tilde{A}_2(\tilde{\varphi})$.

For the matrix elements of $\tilde{A}(\tilde{\varphi})$ we obtain formally

$$\begin{aligned}(\mathrm{X}, \tilde{A}(\tilde{\varphi})\Psi) = \sum_{n=0}^{\infty} \Big\{ & \sqrt{n} \int \bar{\chi}_n(p_1 \cdots p_n)\tilde{\varphi}(p_1)\psi_{n-1}(p_2 \cdots p_n)\, d\rho^{\times n} \\ & + \sqrt{(n+1)} \int \bar{\chi}_n(p_1 \cdots p_n)\tilde{\varphi}(-p)\psi_{n+1}(p, p_1 \cdots p_n)\, d\rho^{\times(n+1)} \Big\}.\end{aligned} \tag{15}$$

If $\Psi \in D_2$ then the formally infinite sum in (15) is finite and we can legitimately reorder the sum to obtain

$$\begin{aligned}(\mathrm{X}, \tilde{A}_2(\tilde{\varphi})\Psi) = \sum_{n=0}^{\infty} \Big\{ & \sqrt{(n+1)} \int \tilde{\varphi}(p)\bar{\chi}_{n+1}(p, p_1 \cdots p_n)\psi_n(p_1 \cdots p_n)\, d\rho^{\times(n+1)} \\ & + \sqrt{n} \int \tilde{\varphi}(-p_1)\bar{\chi}_{n-1}(p_2 \cdots p_n)\psi_n(p_1 \cdots p_n)\, d\rho^{\times n} \Big\}\end{aligned} \tag{16}$$

and we find that

$$(\mathrm{X}, \tilde{A}_2(\tilde{\varphi})\Psi) = (\tilde{A}(\tilde{\varphi}^*)\mathrm{X}, \Psi), \tag{17}$$

where

$$\tilde{\varphi}^*(p) = \overline{\tilde{\varphi}(-p)}, \tag{18}$$

provided $\tilde{A}(\tilde{\varphi}^*)\mathrm{X}$ *exists*, provided therefore that the expressions, constructed according to (13) with $\tilde{\varphi}$ replaced by $\tilde{\varphi}^*$, actually are the components of a vector in $\mathfrak{H}$ (≡ lead to a finite norm (4)). Let us denote the vectors for which this is true by $D_{\tilde{\varphi}^*}$. $D_{\tilde{\varphi}^*}$ is the domain of $\tilde{A}(\tilde{\varphi}^*)$ and correspondingly $D_{\tilde{\varphi}}$ the domain of $\tilde{A}(\tilde{\varphi})$. What (17) tells us is that

$$\tilde{A}(\tilde{\varphi}^*) = [\tilde{A}_2(\tilde{\varphi})]^*. \tag{19}$$

The rest of the analysis depends on the

LEMMA. *Let* $\mathrm{X} \in D_{\tilde{\varphi}^*}$ *and* $\Psi \in D_{\tilde{\varphi}}$, *and*

$$R_N = (P_N\mathrm{X}, \tilde{A}(\tilde{\varphi})\Psi) - (\tilde{A}(\tilde{\varphi}^*)\mathrm{X}, P_N\Psi) \tag{20}$$

then $\lim R_N = 0$ *as* $N \to \infty$.

PROOF. R_N certainly has a limit for $N \to \infty$, in fact

$$\lim_{N\to\infty} R_N = (\mathrm{X}, \tilde{A}(\tilde{\varphi})\Psi) - (\tilde{A}(\tilde{\varphi}^*)\mathrm{X}, \Psi). \tag{21}$$

Now (13) yields for R_N the equation

$$\begin{aligned}(N+1)^{-1/2}R_N = &\int \bar{\chi}_N(p_1 \cdots p_N)\tilde{\varphi}(-p)\psi_{N+1}(p, p_1 \cdots p_N)\, d\rho^{\times(N+1)} \\ &- \int \bar{\chi}_{N+1}(p, p_1 \cdots p_N)\tilde{\varphi}(p)\psi_N(p_1 \cdots p_N)\, d\rho^{\times(N+1)}\end{aligned} \tag{22}$$

and this can be majorized with Schwarz's inequality, using the definition of $\|\tilde{\varphi}\|$ (12), by

$$\begin{aligned}(N+1)^{-1/2}|R_N| &\leqq \|\chi_N\|\,\|\tilde{\varphi}\|\,\|\psi_{N+1}\| + \|\chi_{N+1}\|\,\|\tilde{\varphi}\|\,\|\psi_N\| \\ &= \|\tilde{\varphi}\|\,[\|\chi_N\|\,\|\psi_{N+1}\| + \|\chi_{N+1}\|\,\|\psi_N\|]\end{aligned} \tag{23}$$

so that, using Schwarz's inequality again

$$\sum_{N=0}^{\infty} (N+1)^{-1/2}|R_N| \leqq 2\|\tilde{\varphi}\| \cdot \|\mathrm{X}\| \cdot \|\Psi\|. \tag{24}$$

(21) and (24) clearly imply $R_N \to 0$ as $N \to \infty$.

Now we are ready for the

THEOREM.

$$\tilde{A}(\tilde{\varphi}^*) = [\tilde{A}(\tilde{\varphi})]^*. \tag{25}$$

PROOF. The lemma states that (see (21))

$$(X, \tilde{A}(\tilde{\varphi})\Psi) = (\tilde{A}(\tilde{\varphi}^*)X, \Psi) \tag{26}$$

for $\Psi \in D_{\tilde{\varphi}}$ and $X \in D_{\tilde{\varphi}^*}$. So we find $\tilde{A}(\tilde{\varphi}^*) \subseteq [\tilde{A}(\tilde{\varphi})]^*$. Since $\tilde{A}(\tilde{\varphi})$ is an extension of $\tilde{A}_2(\tilde{\varphi})$ we also have in view of (19) $\tilde{A}(\tilde{\varphi}^*) \supseteq [\tilde{A}(\tilde{\varphi})]^*$ and therefore (25).

As a special case of (25) we find the

COROLLARY. *If $\tilde{\varphi}^* = \tilde{\varphi}$ then $\tilde{A}(\tilde{\varphi})$ is selfadjoint.*

C. RESTRICTIONS OF THE DOMAINS. THE FIELD OPERATOR IN x-SPACE.

DEFINITION. A domain $D \subset D_2$ is *essential* if the restrictions of $\tilde{A}(\tilde{\varphi})$ to D, which we call $\tilde{A}_0(\tilde{\varphi})$ has the property

$$[\tilde{A}_0(\tilde{\varphi})]^* = \tilde{A}(\tilde{\varphi}^*). \tag{27}$$

Hence, if $\tilde{A}(\tilde{\varphi})$ is restricted to an essential domain we can always recover $\tilde{A}(\tilde{\varphi})$ completely by passing to the adjoint. In particular, if $\tilde{\varphi}^* = \tilde{\varphi}$ then $\tilde{A}_0(\tilde{\varphi})$ is essentially selfadjoint.

THEOREM. *The following domains are essential:*

D, which contains all the vectors of D_2, for which the components are strongly decreasing Schwartz test functions. In the notation of Chapter I, §1A, (18)

$$D = D_2 \cap \underline{\tilde{\mathscr{S}}}; \tag{28}$$

D_1, which contains all the vectors of D_2, for which, for all n, the nth component is in $\tilde{\mathscr{S}}^{\otimes n}$.

The restriction of $\tilde{A}(\tilde{\varphi})$ to D will be denoted by $\tilde{A}_0(\tilde{\varphi})$ and to D_1 by $\tilde{A}_1(\tilde{\varphi})$.

The verification of (27) and the corresponding equation for $\tilde{A}_1$ is identical with the derivation of (17).

Next we consider the dependence of $\tilde{A}_2(\tilde{\varphi})$ on $\tilde{\varphi}$. According to the definition (13) $\tilde{A}_2(\tilde{\varphi})$ is continuous in $\tilde{\varphi}$ (on D_2) in the topology given by (12). Therefore we can (and in fact we shall) restrict $\tilde{\varphi}$ to a dense subset in $L_2(\rho_1)$. We choose the subset $\tilde{\mathscr{S}}$, the test function space over the momentum space $\tilde{R}^4$. Since the topology in $\tilde{\mathscr{S}}$ is finer than the topology induced by $L_2(\rho_1)$, $\tilde{A}_2(\tilde{\varphi})$ becomes a *tempered operator-valued distribution.* The same is correct for $\tilde{A}_1(\tilde{\varphi})$ and $\tilde{A}_0(\tilde{\varphi})$.

With this restriction, D, D_1 and D_2 are stable under $\tilde{A}(\tilde{\varphi})$, so that we have, for instance,

$$\tilde{A}(\tilde{\varphi})D \subset D, \tag{29}$$

and an identical equation for D_1 and D_2.

This means that we can freely multiply $\tilde{A}_k(\tilde{\varphi})$, $k = 0, 1, 2$, and can consider the algebra $\mathfrak{A}$ generated by the field operators. If $\mathfrak{A}$ is applied to Ω (the vacuum state) then we obtain D_1:

$$D_1 = \mathfrak{A}\Omega. \tag{30}$$

Ω is therefore a *cyclic vector* of $\mathfrak{A}$.

The operators in x-space are obtained by the usual rules for Fourier transformation of tempered distributions (Chapter I, §IC):

$$A_0(\varphi) = \int A_0(x)\varphi(x)\, d^4x = \tilde{A}_0(\tilde{\varphi}) \tag{31}$$

and similarly for A_1 and A_2.

$\tilde{\varphi}^* = \tilde{\varphi}$ means that φ is real. For real φ the operators $A_k(\varphi)$ are therefore *essentially selfadjoint*. For general φ we have (identical to (27))

$$A_0^*(\varphi) = A^{**}(\bar{\varphi}) \equiv A(\bar{\varphi}). \tag{32}$$

A simple calculation leads to the commutation relations

$$[A_0(x), A_0(y)] = \int \epsilon(p) e^{-i(p,x-y)}\, d\rho_1. \tag{33}$$

The commutator vanishes if $x - y$ is space-like. Thus the theory is *local.*

Finally $U(a, \Lambda)$ defined by (5) acts on $A_0(x)$ as follows

$$U(a, \Lambda)A_0(x)U^{-1}(a, \Lambda) = A_0(\Lambda x + a). \tag{34}$$

The ordinary free scalar field is, up to normalization, obtained if the measure $d\rho(p)$ is carried by the positive sheet of the hyperboloid $p^2 = m^2$.

CHAPTER III

The Axioms and the Wightman Distributions

1. **Introductory remarks.** With this chapter we start the subject proper of this volume, the "general theory of quantized fields". Several axiomatic treatments of the theory of quantized fields exist [Wi 1, 2, 3; LSZ 1; GLZ 1; Sm 1]. They all have the same intention, namely, to clear up the relation between the fundamental assumptions which underlie all specific models of quantized fields. In addition they all avoid those specific properties of the classical Lagrangian theory which definitely seem to lead to mathematical ambiguities.

Among the different approaches we mention Haag's [Ha 1, 2, 3] extremely fruitful ideas, to which we shall in part come back in the last chapters, and the theory of Lehmann, Symanzik and Zimmermann (LSZ-theory) [LSZ 1, 2; GLZ 1]. The latter theory, though mathematically less developed than the Wightman theory, has led to certain experimentally verifiable and verified predictions (dispersion relations): [Bog 1, 1*; Sy 1; Le 1, 2], for experiments [No 1].[1] The chapter describes first the axioms for a neutral scalar field (§2). In §3 a sequence of distributions is introduced (the Wightman distributions), which characterize the theory completely (§4). In §5 we make some additional remarks and introduce the truncated vacuum expectation values of R. Haag. §6 discusses the properties of the translation operator and its matrix elements.

2. **The axioms of Wightman for a neutral scalar field.** We shall take the theory of a free scalar field as a model and try to abstract from it general properties (formulated as axioms), which we can expect to be true in more general situations, as they may occur in a realistic description of natural phenomena.

Our restriction (in the process of deriving and in formulating the axioms) to one neutral scalar field is to a large extent immaterial in the

[1]Recently K. Hepp [Hep 4] succeeded in deriving dispersion relations from the Wightman-axioms. He made use of the Haag-Ruelle theory (Chapter VI).

sense that a generalization to (finitely or countably) many fields of other transformation properties (arbitrary spinor fields) would require only minor and obvious modifications. Later, in the applications, we shall need such a more general framework, and there will be a suitable place to make a few comments.

A. THE HILBERT SPACE. Our scalar field will, in some sense to be specified, be an operator acting on a linear vector space, the *space of states*. The zeroth axiom postulates that this space should be a Hilbert space.[2]

Zeroth axiom. The space of states is a Hilbert space $\mathfrak{H}$ over the complex numbers **C**. We denote the elements of $\mathfrak{H}$ by $\Phi, \Psi, \cdots$ and the positive, hermitian scalar product by (Φ, Ψ). It is antilinear in Φ and linear in Ψ.

B. THE SCALAR FIELD. Next we have to introduce as our fundamental quantity the operator of the scalar field. We already know from the discussion of the free scalar field $A_0(x)$ that only mean values over test functions $A_0(\varphi) = \int A_0(x)\varphi(x)\, d^4x$ are reasonable (though unbounded) operators.

A great variety of test functions $\varphi(x)$ are admissible in this case (Chapter II, §6). In the general case, however, we want to be rather conservative and restrict the test functions to the space $\mathscr{S}$ of C_∞ functions in space-time of rapid decrease (L. Schwartz) [Sw 2*, p. 89]. We remind the reader that a natural definition of convergence in $\mathscr{S}$ exists and, finally, that linear, continuous functionals over $\mathscr{S}$ are tempered distributions (Chapter I, §1).

First axiom. $\mathscr{S}$ is mapped into linear operators $\{A(\varphi)\}$ over $\mathfrak{H}$. $A(\varphi)$ is defined on a dense set D, independent of φ. For $\Phi, \Psi \in D$, $(\Phi, A(\varphi)\Psi)$ is a distribution and

$$(1) \qquad (\Phi, A(\varphi)\Psi) = (A(\bar{\varphi})\Phi, \Psi).$$

Finally we require that

$$(2) \qquad A(\varphi)D \subset D.$$

REMARKS. 1. A weaker form of the first axiom could be postulated if the space $\mathscr{S}$ is replaced by $\mathscr{D}$ (C_∞ functions in space-time of compact support). We do not discuss the question of whether this weaker form of the first axiom together with the other axioms does or does not imply the above stronger form.

2. If $\varphi = \bar{\varphi}$ then $A(\varphi)$ is a symmetric operator on D. We do not discuss here the question of whether $A(\varphi)$ has a selfadjoint extension.

[2]There is in fact no one-to-one correspondence between physical states and the elements of a Hilbert space, but there is a unique correspondence between the physical states and certain "rays" in a Hilbert space [Wey 1*]. A ray is a set $\{\psi = e^{i\alpha}\psi_0,\ \alpha$ real$\}$. In spite of this, we shall call the Hilbert space the space of states.

3. We shall sometimes formally write

$$A(\varphi) = \int A(x)\varphi(x)\, d^4x \tag{3}$$

or

$$(\Phi, A(\varphi)\Psi) = \int \varphi(x)(\Phi, A(x)\Psi)\, d^4x$$

and thus extend the definition of integrals to distributions.

4. The postulate $A(\varphi)D \subset D$ allows the free multiplication of operators $A(\varphi)$, $A(\psi)$, etc.

C. THE LORENTZ INVARIANCE. All that we have introduced so far is a one-component operator $A(\varphi)$ with its behavior under the inhomogeneous Lorentz transformations still unspecified. We know, however, how the transformation property of a *free* scalar field expresses itself through the existence of a unitary representation of the inhomogeneous Lorentz group. In order to formulate the corresponding postulate in the general case, we shall introduce the notation $\varphi_{(a,\Lambda)}(x) = \varphi(\Lambda^{-1}(x - a))$. $\varphi \to \varphi_{(a,\Lambda)}$ defines a well-behaved mapping of $\mathscr{S}$ onto $\mathscr{S}$.

Second axiom. A unitary (continuous) representation $U(a, \Lambda)$ of the restricted inhomogeneous Lorentz group exists and satisfies

$$U(a, \Lambda)A(\varphi)U^{-1}(a, \Lambda) = A(\varphi_{(a,\Lambda)}). \tag{4}$$

The domain D is Lorentz invariant:

$$U(a, \Lambda)D = D. \tag{5}$$

REMARKS. 1. According to the footnote on p. 52 the restricted Lorentz group first induces a ray representation in $\mathfrak{H}$. For details on the reduction of ray representations to ordinary representations, see [Ba 1, 2; Wi 4; Wig 1, 1*].

2. The representation of the translation group $\{(a, I)\}$ will be alternatively denoted by $T(a)$.

$T(a)$ is a representation of a (locally compact) abelian group and therefore allows a spectral resolution

$$T(a) = \int e^{i(p,a)}\, dE(p), \tag{6}$$

where E is a spectral measure with Lorentz invariant support [RN 1*] (Chapter I, §1E).

3. In the case of a spinor field, we would of course have to deal with a representation U of the covering group of the restricted inhomogeneous Lorentz group.

D. THE STABILITY OF THE VACUUM. We come now to one of the most characteristic postulates of Wightman's field theory. It deals with the spectrum of the energy momentum vector P, defined by $P_\mu = \int p_\mu \, dE(p)$, which is simultaneously the support of the spectral measure E.

Third axiom. (a) $\{p = 0\}$ is an isolated eigenvalue of P. The corresponding eigenspace is one-dimensional and corresponds to the vacuum Ω, $\Omega \in D$.

(b) The rest of the spectrum of P is in V_+.

REMARKS. 1. The eigenspace to $\{p = 0\}$ is invariant under $L_+^\uparrow$. Since $L_+^\uparrow$ has only the trivial one-dimensional representation, Ω satisfies $U(0, \Lambda)\Omega = \Omega$ and therefore $U(a, \Lambda)\Omega = \Omega$.

2. Since the spectrum of P is closed and Lorentz invariant, $\mu_0 > 0$ exists such that the spectrum is in fact contained in $\{p = 0\} \cup \bar{V}_+^{\mu_0}$, where $\bar{V}_+^{\mu_0} = \{p \in V_+, (p, p) \geqq \mu_0^2\}$. This is in part also implied by the postulate that $\{p = 0\}$ be an isolated eigenvalue.

3. There are important cases of fields occurring in nature, the electromagnetic field and the neutrino field, for which the third axiom is not satisfied in its above, strict form. In these cases the light cone N_+ also belongs to the spectrum, because the corresponding particles, the light quantum and the neutrino, have mass zero. We do not discuss these cases, and in fact their direct treatment may lead to difficulties. There is, however, the more or less justified hope that these fields could be treated as limiting cases of a fictional theory in which the photon and neutrino have positive mass, taking the limit for this mass going to zero.

4. If we assume the third axiom in its above form, then any state Φ orthogonal to Ω has an energy expectation value $(\Phi, P_0\Phi)/(\Phi, \Phi) \geqq \mu_0$ and the vacuum is *defined* by $(\Omega, P_0\Omega) = 0$.

5. For specific problems, an assumption of more detailed information about the spectrum of P may be essential and indicated. For example, if one wants to describe one kind of neutral spin 0 particle, which does not form bound states, then the spectrum of P (including multiplicity) will be identical with the corresponding spectrum for a *free* scalar field. Instances for which such additional information becomes essential are the definition of asymptotic states and the derivation of dispersion relations.

E. LOCALITY.

DEFINITION. Two sets $\mathfrak{s}_1$ and $\mathfrak{s}_2$ have a space-like separation if any pair of points (x_1, x_2), $x_1 \in \mathfrak{s}_1$, $x_2 \in \mathfrak{s}_2$ satisfies $(x_1 - x_2)^2 < 0$.

Fourth axiom. If supp φ_1 and supp φ_2 are compact and have a space-like separation, then

$$(7) \qquad [A(\varphi_1)A(\varphi_2) - A(\varphi_2)A(\varphi_1)]\Phi \equiv [A(\varphi_1), A(\varphi_2)]\Phi = 0$$

for all $\Phi \in D$.

REMARKS. 1. It follows from §3B that (7) also holds for testing functions without compact support.

2. We shall sometimes simply write

$$[A(x), A(y)] = 0 \tag{8}$$

for $(x - y)^2 < 0$ instead of the more careful formulation above. Whereas the distribution theoretic sense of (7) is perfectly clear, its operator-theoretic implications are only specified if we restrict the operators $A(\varphi)$ to the domain D.

3. The heuristic implication of equation (7) is, for the case of a measurable field $A(x)$, that measurements at a space-like separation do not disturb one another, since no action travels with a velocity greater than c. Locality is certainly implied by this argument. It is, however, unclear whether or not it is equivalent to it.

4. The situation becomes more complicated if we have more fields in our theory and if $A(x)$ is, for example, the real part of a complex field ψ subjected to a gauge group. Then the arguments we made in connection with the Dirac free field should be remembered. Observable local fields (e.g. bilinear in ψ^* and ψ) would still commute at space-like separation, if in the above axiom we took anticommutativity instead of commutativity. In what way, however, this would lead to a contradiction with the other axioms will be shown later.

5. We shall also discuss later and in great detail the situation arising in a theory of several fields with arbitrary transformation properties. The necessary generalization of the fourth axiom will be given there.

F. COMPLETENESS. The fifth axiom expresses the fact that there "should be no other field independent of $A(x)$ in our theory".

Fifth axiom. Let $\mathfrak{P}(A)$ be the ring of polynomials (over $\mathbf{C}$) in the operators $A(\varphi)$, $\varphi \in \mathscr{S}$. Then $\mathfrak{P}(A)\Omega$ should be dense in $\mathfrak{H}$. Expressed differently: Ω should be cyclic with respect to the operators $\mathfrak{P}(A)$.

GENERAL REMARK ABOUT THE AXIOMS. The notion of particles enters nowhere into the axioms. It will appear in Chapter VI together with an additional postulate which guarantees a complete particle interpretation of our field theory.

3. **The Wightman distributions.** One of the principal tools for our later work consists of a certain sequence of distributions, the so-called Wightman distributions [Wi 1]. As we shall show in this and the next section, the content of the axioms can easily and completely be translated into properties of these distributions. Thus the analysis of the axioms can be replaced by a study of the Wightman distributions. This is in many cases an advantage.

A. DEFINITION OF THE WIGHTMAN DISTRIBUTIONS. The existence of a vacuum state Ω, the fact that $\Omega \in D$ and finally the postulate that $A(\varphi)D \subset D$ allows us to define the quantities

$$(\Omega, A(\varphi_1)A(\varphi_2) \cdots A(\varphi_n)\Omega) \equiv \mathfrak{W}_n(\varphi_1, \varphi_2, \cdots, \varphi_n) \tag{1}$$

for any $\varphi_k \in \mathscr{S}(R^4)$. The functional $\mathfrak{W}_n(\varphi_1, \varphi_2, \cdots, \varphi_n)$ is a tempered distribution in each variable φ_k separately. The nuclear theorem of L. Schwartz [Sw 1; Gå 3] then implies that $\mathfrak{W}_n(\varphi_1, \varphi_2, \cdots, \varphi_n)$ uniquely determines a tempered distribution $\mathfrak{W}_n(\varphi)$ for testing functions $\varphi(x_1, x_2, \cdots, x_n)$ over R^{4n} in such a way that for the special choice

$$\begin{aligned}\varphi(x_1, x_2, \cdots, x_n) &= \varphi_1(x_1)\varphi_2(x_2) \cdots \varphi_n(x_n)\\ &= (\varphi_1 \otimes \varphi_2 \otimes \cdots \otimes \varphi_n)(x_1, x_2, \cdots, x_n),\end{aligned}$$

$\mathfrak{W}_n(\varphi)$ reduces to $\mathfrak{W}_n(\varphi_1, \varphi_2, \cdots, \varphi_n)$.

The symmetry property $(\Phi, A(\varphi)\Psi) = (A(\bar{\varphi})\Phi, \Psi)$ leads to a symmetry of $\mathfrak{W}_n(\varphi)$, expressed by

$$\mathfrak{W}_n(\varphi) = \overline{\mathfrak{W}}_n(\varphi^*), \tag{2}$$

where

$$\varphi^*(x_1, x_2, \cdots, x_n) = \bar{\varphi}(x_n, \cdots, x_2, x_1). \tag{3}$$

B. AN APPLICATION. We define for $\chi(x_1, \cdots, x_n) = \varphi_1(x_1) \cdots \varphi_n(x_n)$ the vector-valued functional

$$\Phi_n(\chi) = A(\varphi_1)A(\varphi_2) \cdots A(\varphi_n)\Omega \tag{4}$$

and extend this definition by linearity

$$\begin{aligned}\Phi_n(\chi_1 + \chi_2) &= \Phi_n(\chi_1) + \Phi_n(\chi_2),\\ \Phi_n(c\chi) &= c\Phi_n(\chi).\end{aligned} \tag{5}$$

Thus we have a mapping of $\mathscr{S}^{\otimes n}(R^4)$ into vectors of $\mathfrak{H}$. We want to extend this mapping to a mapping of $\mathscr{S}(R^{4n})$ into $\mathfrak{H}$. Now $\mathscr{S}^{\otimes n}(R^4)$ is dense in $\mathscr{S}(R^{4n})$ [Sw 1*]. Let $\varphi \in \mathscr{S}(R^{4n})$ be arbitrary and $\chi_k \in \mathscr{S}^{\otimes n}(R^4)$ satisfy $\chi_k \to \varphi$ for $k \to \infty$. $\Phi_n(\chi_k - \chi_l) = \Phi_n(\chi_k) - \Phi_n(\chi_l)$ then satisfies

$$\|\Phi_n(\chi_k - \chi_l)\|^2 = \mathfrak{W}_{2n}((\chi_k - \chi_l)^* \otimes (\chi_k - \chi_l)) \tag{6}$$

and tends to zero for $k \to \infty, l \to \infty$. Thus $\Phi_n(\chi_k)$ converges and since $\mathfrak{H}$ is complete it tends to a vector $\Phi_n(\varphi) \in \mathfrak{H}$. We formally write

$$\Phi_n(\varphi) = \int A(x_1) \cdots A(x_n)\varphi(x_1, \cdots, x_n)\, d^4x_1 \cdots d^4x_n\Omega. \tag{7}$$

$\Phi_n(\varphi)$ is a tempered distribution with values in $\mathfrak{H}$.

For the operator

$$\int A(x_1) \cdots A(x_n) \varphi(x_1, \cdots, x_n)\, d^4x_1 \cdots d^4x_n$$

we shall sometimes write $\langle A^n, \varphi \rangle$. It is clearly defined on D. Finally we have the equations

$$(8) \qquad (\Phi_n(\varphi), \Phi_m(\psi)) = \mathfrak{W}_{n+m}(\varphi^* \otimes \psi)$$

and

$$(9) \qquad (\Omega, \Phi_m(\psi)) = \mathfrak{W}_m(\psi).$$

This suggests the notation $\Phi_0(\varphi) = \varphi\Omega$. φ in this case depends on no argument and is a constant. Similarly we put

$$\mathfrak{W}_0(\varphi) = \varphi.$$

C. The zeroth axiom. It implies

$$(10) \qquad \left\| \sum_{n=0}^{N} \Phi_n(\varphi_n) \right\|^2 \geqq 0$$

or, expressed in Wightman distributions,

$$(11) \qquad \sum_{n,m=0}^{N} \mathfrak{W}_{n+m}(\varphi_n^* \otimes \varphi_m) \geqq 0.$$

D. The second axiom. If we define

$$(12) \qquad \varphi_{(a,\Lambda)}(x_1, \cdots, x_n) = \varphi(\Lambda^{-1}(x_1 - a), \cdots, \Lambda^{-1}(x_n - a))$$

it implies

$$(13) \qquad \mathfrak{W}_n(\varphi_{(a,\Lambda)}) = \mathfrak{W}_n(\varphi).$$

Proof.

$$\begin{aligned}(\Omega, A(\varphi_1) \cdots A(\varphi_n)\Omega) &= (U^*(a, \Lambda)\Omega, A(\varphi_1) \cdots A(\varphi_n) U^{-1}(a, \Lambda)\Omega) \\ &= (\Omega, A(\varphi_{1(a,\Lambda)}) \cdots A(\varphi_{n(a,\Lambda)})\Omega),\end{aligned}$$

or, written in Wightman distributions,

$$\mathfrak{W}_n(\varphi_1 \otimes \cdots \otimes \varphi_n) = \mathfrak{W}_n((\varphi_1 \otimes \cdots \otimes \varphi_n)_{(a,\Lambda)})$$

which leads by the nuclear theorem to the result.

As a special case we have the translation invariance of $\mathfrak{W}_n(\varphi)$ and therefore the consequence that $\mathfrak{W}_{m+1}(\varphi)$ can be expressed as a distribution in m vector variables only [Sw 1*]. This change of variables is indicated formally by

(14) $\mathfrak{W}_{m+1}(x_0, x_1, \cdots, x_m) = W_m(x_1 - x_0, x_2 - x_1, \cdots, x_m - x_{m-1})$.

$W_m(\xi_1, \cdots, \xi_m)$ is still invariant under $L_+^\uparrow$:

(15) $$W_m(\Lambda\xi_1, \cdots, \Lambda\xi_m) = W_m(\xi_1, \cdots, \xi_m), \qquad \Lambda \in L_+^\uparrow.$$

E. THE THIRD AXIOM, FIRST PART. We come now to the restrictions imposed on the Wightman distributions by the third axiom. These are best expressed in terms of the Fourier transforms. A word on the Fourier transformation of tempered distributions [Sw 2*] may be in order (Chapter I, § 1C). The Fourier decomposition

(16) $$\varphi(x_1, \cdots, x_n) = \frac{1}{(2\pi)^{4n}} \int \exp\,[-i[(p_1, x_1) + \cdots + (p_n + x_n)]]\tilde{\varphi}(p_1, \cdots, p_n)\, d^{4n}p$$

of functions in $\mathscr{S}(R^{4n})$ is trivially possible.

$\tilde{\varphi}(p_1, \cdots, p_n)$ is again a C_∞-function of fast decrease, i.e., a function belonging to $\mathscr{S}(\tilde{R}^{4n})$, where $\tilde{R}^4$ denotes the vector space of the "momentum vectors" (or the dual space of R^4). This mapping is a (topological) isomorphism of $\mathscr{S}(\tilde{R}^{4n})$ onto $\mathscr{S}(R^{4n})$ [Sw 2*]. If S is a tempered distribution then the linear functional on $\mathscr{S}(\tilde{R})$ defined by

(17) $$\tilde{S}(\tilde{\varphi}) \equiv S(\varphi)$$

is again a tempered distribution. It is the Fourier transform of S. In this way we define $\tilde{\mathfrak{W}}_n(\tilde{\varphi})$, $\tilde{A}(\tilde{\varphi})$, $\tilde{\Phi}_n(\tilde{\varphi})$ and $\langle \tilde{A}^n, \tilde{\varphi}\rangle$.

The action of $T(a)$ on $\tilde{\Phi}_n(\tilde{\varphi})$ is easily computed:

(18) $$T(a)\tilde{\Phi}_n(\tilde{\varphi}) = T(a)\Phi_n(\varphi_n) = \Phi_n(\varphi_{(a,1)}) = \tilde{\Phi}_n\left(\tilde{\varphi}\,\exp\left[i\left(\sum_{k=1}^{n} p_k, a\right)\right]\right).$$

Thus one finds that for a sufficiently regular function $\chi(p)$, using the spectral decomposition of $T(a)$,

(19) $$\int \chi(p)\, dE(p)\tilde{\Phi}_n(\tilde{\varphi}) = \tilde{\Phi}_n(\chi(p_1 + \cdots + p_n)\tilde{\varphi}).$$

But the left-hand side of (19) vanishes if supp $\chi(p) \cap$ supp $(dE) = \emptyset$. Thus as a first conclusion the support of $\tilde{\Phi}_n(\tilde{\varphi})$ in the vector variable $p_1 + p_2 + \cdots + p_n$ is contained in the spectrum of P (i.e., the support of dE).

However, further results are immediate because

$$(20) \qquad (\tilde{A}^m, \tilde{\psi})\tilde{\Phi}_n(\tilde{\varphi}) = \tilde{\Phi}_{m+n}(\tilde{\psi} \otimes \tilde{\varphi})$$

and therefore

$$(21) \qquad \langle \tilde{A}^m, \tilde{\psi} \rangle \int \chi(p)\, dE(p)\tilde{\Phi}_n(\tilde{\varphi}) = \tilde{\Phi}_{n+m}(\tilde{\psi} \otimes \chi(p_1 + \cdots + p_n)\tilde{\varphi}).$$

This last expression vanishes again under the above condition on $\chi(p)$. But this equation implies that the support of $\tilde{\Phi}_n(\tilde{\varphi})$ is contained in $p_k + p_{k+1} + \cdots + p_n \in \operatorname{supp}(dE)$, $1 \leqq k \leqq n$. This result suggests a transformation of variables:

$$(22) \qquad q_k \equiv p_k + p_{k+1} + \cdots + p_n, \qquad 1 \leqq k \leqq n.$$

In these new variables we have the following

THEOREM. *Let $\tilde{\varphi}_q = \tilde{\varphi}(q_1, \cdots, q_n) \in \mathscr{S}(\tilde{R}^{4n})$. The support of $\tilde{\Phi}_n(\tilde{\varphi}_q)$ is contained in* [supp $dE]^{\times n}$.

This theorem leads to a corresponding statement about the support of

$$(23) \qquad \tilde{\mathfrak{W}}_n(\tilde{\varphi}_q) = (\Omega, \tilde{\Phi}_n(\tilde{\varphi}_q)) = (\Omega, \langle A^n, \varphi \rangle \Omega).$$

But this quantity is in addition translation invariant:

$$(24) \qquad (\Omega, T(a)\tilde{\Phi}_n(\tilde{\varphi}_q)) = (\Omega, \tilde{\Phi}_n(\tilde{\varphi}_q))$$

or

$$(25) \qquad \tilde{\mathfrak{W}}_n(\tilde{\varphi}_q e^{i(q_1, a)}) = \tilde{\mathfrak{W}}_n(\tilde{\varphi}_q),$$

which implies the formal equation

$$(26) \qquad \tilde{\mathfrak{W}}_n(q_1, q_2 \cdots q_n) = (2\pi)^4\, \delta(q_1)\tilde{W}_{n-1}(q_2, \cdots, q_n).$$

It is simple to verify, that (again in formal notation)

$$(27) \qquad \begin{aligned} &W_m(\xi_1, \cdots, \xi_m) \\ &\quad = \int \exp[i[(q_1\xi_1) + \cdots + (q_m\xi_m)]]\tilde{W}_m(q_1 \cdots q_m)\, d^{4m}q. \end{aligned}$$

Thus we have the

THEOREM.

$$(28) \qquad \operatorname{supp} \tilde{W}_m(q_1 \cdots q_m) \subset (\operatorname{supp} dE)^{\times m}.$$

F. THE THIRD AXIOM, SECOND PART. The third axiom is not exhausted by the theorem (28). (28) would also be true if the vacuum were degenerate.

The condition [Hep 1] which excludes this possibility follows easily from (19). If supp $\chi(p) \cap$ supp $dE = \{p \mid p = 0\}$ then $\Phi_n(\chi(p_1 + \cdots + p_n)\tilde{\varphi})$ has to be a multiple of Ω. Formulated in another way: If the support of $\tilde{\varphi}(p_1, \cdots, p_n)$ in the variable $p_1 + \cdots + p_n$ has only the point $p_1 + p_2 + \cdots + p_n = 0$ in common with the spectrum of P (the energy momentum operator), then $\tilde{\Phi}_n(\tilde{\varphi})$ is a multiple of Ω or

$$\|\tilde{\Phi}_n(\tilde{\varphi})\|^2 = (\tilde{\Phi}_n(\tilde{\varphi}), \Omega)(\Omega, \tilde{\Phi}_n(\tilde{\varphi})). \tag{29}$$

This last condition is in fact a restriction on Wightman distributions:

THEOREM. *If the support of $\tilde{\varphi}(p_1, \cdots, p_n)$ in the variable $p_1 + \cdots + p_n$ intersects the spectrum of P at most in the point $p_1 + \cdots + p_n = 0$, then*

$$\mathfrak{W}_{2n}(\varphi^* \otimes \varphi) = |\mathfrak{W}_n(\varphi)|^2. \tag{30}$$

G. THE FOURTH AXIOM. This axiom allows an immediate transcription into Wightman distributions. Let

$$\varphi(x_1 \cdots x_n) = \varphi_1(x_1) \cdots \varphi_k(x_k)\varphi_{k+1}(x_{k+1}) \cdots \varphi_n(x_n) \tag{31}$$

and

$$\varphi_{\mathrm{tr}}(x_1 \cdots x_n) = \varphi_1(x_1) \cdots \varphi_k(x_{k+1})\varphi_{k+1}(x_k) \cdots \varphi_n(x_n) \tag{32}$$

and suppose that supp $\varphi_k(x)$ and supp $\varphi_{k+1}(x)$ are compact and space-like separated then

$$\mathfrak{W}_n(\varphi) = \mathfrak{W}_n(\varphi_{\mathrm{tr}}). \tag{33}$$

H. SUMMARY. The restrictions on Wightman distributions can naturally be decomposed into linear and nonlinear ones.

a. *Linear restrictions.*

a1. $\mathfrak{W}_n$ is a tempered distribution in $\mathscr{S}'(R^{4n})$ and satisfies $\bar{\mathfrak{W}}_n(\varphi^*) = \mathfrak{W}_n(\varphi)$, where $\varphi^*(x_1 \cdots x_n) = \bar{\varphi}(x_n, \cdots, x_1)$.

a2. $\mathfrak{W}_n$ is invariant under the restricted inhomogeneous Lorentz group:

$$\mathfrak{W}_n(\varphi_{(a,\Lambda)}) = \mathfrak{W}_n(\varphi).$$

DEFINITION. $W_m(\xi_1, \cdots, \xi_m) \equiv \mathfrak{W}_{m+1}(x_0, \ x_1, \cdots, x_m)$ with $\xi_k \equiv x_k - x_{k-1}$.

a3. The support of $\tilde{W}_m(q_1 \cdots q_m)$ is contained in $\{q_k \in \mathfrak{s}_0, \mathfrak{s}_0 \subset \mathring{V}\}$.

a4. If supp φ_k and supp φ_{k+1} are compact and of space-like separation, then

$$\mathfrak{W}_n(\varphi_1 \otimes \cdots \otimes \varphi_k \otimes \varphi_{k+1} \otimes \cdots \otimes \varphi_n) = \mathfrak{W}_n(\varphi_1 \otimes \cdots \otimes \varphi_{k+1} \otimes \varphi_k \otimes \cdots \otimes \varphi_n).$$

b. *Nonlinear restrictions.*

b1. For any $\varphi_n(x_1 \cdots x_n) \in \mathscr{S}(R^{4n})$, $n = 0, 1, \cdots, N$, N arbitrary,

$$\sum_{m,n=0}^{N} \mathfrak{W}_{n+m}(\varphi_n^* \otimes \varphi_m) \geqq 0.$$

b2. If the support of $\tilde{\varphi}(p_1, \cdots, p_n)$ in the variable $p_1 + \cdots + p_n$ intersects the spectrum of P at most in the point $p_1 + \cdots + p_n = 0$, then

$$\mathfrak{W}_{2n}(\varphi^* \otimes \varphi) = |\mathfrak{W}_n(\varphi)|^2.$$

In the next section we shall show that the properties (a) and (b) form a complete characterization of the Wightman distributions.

4. The main theorem.

THEOREM [Wi 1]. *To a given sequence of distributions* $\mathfrak{W}_n$ *satisfying the conditions* (a) *and* (b) *of the last section, there corresponds uniquely a neutral scalar field* $A(x)$, *satisfying all the axioms and having the distributions* $\mathfrak{W}_n$ *as Wightman distributions.*

PROOF. (a) Let $\mathscr{S}_n = \mathscr{S}(R^{4n})$ for $n = 1, 2, 3, \cdots$ and $\mathscr{S}_0 = \mathbf{C}$ the field of the complex numbers. In this section we denote an element of $\mathscr{S}_n$ by φ_n.

(b) *Construction of the Hilbert space* $\mathfrak{H}$. To each φ_n corresponds a vector $\Phi_n(\varphi_n)$ of a linear space in such a way that $\Phi_n(\varphi_n + \psi_n) = \Phi_n(\varphi_n) + \Phi_n(\psi_n)$ and $\Phi_n(c\varphi_n) = c\Phi_n(\varphi_n)$ for $c \in \mathbf{C}$.

A scalar product is introduced by

$$(\Phi_n(\varphi_n), \Phi_m(\varphi_m)) \equiv \mathfrak{W}_{n+m}(\varphi_n^* \otimes \varphi_m) \tag{1}$$

and by linear extension in the second and antilinear extension in the first variable. This scalar product is symmetrical and positive semi-definite from condition b1. If Φ and Ψ are finite linear combinations of vectors $\Phi_n(\varphi_n)$, then (Φ, Ψ) is defined and satisfies the Schwarz inequality.

$$|(\Phi, \Psi)|^2 \leqq (\Phi, \Phi)(\Psi, \Psi). \tag{2}$$

The vector space has a radical, which from (2) corresponds exactly to the vectors with vanishing squares. The factor space with respect to this radical is, after completion, our Hilbert space $\mathfrak{H}$.

REMARK. The above construction of $\mathfrak{H}$ can, in more modern terms, be described in the following way [Bo 3] (Chapter I, § 1A). Let

$$\underline{\mathscr{S}} = \bigoplus_{n=0}^{\infty} \mathscr{S}_n \tag{3}$$

with the elements $\underline{\varphi}, \underline{\psi}, \cdots$ equipped with the locally convex direct sum topology [Kö 1*, p. 217] induced by the topologies in $\mathscr{S}_n$. $\underline{\mathscr{S}}$ is a module, it further allows a multiplication $\otimes$, where the n component of $\underline{\varphi} \otimes \underline{\psi}$ is defined as

$$(4) \qquad (\underline{\varphi} \otimes \underline{\psi})_n \equiv \sum_{k=0}^{n} \varphi_{n-k} \otimes \psi_k$$

and it possesses the antilinear involution defined by

$$(5) \qquad (\underline{\varphi}^*)_n \equiv \varphi_n^*.$$

$\underline{\mathscr{S}}$ is thus a topological* algebra.

Now the scalar product

$$(6) \qquad (\underline{\varphi}, \underline{\psi}) = \sum_{n,m} \mathfrak{W}_{n+m}(\varphi_n^* \otimes \psi_m)$$

and the corresponding metric $\|\underline{\varphi}\| = \sqrt{(\underline{\varphi}, \underline{\varphi})}$ is introduced. From conditions a1 and b1 this metric is defined and equips $\underline{\mathscr{S}}$ with a new and weaker topology.

Let $\underline{\mathscr{S}}_0 = \{\underline{\varphi} \mid (\underline{\varphi}, \underline{\varphi}) = 0\}$, then the completion of the factor space $\underline{\mathscr{S}}/\underline{\mathscr{S}}_0$ is identical to $\mathfrak{H}$ [Ne 1*, Chapter IV].

(c) *The dense domain D and the field operator A*. The domain D consists of all finite linear combinations of vectors $\Phi_n(\varphi_n)$. $A(\varphi)$ is defined by linear extension from the formula

$$(7) \qquad A(\varphi)\Phi_n(\varphi_n) = \Phi_{n+1}(\varphi \otimes \varphi_n).$$

The matrix elements of $A(\varphi)$ are given by

$$(8) \qquad (\Phi_m(\psi_m), A(\varphi)\Phi_n(\varphi_n)) = \mathfrak{W}_{m+n+1}(\psi_m^* \otimes \varphi \otimes \varphi_n)$$

and

$$(9) \qquad (A(\bar{\varphi})\Phi_m(\psi_m), \Phi_n(\varphi_n)) = \mathfrak{W}_{m+n+1}(\psi_m^* \otimes \varphi \otimes \varphi_n)$$

such that, for $\Phi, \Psi \in D$

$$(10) \qquad (\Psi, A(\varphi)\Phi) = (A(\bar{\varphi})\Psi, \Phi).$$

This last equation shows that the radical of the original vector space is mapped into itself by $A(\varphi)$. Finally we clearly have $A(\varphi)D \subset D$ and, from a1, $A(\varphi)\Phi \to 0$ strongly as $\varphi \to 0$.

Thus even a strengthened version of the first axiom is true here.

REMARKS. 1. For the rest of this work we shall stick to the above definition of D.

2.

(11) $$\langle A^m, \psi_m\rangle \Phi_n(\varphi_n) = \Phi_{m+n}(\psi_m \otimes \varphi_n).$$

3.

(12) $$\Phi_n(\varphi_n) \to 0$$

strongly as $\varphi_n \to 0$.

Φ_n is a tempered vector-valued distribution and has a Fourier transform $\tilde{\Phi}_n$. The support property a3 implies that $(\Psi, \tilde{\Phi}_n(\tilde{\varphi}_n)) = 0$ for $\Psi \in D$ unless a point with $p_1 + p_2 + \cdots + p_n \in \mathfrak{s}_0$ is contained in supp $\tilde{\varphi}_n$. Thus $\tilde{\Phi}_n(\tilde{\varphi}_n) = 0$ in this case.

(d) *The representation* $U(a, \Lambda)$. Linear extension of

(13) $$U(a, \Lambda)\Phi_n(\varphi_n) = \Phi_n(\varphi_{n(a,\Lambda)})$$

leads, from a2, to a unitary transformation of $\mathfrak{H}$ and a representation of the restricted inhomogeneous Lorentz group. A simple verification leads to

(14) $$U(a, \Lambda)\langle A^n, \varphi\rangle U^{-1}(a, \Lambda) = \langle A^n, \varphi_{(a,\Lambda)}\rangle.$$

Finally we have

(15) $$U(a, \Lambda)D = D.$$

Thus the second axiom is satisfied.

(e) *The spectrum of P*. Again we put

(16) $$T(a) = U(a, I) = e^{i(P,a)} = \int e^{i(p,a)}\, dE(p).$$

We have

(17) $$T(a)\tilde{\Phi}_n(\tilde{\varphi}_n) = \tilde{\Phi}_n(\tilde{\varphi}_n \exp[i((p_1 + \cdot \quad + p_n), a)])$$

and, for sufficiently smooth $\chi(q)$

(18) $$\int \chi(q)\, dE(q)\tilde{\Phi}_n(\tilde{\varphi}) = \tilde{\Phi}_n(\tilde{\varphi}_n \cdot \chi(p_1 + \cdots + p_n)).$$

The right-hand side vanishes if supp $\chi(q) \cap \mathfrak{s}_0 = \emptyset$.

From this one deduces that the spectrum of P is completely contained in $\mathfrak{s}_0$. Thus one part of the third axiom is verified.

(f) *The uniqueness of the vacuum.* Let $\chi(q) \in \mathscr{S}(\tilde{R}^4)$ satisfy

(19) $$\text{supp}\, \chi \cap \mathfrak{s}_0 = \{q \mid q = 0\}$$

and

(20) $$\chi(0) = 1.$$

Then the projection

$$E_0 = \int \chi(q)\, dE(q) \tag{21}$$

projects on the translation invariant states. $\Phi_0(\varphi_0) = \varphi_0\Omega$ gives one set of such states. We have to show that there are no others.

According to (14)–(17)

$$E_0 D \subset D \tag{22}$$

and therefore

$$E_0\mathfrak{H} = \overline{E_0 D \cap D}, \tag{23}$$

where the bar indicates closure. Thus we only have to look for translation invariant states in D. These are finite linear combinations of translation invariant states of the form $\tilde{\Phi}_n(\tilde{\varphi}_n)$ and these are states of the form $\tilde{\Phi}_n(\tilde{\varphi}_n\chi(p_1 + \cdots + p_n))$. From (15), (16) and b2, these states satisfy

$$\| \tilde{\Phi}_n \|^2 = |(\tilde{\Phi}_n, \Omega)|^2 \tag{24}$$

and therefore are multiples of Ω.

(g) *Locality* is trivially satisfied according to a4.

(h) *Completeness*. This axiom states that the linear manifold spanned by the states $\Phi_n(\varphi_n)$ with $\varphi_n \in \mathscr{S}^{\otimes n}(R^4)$ is dense in $\mathfrak{H}$. But $\mathscr{S}^{\otimes n}(R^4)$ is dense in $\mathscr{S}(R^{4n})$ and $\Phi_n(\varphi_n)$ is continuous in φ_n. Thus the linear manifold under discussion is dense in D and the last axiom is verified.

This completes the proof.

5. **Additional remarks.** We continue this chapter with four additional remarks.

A. Separability of $\mathfrak{H}$.

Theorem [Ru 4; Bo 3]. *$\mathfrak{H}$ is separable.*

Proof. D is dense in $\mathfrak{H}$ and is generated by the vectors $\Phi_n(\varphi_n)$, $\varphi_n \in \mathscr{S}_n = \mathscr{S}(R^{4n})$. The vectors $\Phi_n(\varphi_n)$ depend continuously on φ_n. Each $\mathscr{S}_n$ is separable [CH 1*; Sw 1*, p. 108]. Let φ_n^k, $k = 1, 2, 3, \cdots$, be a dense set in $\mathscr{S}_n$. $\Phi_n(\varphi_n)$ for arbitrary $\varphi_n \in \mathscr{S}_n$ appears as the limit of a subsequence $\Phi_n(\varphi_n^{k_s})$. $\mathfrak{H}$ is therefore the closed linear space generated by the countable set $\Phi_n(\varphi_n^k)$, $n = 0, 1, 2, \cdots$, $k = 1, 2, 3, \cdots$, and is hence separable.

B. Completeness [Ru 4]. We defined completeness by the requirement that Ω be cyclic with respect to the ring of all polynomials in $A(\varphi)$, $\varphi \in \mathscr{S}_1$. Another notion by which one could attempt to characterize the completeness of the theory would be by irreducibility in the sense, "that every bounded operator C, which commutes with $A(\varphi)$ for all $\varphi \in \mathcal{S}_1$, is a multiple of the identity". As they stand, the words in quotation marks lack a meaning. A related and meaningful statement appears in the following

THEOREM (RUELLE). *If the bounded operator C satisfies for all $\Psi, \Phi \in D$ and all $\varphi \in \mathcal{S}_1$*

(1) $$(\Psi, CA(\varphi)\Phi) = (A(\bar{\varphi})\Psi, C\Phi)$$

then

(2) $$C = c \cdot I.$$

PROOF. (α) Clearly

(3) $$c = (\Omega, C\Omega).$$

(β) Successive application of (1) leads to

(4) $$(\Psi, C\langle A^n, \varphi\rangle\Phi) = (\langle A^n, \varphi^*\rangle\Psi, C\Phi)$$

for $\varphi \in \mathcal{S}_1^{\otimes n}$ and, from the continuity of both sides of (4) and the fact that $\mathcal{S}_1^{\otimes n}$ is dense in $\mathcal{S}_n$, also for $\varphi \in \mathcal{S}_n$.

(γ) From (4) we derive

(5) $$(\Omega, CT(a)\langle A^n, \varphi\rangle T(-a)\Omega) = (T(a)\langle A^n, \varphi^*\rangle T(-a)\Omega, C\Omega)$$

or

(6) $$(\Omega, CT(a)\langle A^n, \varphi\rangle\Omega) = (\langle A^n, \varphi^*\rangle\Omega, T(-a)C\Omega).$$

Let Δ be a Borel set in $\tilde{R}^4$ and write

$$E(\Delta) = \int_\Delta dE(p);$$

then (6) leads to

(7) $$(\Omega, CE(\Delta)\langle A^n, \varphi\rangle\Omega) = (\langle A^n, \varphi^*\rangle\Omega, E(-\Delta)C\Omega).$$

If we choose for Δ the closed forward cone $\bar{V}_+$, then $E(\Delta) = I$ and $E(-\Delta) = E_0$, the projection on the vacuum Ω. Thus, with (3),

(8) $$(\Omega, C\langle A^n, \varphi\rangle\Omega) = c(\Omega, \langle A^n, \varphi\rangle\Omega)$$

and, according to the definition of D,

(9) $$(\Omega, C\Phi) = c(\Omega, \Phi)$$

for any $\Phi \in D$.

(δ) Finally

$$(10) \qquad (\langle A^m, \psi\rangle\Omega, C\Phi) = (C^*\Omega, \langle A^m, \psi^*\rangle\Phi) = c(\langle A^m, \psi\rangle\Omega, \Phi)$$

and again from the definition of D, for any $\Phi, \Psi \in D$

$$(11) \qquad (\Psi, C\Phi) = c(\Psi, \Phi).$$

(2) follows from the density of D.

C. The truncated vacuum expectation values (TVEV). It is advantageous for many purposes to eliminate symmetrically the contribution of the vacuum state of the Wightman distributions. According to R. Haag [Ha 3] this can be achieved by the introduction of the TVEV. These are recursively defined by the equations

$$(12) \qquad \begin{aligned} \mathfrak{W}_n(x_1, \cdots, x_n) = \sum_{\text{part}} & \mathfrak{W}^T_{r_1}(x_{l_{1,1}}, \cdots, x_{l_{1,r_1}}) \\ & \times \mathfrak{W}^T_{r_2}(x_{l_{2,1}}, \cdots, x_{l_{2,r_2}}) \cdots \mathfrak{W}^T_{r_s}(x_{l_{s,1}}, \cdots, x_{l_{s,r_s}}), \end{aligned}$$

where the sum on the right-hand side runs over all partitions of the indices $1, \cdots, n$ and in each subset $l_{k,1} \cdots l_{k,r_k}$ the indices are taken in natural order. For $n = 1$ and 2 the equations (12) read

$$(13) \qquad \mathfrak{W}_1(x_1) = \mathfrak{W}^T_1(x_1),$$

$$(14) \qquad \mathfrak{W}_2(x_1, x_2) = \mathfrak{W}^T_1(x_1)\mathfrak{W}^T_1(x_2) + \mathfrak{W}^T_2(x_1, x_2).$$

The TVEV clearly satisfy all the linear restrictions (a1-4). According to a2 they are translation invariant and therefore allow the definition of

$$(15) \qquad W^T_m(\xi_1, \cdots, \xi_m) \equiv \mathfrak{W}^T_{m+1}(x_0, \cdots, x_n), \qquad \xi_k \equiv x_k - x_{k-1}.$$

$W_0 = W^T_0 = \mathfrak{W}_1(x_0) = \mathfrak{W}^T_1(x_0)$ is a constant (and vanishes in all reasonable cases).

We want to discuss the support of $\tilde{W}^T_m(q_1, \cdots, q_m)$ and to prove the

Theorem. *The support of* $\tilde{W}^T_m(q_1, \cdots, q_m)$ *is contained in* $q_k \in V_+$, $k = 1, 2, \cdots, m$.

If $\mathfrak{s}_0 \subset \{q \mid q = 0\} \cup \bar{V}^{\mu_0}_+$, *then* supp $\tilde{W}^T_m(q_1, \cdots, q_m)$ *is contained in* $\{q_k \in \bar{V}^{\mu_0}_+, k = 1, 2, \cdots, m\}$.

Proof. (α) It has already been anticipated and follows by induction on m from (12) that the support of $\tilde{W}^T_m(q_1, \cdots, q_m)$ is contained in $\mathfrak{s}_0^{\times m}$.

(β) If $\chi(\xi)$ satisfies supp $\tilde{\chi} \cap \mathfrak{s}_0 = \{q \mid q = 0\}$ then

$$\int \chi(a)\mathfrak{W}_{m+1}(x_0, \cdots, x_{l-1}, x_l + a, x_{l+1} + a, \cdots, x_m + a)\, d^4a$$

$$= \int \chi(a)\mathfrak{W}_m(\xi_1, \cdots, \xi_l + a, \xi_{l+1}, \cdots, \xi_m)\, d^4a$$

$$= \left(\Omega, A(x_0) \cdots A(x_{l-1}) \int T(a)\chi(a)\, d^4a A(x_l) \cdots A(x_m)\Omega\right) \tag{16}$$

$$= \tilde{\chi}(0)(\Omega, A(x_0) \cdots A(x_{l-1})\Omega)(\Omega, A(x_l) \cdots A(x_m)\Omega)$$

$$= \tilde{\chi}(0)\mathfrak{W}_l(x_0, \cdots, x_{l-1})\mathfrak{W}_{m+1-l}(x_l, \cdots, x_m).$$

We now make the induction assumption that, for $l < m + 1$,

$$\int \chi(a)\mathfrak{W}_l^T(x_0 \cdots x_k + a, \cdots, x_{l-1} + a)\, da = 0.$$

Using (14) this assumption is easily checked for $l = 2$. Then we substitute the TVEV's for $\mathfrak{W}_{m+1}$ for the first term in (16). Apart from the term

$$\int \chi(a)\mathfrak{W}_{m+1}^T(x_0, \cdots, x_l + a, \cdots, x_m + a)\, d^4a \tag{17}$$

the only terms which do not give a vanishing contribution on the right-hand side of (12) can be written as

$$\tilde{\chi}(0) \sum_{(\text{part})'} \mathfrak{W}_{r_1}^T(\cdots)\mathfrak{W}_{r_2}^T(\cdots) \cdots \mathfrak{W}_{r_s}^T(\cdots), \tag{18}$$

where (part)′ indicates a summation over all subpartitions of the partition

$$(0, 1, \cdots, l - 1)(l, l + 1, \cdots, m).$$

This sum, however, is just

$$\tilde{\chi}(0)\mathfrak{W}_l(x_0, \cdots, x_{l-1})\mathfrak{W}_{m+1-l}(x_l, \cdots, x_m) \tag{19}$$

so from (16) (assuming $\tilde{\chi}(0) \neq 0$)

$$\begin{aligned} &\int \chi(a)\mathfrak{W}_{m+1}^T(x_0, \cdots, x_l + a, \cdots, x_m + a)\, d^4a \\ &\qquad = \int \chi(a)W_m^T(\xi_1, \cdots, \xi_l + a, \cdots, \xi_m)\, d^4a = 0. \end{aligned} \tag{20}$$

By induction (20) is valid for all m. This, together with the assumed properties of $\chi(\xi)$, proves the theorem.

The proof gives us immediately the following

COROLLARY. *If the sequence of distributions* $\mathfrak{W}_n^T(x_1, \cdots, x_n)$ *satisfies the conditions* a1, 2, 4 *and in addition*

$$W_m^T(\xi_1, \cdots, \xi_m) \equiv \mathfrak{W}_{m+1}^T(x_0, \cdots, x_n), \qquad \xi_k = x_k - x_{k-1},$$

satisfies

$$\text{supp}\, \tilde{W}_m^T(q_1, \cdots, q_m) \subset V_+^{\times \mu}$$

then the distributions $\mathfrak{W}_n$ *defined by* (12) *satisfy* a1–4 *and* b2. *If the* $\mathfrak{W}_n$ *satisfy* b1 *then they define a Wightman theory.*

PROOF. The distributions (12) satisfy (16) (equality of first and last terms). Thus a3 is satisfied. However (16) also implies b1, as one easily sees. We see that the introduction of the TVEV in a way linearizes the nonlinear condition b2. b1, however, looks revolting if expressed in TVEV.

D. THE INFINITESIMAL LORENTZ TRANSFORMATIONS AND THE DOMAIN *D*. The infinitesimal Lorentz transformations act on the test functions as follows (Chapter I, § 1C):

(α) *Infinitesimal translations.*

$$\varphi(x_1, \cdots, x_n) \to -\sum_{s=1}^{n} \frac{\partial \varphi}{\partial x_s^k}.$$

(β) *Infinitesimal homogeneous Lorentz transformations.*

$$\varphi(x_1, \cdots, x_n) \to -\sum_{s=1}^{n} \left(x_{sk} \frac{\partial \varphi}{\partial x_s^l} - x_{sl} \frac{\partial \varphi}{\partial x_s^k} \right).$$

In any case φ is mapped continuously [Sw 1*] into a function from $\mathscr{S}_n$. Since the generating vectors $\Phi_n(\varphi)$ of D are strongly continuous in φ, the representations of the infinitesimal transformations are defined on D and map D into itself. Their products can therefore be applied freely to any vector from D [Gå 1].

6. **The matrix elements of the translation operator.** [De 1; Ar 2; Jo 7.] The spectral decomposition

$$T(a) = \int e^{i(p,a)}\, dE(p) = e^{i(P,a)} \tag{1}$$

defines the spectral measure E. Let B be the Banach space of the continuous functions of the vector variable p with the norm $\sup |\chi(p)|$. As a measure E defines a continuous operator-valued linear functional on B

which in turn defines E uniquely [RN 1*]. For this functional we use alternatively the notations

$$(2) \qquad \int \chi(p)\, dE(p) = \langle E, \chi \rangle = \chi(P).$$

The second notation is borrowed from the theory of distributions, the last one corresponds to the definition of a function of the energy momentum operator. The continuity of $\langle E, \chi \rangle$ follows from the equation

$$(3) \qquad \|\langle E, \chi \rangle\| = \|\chi(P)\| \leqq \sup |\chi(p)|.$$

To each pair of states Φ, Ψ a bounded complex-valued measure is determined by

$$(4) \qquad \langle m, \chi \rangle = (\Phi, \langle E, \chi \rangle \Psi).$$

It satisfies

$$(5) \qquad |\langle m, \chi \rangle| \leqq \|\Phi\| \cdot \|\Psi\| \sup |\chi(p)|.$$

We are interested in this measure for states Φ and Ψ from D. We collect the properties of $\langle m, \chi \rangle$:

First property. $\langle m, \chi \rangle$ is strongly decreasing.

PROOF. Let $n = (n_0, n_1, n_2, n_3)$ be a set of four natural numbers and P^n the corresponding power of the energy momentum operator. The operator $\chi(P)P^n$ will in general be unbounded. It is, however, defined on D since P maps D into itself. Thus

$$(6) \qquad |(\Phi, \chi(P)P^n\Psi)| = |\langle m \cdot p^n, \chi \rangle| \leqq \|\Phi\| \, \|P^n\Psi\| \sup |\chi(p)|.$$

The measure obtained from m by the multiplication by p^n is therefore still bounded. This proves the first property.

The second property follows from the fact that the infinitesimal homogeneous Lorentz transformations P_{ik} map D into itself. If we write $U(\Lambda) = U(0, \Lambda)$ then

$$(7) \qquad U^{-1}(\Lambda)\chi(P)U(\Lambda) = \chi(\Lambda^{-1}P).$$

Thus

$$(8) \qquad (U(\Lambda)\Phi, \langle E, \chi \rangle U(\Lambda)\Psi) = \langle m_\Lambda, \chi \rangle,$$

where

$$(9) \qquad m_\Lambda(p) = m(\Lambda p).$$

The left-hand side of (8), however, is infinitely differentiable on the restricted Lorentz group. Thus we find, e.g.

$$(10) \qquad |\langle \partial_{kl} m, \chi \rangle| \leqq \{\|P_{kl}\Psi\| \cdot \|\Phi\| + \|\Psi\| \cdot \|P_{kl}\Phi\|\} \sup |\chi(p)|,$$

where $\partial_{kl} = p_k(\partial/\partial p_l) - p_l(\partial/\partial p_k)$ and P_{kl} the corresponding representation. We have therefore the

Second property. Application of an arbitrary polynomial in ∂_{kl} to the measure m leads again to a bounded measure.

Now we split the measure m into a trivial part with support in $\{p \mid p = 0\}$ and the rest m_1 with support in $\bar{V}_+^{\mu_0}$:

$$(\Phi, \langle E, \chi \rangle \Psi) = (\Phi, \Omega)(\Omega, \Psi)\chi(0) + \langle m_1, \chi \rangle. \tag{11}$$

m_1 has both properties mentioned above. For m_1, however, we can introduce new (on $\bar{V}_+^{\mu_0}$ regular) coordinates by

$$(p_0, \vec{p}) = (\sqrt{(\mu^2 + \vec{p}^2)}, \vec{p}). \tag{12}$$

This transformation of coordinates will be indicated by the notation $\langle \tilde{m}_1, \tilde{\chi} \rangle$. The operator ∂_{0k} now takes the form

$$\partial_{0k} = -\omega D^k, \qquad D^k = \frac{\partial}{\partial p_k}, \qquad \omega = p_0 = \sqrt{(\mu^2 + \vec{p}^2)}. \tag{13}$$

Finally we notice that ω^{-1} is bounded on supp $\tilde{m}$. This leads us to the

THEOREM [Jo 7]. *Let* $\mathfrak{p}_1(\omega, \vec{p})$ *and* $\mathfrak{p}_2(D)$ *be arbitrary polynomials in the indicated variables, and let n be an arbitrary natural number, then*

$$\omega^{-n}\mathfrak{p}_1(\omega, \vec{p})\mathfrak{p}_2(\vec{D})\tilde{m}_1 \tag{14}$$

is a bounded measure.

COROLLARY. *The function*

$$t_1(\vec{a}) = (\Phi, T(\vec{a})\Psi) - (\Phi, \Omega)(\Omega, \Psi) \tag{15}$$

for $\Phi, \Psi \in D$ *and* $\vec{a} \equiv (0, \vec{a})$ *is strongly decreasing as* $\vec{a} \to \infty$ *and* C_∞. *Therefore* $t_1 \in \mathscr{S}(R^3)$.

PROOF OF THE COROLLARY. With the notation $e_{\vec{a}}(\vec{p}) = e^{-i(\vec{p}\cdot\vec{a})}$ the function (15) takes the form

$$t_1(\vec{a}) = \langle \tilde{m}, e_{\vec{a}} \rangle. \tag{16}$$

The fact that $\tilde{m}$ is strongly decreasing leads to the statement that $t_1(\vec{a})$ is C_∞, the fact that $\vec{p}(D)\tilde{m}$ is again a bounded measure, to the strong decrease of $t_1(\vec{a})$.

Finally the corollary leads immediately to the following cluster property of the Wightman distributions:

Cluster property.

$$\iint \mathfrak{W}_{n+m}(x_1, \cdots, x_n, y_1 + \vec{a}, \cdots, y_m + \vec{a}) \times \varphi(x_1, \cdots, x_n)\psi(y_1, \cdots, y_m)\, d\underline{x}d\underline{y} - \mathfrak{W}_n(\varphi)\mathfrak{W}_m(\psi) \to 0 \tag{17}$$

as $\vec{a} \to 0$ stronger than any power of $[\vec{a} \cdot \vec{a}]^{-1/2}$.

REMARKS. 1. Nowhere in this section have we used locality. The following theorem can also be proved without locality.

THEOREM [Jo 7]. *In the sense of convergence of distributions one has for any natural number N and uniformly in* $(a, a) < 0$

$$\lim_{-(a,a)\to\infty} |(a, a)|^{N/2}[\mathfrak{W}_{n+m}(x_1, \cdots, x_n, y_1 + a, \cdots, y_n + a) - \mathfrak{W}_n(x_1, \cdots, x_n)\mathfrak{W}_m(y_1, \cdots, y_m)] = 0. \quad (18)$$

2. For special points, namely, the real regularity points, a stronger result follows trivially [Ar 2].

3. Interesting cluster properties have been derived from locality by D. Ruelle ([Ru 4] Chapter VI), and by H. Araki, K. Hepp and D. Ruelle [Ar 8].

CHAPTER IV

The Wightman Functions

1. **Introductory remarks.** It turns out that the Wightman distributions are boundary values of analytic functions, the Wightman functions, and these have proved to be a very useful tool for investigating the theory. Almost all the important physical applications of the theory use to some extent the fundamental property of these functions that they are invariant under the identity component of the complex inhomogeneous Lorentz group.[1] This fact forms the content of a deep theorem of Bargmann, Hall and Wightman (BHW-Theorem) (§ 4 [Hall 1]). The proof we give of this theorem is in its essential ideas the original proof of the above-named authors. A considerable simplification is due to D. Ruelle and remained unpublished until now.

The BHW-Theorem can be applied to the problems raised by the fourth axiom (locality) (§ 5), but new problems, unsolved till now, immediately arise (§ 6). We close this chapter with two interesting theorems: one of V. Glaser and R. F. Streater [Str 1], which sheds new light on the regularity domain of the Wightman functions and a simple but remarkable theorem due to H. Reeh and S. Schlieder.

2. **Analytic continuation of the distributions $\Phi_n(x_1, \cdots, x_n)$ and $\mathfrak{W}_n(x_1, \cdots, x_n)$; the Wightman functions.** We come now to the most characteristic consequences of the spectral assumption (third axiom and property a3).

As we know from Chapter III, § 3, this axiom has the consequence that the support of the vector-valued distribution

$$(1) \qquad \tilde{A}(p_1)\tilde{A}(p_2) \cdots \tilde{A}(p_n)\Omega = \tilde{\Phi}_n(p_1, p_2, \cdots, p_n)$$

is contained in

$$(2) \quad q_k = p_k + p_{k+1} + \cdots + p_n \in \operatorname{supp} dE = \mathfrak{s}_0, \qquad k = 1, 2, \cdots, n.$$

[1] This statement is no more accurate. Real Analysis, e.g. the methods of D. Ruelle, described in Chapter VI, has recently proved to be equally powerful as Complex Analysis. See also Chapter III, footnote 1.

This support property has the consequence that $\tilde{\Phi}_n(\tilde{\varphi})$ exists for a much wider class of test functions $\tilde{\varphi}$ than was originally considered. The most important such test functions are the exponentials

$$\text{(3)}\quad \exp i[q_1 \cdot z_1 + q_2 \cdot (z_2 - z_1) + q_3 \cdot (z_3 - z_2) + \cdots + q_n \cdot (z_n - z_{n-1})] = \exp i \sum p_k \cdot z_k$$

for

$$\text{(4)}\qquad \operatorname{Im} z_1 \in V_+, \qquad \operatorname{Im}(z_k - z_{k-1}) \in V_+, \qquad k = 2, 3, \cdots, n.$$

These exponentials clearly decrease fast on the support of $\tilde{\Phi}_n$ as do their derivatives. Thus

$$\text{(5)}\qquad \Phi_n(z_1, z_2, \cdots, z_n) = \int \exp[i \sum p_k \cdot z_k] \tilde{\Phi}(p_1, \cdots, p_n)\, d\underline{p}$$

exists and is even a holomorphic (vector-valued) function in $(z_1, \cdots, z_n)$ [Die 1*].

In order to analyze the relation between $\Phi_n(\underline{z})$ and $\Phi_n(\underline{x})$ we write for the moment $z_k = x_k + iy_k$, $\eta_1 = y_1$, $\eta_k = y_k - y_{k-1}$, $k = 2, 3, \cdots, n$, and

$$\text{(6)}\qquad \Phi_n(z_1, z_2, \cdots, z_n) = \Phi_n(x_1, x_2, \cdots, x_n;\ \eta_1, \eta_2, \cdots, \eta_n).$$

We interpret the right-hand side of (6) as a distribution in the variables $x_1, x_2, \cdots, x_n$, which depends on the parameters $\eta_1, \eta_2, \cdots, \eta_n$. These parameters are all in V_+. Finally we introduce the function

$$\text{(7)}\qquad e_\eta(p_1, \cdots, p_n) = \exp\left[- \sum_k \eta_k (p_k + p_{k+1} + \cdots + p_n) \right].$$

Then the relation between $\Phi_n(\varphi)$ and $\Phi_n(\varphi; \underline{\eta})$ is given by

$$\text{(8)}\qquad \Phi_n(\varphi; \underline{\eta}) = \tilde{\Phi}_n(\tilde{\varphi} \cdot e_{\underline{\eta}}).$$

In view of the support condition (2) $\tilde{\varphi} \cdot e_{\underline{\eta}}$ is an admissible test function and it converges, as $\eta_k \to 0$ inside V_+ to the test function $\tilde{\varphi}$. Thus we find

$$\text{(9)}\qquad \lim_{\substack{\underline{\eta} \to 0 \\ \eta_k \in V_+}} \Phi_n(\varphi, \underline{\eta}) = \tilde{\Phi}_n(\tilde{\varphi}) = \Phi_n(\varphi).$$

In this sense

$$\text{(10)}\qquad \lim_{\substack{\underline{\eta} \to 0 \\ \eta_k \in V_+}} \Phi_n(\underline{x}, \underline{\eta}) = \Phi_n(\underline{x}).$$

Thus we have the

THEOREM. *The distribution* $\Phi_n(\underline{x})$ *is the boundary value of the analytic function* $\Phi_n(\underline{z})$ *regular in*

$$\text{(11)}\qquad \operatorname{Im} z_1 \in V_+, \qquad \operatorname{Im}(z_k - z_{k-1}) \in V_+, \qquad k = 2, 3, \cdots, n.$$

COROLLARY. *For any* $\Psi \in \mathfrak{H}$ *the function*

$$(\Psi, \Phi_n(\underline{z})) = F_n(\Psi)(\underline{z}) \tag{12}$$

is holomorphic in (11). *The sequence of analytic functions* $F_n(\Psi)$ *defines* Ψ *uniquely.*

If we choose for Ψ the vacuum state Ω, then we obtain the

THEOREM. *The Wightman distributions* $\mathfrak{W}_n(x_1, \cdots, x_n)$ *are boundary values of analytic functions* $\mathfrak{W}_n(z_1, \cdots, z_n)$, *holomorphic in*

$$\mathfrak{S}_n = \{(z_1, \cdots, z_n) \mid \operatorname{Im}(z_k - z_{k-1}) \in V_+\}. \tag{13}$$

The Wightman functions are invariant under the restricted inhomogeneous Lorentz group.

The fact that z_1 remains unrestricted follows from the translational invariance of $\mathfrak{W}_n(z_1, \cdots, z_n)$.

COROLLARY. *The Wightman distribution*

$$W_n(\xi_1, \cdots, \xi_n) = \mathfrak{W}_{n+1}(x_0, x_1, \cdots, x_n), \qquad \xi_k = x_k - x_{k-1},$$

is the boundary value of an analytic function $W_n(\zeta_1, \cdots, \zeta_n)$ *regular in* $(\zeta_1, \cdots, \zeta_n) \in \mathfrak{T}^n$, $\mathfrak{T} = \{\zeta \mid \operatorname{Im} \zeta \in V_+\}$. $\mathfrak{T}$ *is the forward tube.*

The scalar product $(\Phi_n(\underline{z}), \Phi_m(\underline{w}))$ is easily expressed in Wightman functions

$$(\Phi_n(\underline{z}), \Phi_m(\underline{w})) = \mathfrak{W}_{n+m}(\overleftarrow{\underline{z}}, \underline{w}) \tag{14}$$

where $\overleftarrow{\underline{z}}$ stands for the n-tuple $(\bar{z}_n, \bar{z}_{n-1}, \cdots, \bar{z}_1)$.

From (14) one obtains the symmetry property

$$\mathfrak{W}_n(\overleftarrow{\underline{z}}) = \overline{\mathfrak{W}_n(\underline{z})} \tag{15}$$

which also follows from $\mathfrak{W}_n(\varphi^*) = \overline{\mathfrak{W}_n(\varphi)}$.

The possibility of the analytic continuation discussed in this section can be traced finally to the analytic continuation of the translation operator $T(a)$. This operator clearly is the boundary value of the analytic operator-valued function

$$T(\alpha) = \int e^{i(p,\alpha)}\, dE(p) \tag{16}$$

which is holomorphic for $\operatorname{Im} \alpha \in V_+$ or $\alpha \in \mathfrak{T}$ [Uh 1].

For $\lambda > 0$

(17)
$$\lim_{\lambda \to \infty} T(\lambda\alpha) = E_0$$

as one easily verifies. E_0 is the projection on $\langle\Omega\rangle$.

3. **The complex Lorentz transformations.** The analytic functions $W_n(\zeta_1, \cdots, \zeta_n)$ introduced in the last section will absorb our attention for the most part of what follows. They form the main tool for the analysis of the linear restrictions a1 to a4 of Chapter III, § 3. We call them Wightman functions. Their arguments are ordered sets of complex vectors ζ_k. It is therefore quite appropriate (and necessary for our further work) to say something about the complex Lorentz space R_c and the corresponding vector space $\mathfrak{B}_c$.

The elements of $R_c(\mathfrak{B}_c)$ are evidently pairs of points (vectors) $z = x + iy$ $(\zeta = \xi + i\eta)$ of $R^N(\mathfrak{B})$. A metric structure is introduced by the scalar product

$$(\zeta_1, \zeta_2) \equiv (\xi_1, \xi_2) - (\eta_1, \eta_2) + i[(\xi_1, \eta_2) + (\eta_1, \xi_2)].$$

This scalar product is symmetric, bilinear with respect to complex numbers, nonsingular and analytic in both factors.

The isometries of $\mathfrak{B}_c$ with respect to the scalar product (ζ_1, ζ_2) form the complex Lorentz group $L(C)$. The elements of $L(C)$ will be denoted by A, B. There is, of course, no intrinsic difference between the complex Lorentz group and the complex orthogonal group. The justification for the name $L(C)$ is simply that we need to look at it as the complex extension of the real Lorentz group.

This again is connected with the fact that the real points (vectors) in $R_c(\mathfrak{B}_c)$ are the quantities of immediate physical significance. Coordinate transformations should therefore be kept real throughout and the elements of $L(C)$ interpreted as mappings.

In an orthonormal coordinate system, A will be represented by a matrix having complex elements. We shall use A interchangeably to denote the transformation and its matrix representation. With G the metric tensor, A satisfies $A^TGA = G$ and is thereby completely characterized as the matrix of a complex Lorentz transformation. Again $\det A = \pm 1$ and again we have homomorphism $A \to \det A$, of which we denote the kernel by $L_+(C)$. But unlike the real Lorentz group, $L_+(C)$ is connected. It therefore contains as real transformations $L_+^\uparrow$ and $L_+^\downarrow$. The fact that $L_+^\uparrow$ and $L_+^\downarrow$ can be connected by a (continuous) path in $L_+(C)$ is, as we shall see later, of physical consequence.

The decomposition of $L(C)$ with respect to $L_+(C)$ may be written as

$$L(C) = L_+(C) + TL_+(C), \tag{1}$$

where T is the time reflection.

For the proof of a fundamental theorem which will occupy us in the next section we need an analytic parameterization of a neighborhood of the identity in $L_+(C)$ and $L_+^\uparrow$. We choose for this parameterization the one given by Cayley [Wey 2*] and characterized by the

THEOREM. (a) *Let* $R = -R^T$ *be a real (complex) skew symmetric matrix. Then* $A = (I - GR)(I + GR)^{-1}$ *(if it exists) is the matrix of a real (complex) Lorentz transformation.*

(b) *Let A be the matrix of a complex (real) Lorentz transformation, then* $R = G(I - A)(I + A)^{-1}$ *is (if it exists) a complex (real) skew symmetric matrix:* $R^T = -R$.

PROOF. 1. The reality properties of matrices and transformations are trivial.

2. In order to prove that $A = (I - GR)(I + GR)^{-1}$ is a Lorentz transformation, we compute

$$A^TGA = (I - RG)^{-1}(I + RG)G(I - GR)(I + GR)^{-1} \tag{2}$$

which, since $G^2 = 1$, equals

$$(I - RG)^{-1}(I - RG)G(I + GR)(I + GR)^{-1} = G. \tag{3}$$

3. For the proof that $R = G(I - A)(I + A)^{-1}$ is skew symmetric we compute

$$\begin{aligned} R^T &= (I + A^T)^{-1}(I - A^T)G = G(I + A^{-1})^{-1}GG(I - A^{-1})GG \\ &= G(A - I)(A + I) = -R. \end{aligned} \tag{4}$$

REMARKS. (a) If R is small enough (i.e., if its matrix elements are small enough in absolute value), then $(I - GR)(I + GR)^{-1}$ exists.

(b) If A is close enough to the identity I, then $G(I - A)(I + A)^{-1}$ exists.

We therefore possess in the matrix elements of R a regular and analytic parameterization of a group germ of $L_+(C)$ and $L_+^\uparrow$, respectively. Real parameters correspond to real Lorentz transformations.

Finally, we need the notion of equivalence of two complex Lorentz transformations with respect to $L_+^\uparrow$ and the characterization of the corresponding equivalence classes.

DEFINITION. The complex Lorentz transformations A and B are equivalent with respect to $L_+^\uparrow$, if $\Lambda_1, \Lambda_2 \in L_+^\uparrow$ exist such that $A = \Lambda_1 B \Lambda_2$.

THEOREM [Jo 6]. *Any $A \in L_+(C)$ is equivalent to one of the following normal forms*:

1. *For even dimension*:

(a) *Normal case*:

$$(5)\quad N = \begin{pmatrix} L(i\varphi) & & & & 0 \\ & K(i\chi_1) & & & \\ & & \cdot & & \\ & & & \cdot & \\ 0 & & & & K(i\chi_k) \end{pmatrix}, \quad |\varphi| \leqq \pi;\ \varphi, \chi_1, \cdots, \chi_k \text{ real};$$

(b) *Exceptional case*:

$$(6)\quad N = \sigma \begin{pmatrix} M(i\tau) & & & & & 0 \\ & K(i\chi_1) & & & & \\ & & \cdot & & & \\ & & & \cdot & & \\ & & & & K(i\chi_{k-1}) & \\ 0 & & & & & 1 \end{pmatrix} \quad \tau \neq 0;\ \tau, \chi_1, \cdots, \chi_{k-1} \text{ real}, \quad \sigma = \pm 1.$$

2. *For odd dimension*:

(a) *Normal case*:

$$(7)\ (\text{a1}) \qquad N = \begin{pmatrix} L(i\varphi) & & & & & 0 \\ & K(i\chi_1) & & & & \\ & & \cdot & & & \\ & & & \cdot & & \\ & & & & K(i\chi_k) & \\ 0 & & & & & 1 \end{pmatrix},$$

$$(8)\ (\text{a}2\alpha) \qquad N = \begin{pmatrix} 1 & & & & 0 \\ & K(i\chi_1) & & & \\ & & \cdot & & \\ & & & \cdot & \\ 0 & & & & K(i\chi_k) \end{pmatrix},$$

$$(9)\ (\text{a}2\beta) \qquad N = \begin{pmatrix} 1 & & & & 0 \\ & K(i\chi_1) & & & \\ & & \cdot & & \\ & & & \cdot & \\ 0 & & & & K(i\chi_k) \end{pmatrix} R;$$

(b) *Exceptional case*:

(10) (b1)
$$N = \begin{pmatrix} M(i\tau) & & & & 0 \\ & K(i\chi_1) & & & \\ & & \cdot & & \\ & & & \cdot & \\ & & & & \cdot \\ 0 & & & & K(i\chi_{k-1}) \end{pmatrix},$$

(11) (b2)
$$N = \begin{pmatrix} M(i\tau) & & & & 0 \\ & K(i\chi_1) & & & \\ & & \cdot & & \\ & & & \cdot & \\ & & & & \cdot \\ 0 & & & & K(i\chi_{k-1}) \end{pmatrix} R.$$

The proof of this theorem and the definitions for $M(i\tau)$, $L(i\varphi)$, $K(i\chi)$ are given in Appendix I. R stands for a diagonal matrix with diagonal elements $-1, -1, 1, \cdots, 1$.

4. **The theorem of Bargmann, Hall and Wightman.** The proof of the following fundamental theorem will occupy us in this section.

BHW-THEOREM [Ha 1]. *If the $L_+^\uparrow$-invariant function $W_n(\zeta_1, \cdots, \zeta_n)$ is regular analytic in $\mathfrak{T}^n$, then it allows a single-valued, $L_+(C)$-invariant, analytic continuation into the domain*

$$\mathfrak{T}'_n = \bigcup_{A \in L_+(C)} A\mathfrak{T}^n.$$

REMARK. We call $\mathfrak{T}'_n$ the extended tube. $\mathfrak{T}'_n$ is, however, not a tube in the variables $(\zeta_1, \cdots, \zeta_n)$.

PROOF. 1. In this proof we shall abbreviate $(\zeta_1, \cdots, \zeta_n)$ by ζ, $\mathfrak{T}^n$ by $\mathfrak{T}$ and W_n by W.

2. The function $W_A(\zeta) \equiv W(A^{-1}\zeta)$ is defined in $A\mathfrak{T}$. $W_A(\zeta)$ and $W(\zeta)$ are simultaneously defined in $\mathfrak{T} \cap A\mathfrak{T}$. Let us assume that $\mathfrak{T} \cap A\mathfrak{T} \neq \emptyset$. If we succeed in proving that the two functions coincide in this domain, we have shown first that $W_A(\zeta)$ is an analytic continuation of $W(\zeta)$ and secondly that this continuation does not lead to any multi-valuedness within $\mathfrak{T}$.

3. This last fact, however, even guarantees the single-valuedness of the continuation by $W_A(\zeta)$ in the whole of $\mathfrak{T}'$. In order to see this let us assume that $W_{A_1}(\zeta) \neq W_{A_2}(\zeta)$ for some $\zeta \in A_1\mathfrak{T} \cap A_2\mathfrak{T}$. Put $\zeta_1 = A_1^{-1}\zeta \in \mathfrak{T}$ and $\zeta_2 = A_2^{-1}\zeta \in \mathfrak{T}$. Then $W(\zeta_1) \neq W(\zeta_2)$ but $\zeta_2 = A_2^{-1}A_1\zeta_1$. Thus $W_{A_1^{-1}A_2}(\zeta_1) \neq W(\zeta_1)$ and $\zeta_1 \in \mathfrak{T} \cap A_1^{-1}A_2\mathfrak{T}$ in contradiction to the statement in point 2.

4. Now $\mathfrak{T} \cap A\mathfrak{T}$ is, as the intersection of two convex sets, itself convex and thus connected. It suffices therefore to prove that $W(\zeta)$ and $W_A(\zeta)$ coincide in the neighborhood of one point. In addition: If $W(\zeta)$ and $W_A(\zeta)$ coincide for some Lorentz transformation A_0 then they coincide also if A varies in a suitable neighborhood of A_0. This can be seen as follows:

5. Keep ζ fixed in $\mathfrak{T} \cap A_0\mathfrak{T}$ and look at $W_A(\zeta)$ as a function of A. Introduce local coordinates by $A = A_0B$, where B is expressed in Cayley parameters. If B varies over a sufficiently small (connected) neighborhood of the identity we still have $\zeta \in \mathfrak{T} \cap A\mathfrak{T}$. If we keep this neighborhood small enough, this will even be true for all the points of a neighborhood of ζ. The $L_+^\uparrow$-invariance now implies $W_A(\zeta) = W_{A_0}(\zeta)$ for $B \in L_+^\uparrow$. $W_A(\zeta)$ is an analytic function of the Cayley parameters of B. This function is constant for real parameters (this corresponds to $B \in L_+^\uparrow$) and therefore [BM 1*] also for complex parameters. Thus $W_A(\zeta) = W_{A_0}(\zeta)$ for all elements B in our neighborhood, and in a neighborhood of ζ. This implies $W_A(\zeta) = W(\zeta)$ in $\mathfrak{T} \cap A\mathfrak{T}$.

6. If in the above argument we choose for A_0 the unit element, we find $W_B(\zeta) = W(\zeta)$ for sufficiently small $B \in L_+(C)$.

7. The rest of the proof depends on the

LEMMA. *The set* $\mathfrak{B} = \{A \in L_+(C) \mid A\mathfrak{T} \cap \mathfrak{T} \neq \emptyset\}$ *is connected.*

We postpone the proof of the lemma to finish the argument. An arbitrary point $A \in \mathfrak{B}$ can be joined, by a finite chain of overlapping neighborhoods of the kind discussed in point 5, to the identity. Application of the statement in point 4 finishes the proof.

Finally we come to the

PROOF OF THE LEMMA. (α) The definition of $\mathfrak{B}$ implies for any $\Lambda_{1,2} \in L_+^\uparrow$ the equation $\Lambda_1\mathfrak{B}\Lambda_2 = \mathfrak{B}$. $\mathfrak{B}$ is therefore a set of equivalence classes of $L_+(C)$ relative to $L_+^\uparrow$. We have therefore only to determine the normal forms contained in $\mathfrak{B}$.

(β) For this we refer to he classification of § 3. $\mathfrak{B}$ contains exactly the following normal forms.

1. *Even dimension*:
   (a) Normal case: $|\varphi| < \pi$, rest of parameters arbitrary;
   (b) Exceptional case: $\sigma = +1$, rest of parameters arbitrary.
2. *Odd dimension*:
   (a) Normal case: (a1) $|\varphi| < \pi$, rest of parameters arbitrary;
   (a2α): all cases;
   (b) Exceptional case: (b1): all cases.

(γ) To verify this statement, one has only to apply the normal forms (in the exceptional cases for τ small enough) to the special points

$$\zeta_k = (i, (\sin\phi)^{-1}, 0, \cdots, 0) \text{ or } (i, 0, 0 \cdots 0).$$

The resulting point $N\zeta$ lies in $\mathfrak{T}$.

No other cases can occur because all other normal forms lead to an imaginary part of $N\zeta_k$, which has a negative zero component (again in the exceptional cases τ has to be chosen small enough).

(δ) All the normal forms in $\mathfrak{B}$ can continuously be connected with I by decreasing the parameters in absolute value to zero. $\mathfrak{B}$ is therefore connected.

This finishes the proof of the lemma and of the theorem.

It might be appropriate to illustrate in two dimensions the situation described by the theorem. A coordinate transformation will simplify the discussion. Instead of (ζ^0, ζ^1) we introduce $u = \zeta^0 + \zeta^1$ and $v = -(\zeta^0 - \zeta^1)^{-1}$ as coordinates of one vector. $\mathfrak{T}$ then consists of the points $\text{Im}\, u > 0$, $\text{Im}\, v > 0$. In the complex plane a vector in $\mathfrak{T}$ is represented by a pair of points in the upper half plane. The normal form of a complex Lorentz transformation amounts to the multiplication of u by v by the same factor of modulus 1: $\tilde{u} = e^{i\varphi}u$, $\tilde{v} = e^{i\varphi}v$ or, in the complex plane, to a solid rotation of both u and v by an angle φ.

A point in $\mathfrak{T}^n$ is represented by a set of $2n$ points in the upper half plane (Figure 1); a point in $\mathfrak{T}_n'$ by $2n$ points contained in an open half plane, the boundary of which passes through the origin (Figure 2).

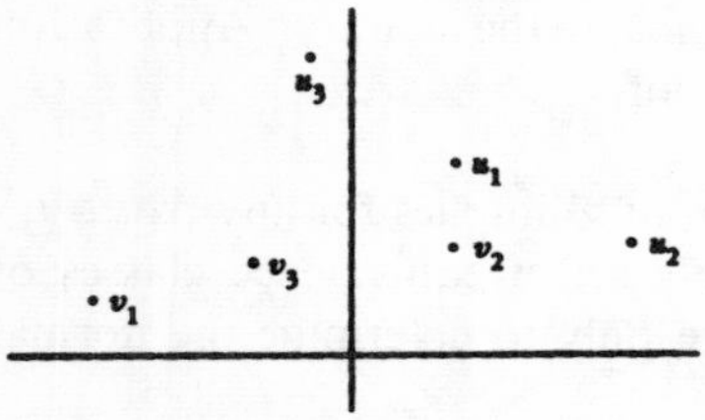

FIGURE 1. POINT IN $\mathfrak{T}_3$.

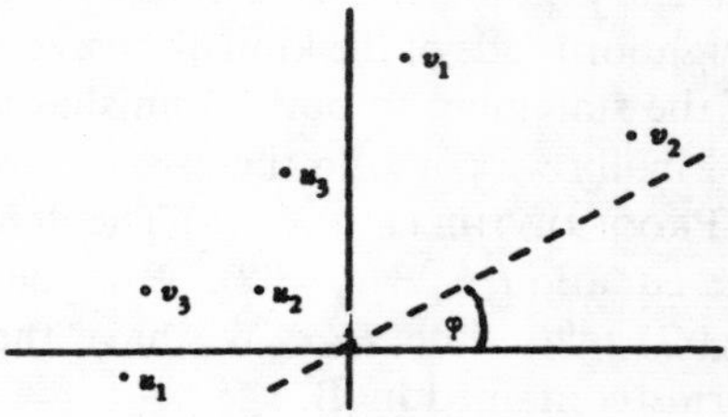

FIGURE 2. POINT IN $\mathfrak{T}_3'$.

We notice that $\mathfrak{T}_n'$ contains real points characterized by $\sigma u_l > 0$ and $\sigma v_l > 0$ for all l and for $\sigma = \pm 1$.

Analytically, points in $\mathfrak{T}_n'$ can be characterized by their property that the convex set generated by $(u_1, \cdots, v_n)$ does not contain the origin: if $\lambda_k \geqq 0$ and $\sum \lambda_k = 1$, then $\lambda_1 u_1 + \cdots + \lambda_{2n} v_n \neq 0$. Points outside $\mathfrak{T}_n'$ have the property that their convex hull does contain the origin. This evidently allows one to construct a function regular in $\mathfrak{T}_n'$ but singular in an arbitrarily prescribed point outside $\mathfrak{T}'_n$. Therefore $\mathfrak{T}'_n$ is a domain of holomorphy [Be 1*].

5. **Application of the BHW-Theorem to locality.** The theorem of the last section has an immediate application (already implied by the notation) to the Wightman functions: $W_n(\zeta_1, \cdots, \zeta_n)$ has a single-valued analytic extension into $\mathfrak{T}'_n$ and is invariant under $L_+(C)$. Correspondingly

$$\text{(1)} \qquad \mathfrak{W}_{n+1}(z_0, z_1, \cdots, z_n) = W_n(z_1 - z_0, \cdots, z_n - z_{n-1})$$

has a single-valued analytic extension into a domain $\mathfrak{S}'_{n+1}$ defined by

$$\mathfrak{S}'_{n+1} \equiv \{(z_0, z_1, \cdots, z_n) \,|\, ((z_1 - z_0), \cdots, (z_n - z_{n-1})) \in \mathfrak{T}'_n\}.$$

After this extension $\mathfrak{W}_n$ is invariant under the identity component of the complex inhomogeneous Lorentz group, generated by the complex translations and $L_+(C)$.

It is interesting that, unlike $\mathfrak{T}^n$ and $\mathfrak{S}_{n+1}$, $\mathfrak{T}'_n$ and $\mathfrak{S}'_{n+1}$ contain real points, which are characterized in the

THEOREM [Jo 3]. *The real point* $(\rho_1, \rho_2, \cdots, \rho_n)$ *is in* $\mathfrak{T}'_n$ *if and only if the convex cone* $\mathfrak{k}(\rho_1, \rho_2, \cdots, \rho_n)$ *generated by* $\rho_1, \rho_2, \cdots, \rho_n$ *contains only space-like points.*

REMARK. The convex cone $\mathfrak{k}\,(\rho_1, \rho_2, \cdots, \rho_n)$ is defined by the set of points $\lambda_1\rho_1 + \lambda_2\rho_2 + \cdots + \lambda_n\rho_n$ with $\lambda_k \geqq 0$ and $\sum \lambda_k > 0$.

PROOF. (a) The condition is necessary: $(\rho_1, \cdots, \rho_n) \in \mathfrak{T}'_n$ implies the existence of $A \in L_+(C)$ in such a way that $\rho_k = A\zeta_k$ and $\zeta_k \in \mathfrak{T}$. If now $\lambda_k \geqq 0$ we find that

$$\text{(2)} \qquad \left(\sum_{k=1}^{n} \lambda_k\rho_k, \sum_{k=1}^{n} \lambda_k\rho_k\right) = (\zeta, \zeta),$$

where $\zeta = \sum_{k=1}^n \lambda_k\zeta_k \in \mathfrak{T}$, because $\mathfrak{T}$ is convex. Writing as usual $\zeta = \xi + i\eta$, we compute $(\zeta, \zeta) = (\xi, \xi) - (\eta, \eta) + 2i(\xi, \eta)$, and this quantity is required to be real. This implies $(\xi, \eta) = 0$ and, since $\eta \in V_+$, $(\xi, \xi) < 0$ so that finally $(\zeta, \zeta) < 0$.

(b) The condition is sufficient. Let us denote by $\bar{\mathfrak{k}}$, $\bar{V}_\pm$, the closed cones corresponding to $\mathfrak{k}$ and $V_\pm$. Since $\bar{\mathfrak{k}} \cap \bar{V}_+ = \bar{\mathfrak{k}} \cap \bar{V}_- = \{0\}$ there exists a tangential plane $(\alpha, \xi) = 0$ to V_+, which separates V_+ from $\mathfrak{k}$ and V_- and another one, $(\beta, \xi) = 0$, which separates V_- from $\mathfrak{k}$ and V_+. Then the following equations hold

$$(\alpha, \xi) > 0 \quad \text{for } \xi \in V_+,$$
$$(\alpha, \xi) < 0 \quad \text{for } \xi \in \mathfrak{k} \text{ and } \xi \in V_+$$

and

$$(\beta, \xi) > 0 \quad \text{for } \xi \in V_-,$$
$$(\beta, \xi) < 0 \quad \text{for } \xi \in \mathfrak{k} \text{ and } \xi \in V_+.$$

α and β are zero vectors, $\alpha \in N_+$ and $\beta \in N_-$. They are in addition linearly independent and this implies $(\alpha, \beta) \neq 0$ and in fact $(\alpha, \beta) < 0$. We normalize α and β by the condition $(\alpha, \beta) = -2$. In a suitable coordinate system α and β take the form

$$\alpha = (1, 1, 0, \cdots, 0), \qquad \beta = (-1, 1, 0, \cdots, 0).$$

The conditions $(\alpha, \xi) < 0$ and $(\beta, \xi) < 0$, both satisfied for $\xi \in \mathfrak{k}$, become $-\xi^0 - \xi^1 < 0$ and $\xi^0 - \xi^1 < 0$, therefore $\xi^1 > |\xi^0|$.

The complex Lorentz transformation

$$A = \left(\begin{array}{cc|ccc} 0 & i & & & \\ i & 0 & & & \\ \hline & & 1 & & \\ & & & \ddots & \\ & & & & 1 \end{array}\right) \in L_+(C) \tag{3}$$

now maps $\xi \in \mathfrak{k}$ into $A\xi = \zeta \in \mathfrak{T}$, as is easily verified. Since $\rho_k \in \mathfrak{k}$ we find a fortiori $A\rho_k = \zeta_k \in \mathfrak{T}$ or $(\rho_1, \cdots, \rho_n) \in A^{-1}\mathfrak{T}^n$. This completes the proof.

We shall systematically denote the real points in $\mathfrak{T}_n'$ by $(\rho_1, \cdots, \rho_n)$. They are regularity points of $W_n(\zeta_1, \cdots, \zeta_n)$. Similarly $(r_0, r_1, \cdots, r_n)$ denotes a real point in $\mathfrak{S}_{n+1}'$ and therefore a real regularity point of $\mathfrak{W}_{n+1}(z_0, z_1, \cdots, z_n)$. They are characterized by

$$(r_1 - r_0, r_2 - r_1, \cdots, r_n - r_{n-1}) = (\rho_1, \rho_2, \cdots, \rho_n). \tag{4}$$

As a simple consequence of the theorem just proved we have the

COROLLARY. *The points $r_0, r_1, \cdots, r_n$ are totally space-like: for $k > l$ arbitrary $(r_k - r_l)^2 < 0$.*

PROOF. Clearly $r_k - r_l = \rho_k + \rho_{k+1} + \cdots + \rho_{l+1} \in \mathfrak{k}(\rho_1, \cdots, \rho_n)$ and therefore $(r_k - r_l)^2 < 0$.

With the help of the points $(r_0, r_1, \cdots, r_n)$ we are now able to get a deeper understanding of locality. Clearly the r-points form a real open set and on this set the Wightman distributions are analytic functions. Now locality implies the invariance under permutation of the vector variables in $\mathfrak{W}_n(x_1, \cdots, x_n)$ in totally space-like points. Since $\mathfrak{W}_n(r_1, r_2, \cdots, r_n)$ is a function, locality has as consequence that $\mathfrak{W}_n$ is a function also in all the permuted points $(r_{k_1}, \cdots, r_{k_n})$, where $k_1, k_2, \cdots, k_n$ is an arbitrary permutation of $1, \cdots, n$. The equation

$$\mathfrak{W}_n(r_1, r_2, \cdots, r_n) = \mathfrak{W}_n(r_{k_1}, r_{k_2}, \cdots, r_{k_n}) \tag{5}$$

can, however, be analytically continued to an equation for Wightman functions

$$\mathfrak{W}_n(z_1, z_2, \cdots, z_n) = \mathfrak{W}_n(z_{k_1}, z_{k_2}, \cdots, z_{k_n}) \tag{6}$$

valid in the smallest domain containing $\mathfrak{S}'_n$ and invariant under all permutations applied to $(z_1, \cdots, z_n)$. Let us denote this new and *extended domain* by $\mathfrak{S}^P_n$. $\mathfrak{S}^P_n$ is the union of all domains generated from $\mathfrak{S}'_n$ by arbitrary permutations of the point variables $z_1, \cdots, z_n$. Thus we have proved the

THEOREM. *The Wightman functions $\mathfrak{W}_n(z_1, \cdots, z_n)$ of a local field theory are regular analytic in the domain $\mathfrak{S}^P_n$ and symmetric in $z_1, \cdots, z_n$.*

Our next aim is the proof of the

THEOREM. *If $\mathfrak{W}_{n+1}(z_0, z_1, \cdots, z_n)$ has all the properties of a Wightman function except the ones derived from locality and if in addition $\mathfrak{W}_{n+1}(z_0, z_1, \cdots, z_n)$ is symmetric in $z_0, z_1, \cdots, z_n$, then it satisfies also the requirements of locality.*

PROOF. From our assumptions,

$$\mathfrak{W}_{n+1}(z_0, z_1, \cdots, z_n) = W_n(z_1 - z_0, \cdots, z_n - z_{n-1})$$

and $W_n(\zeta_1, \cdots, \zeta_n)$ is holomorphic in $\mathfrak{T}^n$ and $L^\uparrow_+$-invariant. In addition, $W_n(\zeta_1, \cdots, \zeta_n)$ tends to a distribution $W_n(\xi_1, \cdots, \xi_n)$ as the imaginary parts of $\zeta_1, \cdots, \zeta_n$ tend to zero inside V_+. The BHW-Theorem then allows the analytic continuation of W_n into $\mathfrak{T}'_n$ and of $\mathfrak{W}_{n+1}$ into $\mathfrak{S}'_{n+1}$ and the symmetry of $\mathfrak{W}_{n+1}(z_0, \cdots, z_n)$ allows the continuation into $\mathfrak{S}^P_{n+1}$.

We have to show now that these properties of $\mathfrak{W}_{n+1}(z_0, \cdots, z_n)$ imply for the boundary distribution

$$\mathfrak{W}_{n+1}(x_0, \cdots, x_n) \equiv W_n(x_1 - x_0, \cdots, x_n - x_{n-1})$$

the equation

$$\mathfrak{W}_{n+1}(x_0, \cdots, x_{k-1}, x_k, \cdots, x_n) = \mathfrak{W}_{n+1}(x_0, \cdots, x_k, x_{k-1}, \cdots, x_n), \tag{7}$$

valid under the condition that $(x_k - x_{k-1})^2 < 0$.

The proof is simple. To the transposition of z_{k-1} and z_k corresponds the linear transformation

$$\zeta_{k-1} \to \zeta_{k-1} + \zeta_k, \quad \zeta_k \to -\zeta_k, \quad \zeta_{k+1} \to \zeta_{k+1} + \zeta_k,$$

all the other ζ_l's staying fixed. In the domain of regularity, e.g. in $\mathfrak{T}^n$, we therefore find

$$W_n(\zeta_1, \cdots, \zeta_{k-1}, \zeta_k, \zeta_{k+1}, \cdots, \zeta_n) \\ = W_n(\zeta_1, \cdots, \zeta_{k-1} + \zeta_k, -\zeta_k, \zeta_k + \zeta_{k+1}, \cdots, \zeta_n).$$

Next we claim that this equation still holds, if we choose for $l \neq k$ all $\zeta_l \in \mathfrak{T}$, but ζ_k, real and space-like: $\zeta_k = \xi_k$ with $(\xi_k, \xi_k) < 0$. This is so, if the point $(\zeta_1 \cdots \zeta_{k-1}, \xi_k \cdots \zeta_n) \in \mathfrak{T}'_n$, because then it is a regularity point. In order to verify this, we have to find an $A \in L_+(C)$, which maps the point under discussion into $\mathfrak{T}^n$. Such a transformation is almost trivially shown to exist. It is no assumption to take $\xi = (0, \xi', 0, \cdots, 0)$ with $\xi' > 0$. If we apply to the first two components the transformation

$$\begin{pmatrix} \cos\varphi & i\sin\varphi \\ i\sin\varphi & \cos\varphi \end{pmatrix}$$

with $\sin\varphi > 0$ the resulting vector is in $\mathfrak{T}$. On the other hand we can restrict φ to be so small that none of the vectors ζ_l, $l \neq k$, are removed from $\mathfrak{T}$.

Thus we have established the equation

$$\text{(8)}\quad W_n(\zeta_1, \cdots, \zeta_{k-1}, \xi_k, \zeta_{k+1}, \cdots, \zeta_n) \\ = W_n(\zeta_1, \cdots, \zeta_{k-1} + \xi_k, -\xi_k, \zeta_{k+1} + \xi_k, \cdots, \zeta_n)$$

for $\zeta_l \in \mathfrak{T}$, $l \neq k$ and $(\xi_k, \xi_k) < 0$. Both sides, however, converge for $\operatorname{Im} \zeta_l \to 0$ in $\mathfrak{T}$ to their respective Wightman distributions and we find

$$\text{(9)}\quad W_n(\xi_1, \cdots, \xi_{k-1}, \xi_k, \xi_{k+1}, \cdots, \xi_n) \\ = W_n(\xi_1, \cdots, \xi_{k-1} + \xi_k, -\xi_k, \xi_{k+1} + \xi_k, \cdots, \xi_n)$$

which equation in terms of $\mathfrak{W}_{n+1}$ reads

$$\text{(10)}\quad \mathfrak{W}_{n+1}(x_0, \cdots, x_{k-1}, x_k, \cdots, x_n) = \mathfrak{W}_{n+1}(x_0, \cdots, x_k, x_{k-1}, \cdots, x_n)$$

and is valid under the single condition that $(x_k - x_{k-1})^2 < 0$. This finishes the proof.

REMARKS. (a) The requirement of locality is therefore completely equivalent (if the other axioms hold) to the symmetry of $\mathfrak{W}_n(z_1, \cdots, z_n)$. Any condition insuring this symmetry also insures the full locality.

(b) The only property we needed of $W_n(\zeta_1, \cdots, \zeta_n)$ beyond the regularity in $\mathfrak{T}^n$ and $L_+^\uparrow$-invariance was the existence of the boundary distribution $W_n(\xi_1, \cdots, \xi_n)$ if $\zeta_k \to \xi_k$ in $\mathfrak{T}$.

As an application of the previous theorem and as an illustration of the strength of the Wightman axioms, we shall next discuss the

THEOREM. *Given that the scalar field $A(x)$ satisfies all the axioms of Wightman except the axiom of locality, and also satisfies*

$$[A(x), A(y)] = 0$$

for x in an arbitrary neighborhood of 0 *and y in an arbitrary neighborhood of a space-like vector a, then it satisfies the full axiom of locality.*

PROOF. Let $l = 1, 2, \cdots, n-1$. We discuss the following real regularity point $(r_1^l, r_2^l, \cdots, r_n^l)$, $r_k^l = (k-l)a$. According to the assumption,

$$\text{(11)} \quad \mathfrak{W}_n(r_1^l, r_2^l, \cdots, r_l^l, r_{l+1}^l, \cdots, r_n^l) = \mathfrak{W}_n(r_1^l, r_2^l, \cdots, r_{l+1}^l, r_l^l, \cdots, r_n^l)$$

and the same is true for a suitable neighborhood of this point. By analytic continuation

$$\text{(12)} \quad \mathfrak{W}_n(z_1, \cdots, z_l, z_{l+1}, \cdots, z_n) = \mathfrak{W}_n(z_1, \cdots, z_{l+1}, z_l, \cdots, z_n).$$

Since l is arbitrary we must have complete symmetry of $\mathfrak{W}_n$ for each n. Q.E.D.

REMARK. This theorem clearly demonstrates the strong interrelation between Lorentz invariance, the positive energy condition and locality. It also shows that, in a sense specified by the theorem, one has only the choice between a strictly local and an everywhere nonlocal theory.

6. The problem connected with the total symmetry of $\mathfrak{W}_n(z_1, z_2, \cdots, z_n)$. Additional remarks on the BHW-Theorem.

A. THE PROBLEM CONNECTED WITH THE TOTAL SYMMETRY OF $\mathfrak{W}_n$. As we have seen, the total symmetry of $\mathfrak{W}_n$ expresses in an elegant and nontrivial way the locality of the underlying field theory. It immediately poses new and unmanageable problems. As we know it implies the holomorphy of $\mathfrak{W}_n$ in $\mathfrak{S}_n^P$. Whereas it is trivial that $\mathfrak{S}_n$ is a domain of holomorphy and very likely that this is also the case for $\mathfrak{S}_n'$ for $n > 2$ this is no longer true for $\mathfrak{S}_n^P$.[2]

In order to illuminate the above statement we have to refer to an elementary but fundamental fact, by which the theory of functions of several complex variables differs from the theory of one complex variable. In the latter, any domain is a domain of holomorphy, which means that there exist functions holomorphic in the domain but without analytic continuation to points outside the domain. This is, however, not the case for more than one complex variable. If, to fix our ideas, $\mathfrak{D}$ is a schlicht

[2]The case $n = 2$ is trivial, for $n = 3$ this was first shown by G. Källén and A. Wightman [Kä 2], for $n = 4$ by G. Källén and J. Toll [Kä 4], for $n = 5$ by Manoharan [Mh 1], Möller [Mö 1] and Luzzatto [Lu 1].

domain in a more than one-dimensional complex number space, then any function holomorphic and one-valued in $\mathfrak{D}$ may necessarily be holomorphic also in certain points outside $\mathfrak{D}$. If this is not the case, i.e., if there are functions holomorphic in $\mathfrak{D}$ which become singular in an arbitrarily prescribed point outside of $\mathfrak{D}$, then $\mathfrak{D}$ is called a domain of holomorphy [Be 1*; Wi 5]. Otherwise $\mathfrak{D}$ is contained in a smallest domain of holomorphy, its envelope of holomorphy $\mathscr{H}(\mathfrak{D})$. Among the complications which may occur in the process of analytic completion, i.e., the transition from $\mathfrak{D}$ to its envelope of holomorphy $\mathscr{H}(\mathfrak{D})$, we mention that $\mathscr{H}(\mathfrak{D})$ of schlicht domain need not be schlicht.

It may be interesting to illustrate these facts by a simple but useful theorem of analytic completion. We are dealing with a complex s-dimensional affine space with coordinates $z_1, z_2, \cdots, z_s$. We shall write $z_l = x_l + iy_l$, where x_l and y_l are real.

DEFINITION. Let $\mathfrak{B}$ be a (connected) domain in the s-dimensional real space with coordinates $y_1, \cdots, y_s$. The domain

$$\mathfrak{T}(\mathfrak{B}) = \{(z_1, \cdots, z_s) \mid (y_1, \cdots, y_s) \in \mathfrak{B}\}$$

is called a *tube* with basis $\mathfrak{B}$.

EXAMPLE. Our domain $\mathfrak{T}$ is a tube which has a basis V_+. Similarly $\mathfrak{T}^n$ is a tube with basis $V_+^{\times n}$. $\mathfrak{T}'_n$, however, is not a tube.

THEOREM. *The envelope of holomorphy of a tube $\mathfrak{T}(\mathfrak{B})$ is the convex hull of $\mathfrak{T}(\mathfrak{B})$ or, equivalently, the tube $\mathfrak{T}(\overline{\mathfrak{B}})$, where $\overline{\mathfrak{B}}$ is the convex hull of $\mathfrak{B}$.*

For a proof e.g. [Wi 5].

REMARK. Any convex set with an interior point in a complex affine space is a domain of holomorphy. This is a consequence of the following two facts:

(1) A convex set is the intersection of half spaces and

(2) A half space is a domain of holomorphy.

The last statement is easily seen to be true, since by an affine transformation (which clearly transforms a domain of holomorphy into a domain of holomorphy), the half space can be brought into the form $\{y_1 < 0\}$. The function $(z_1 - a)^{-1}$ with $\operatorname{Im} a \geqq 0$ then becomes singular in an arbitrarily prescribed point outside our (open) half space.

In order to demonstrate the power of analytic completion even in the form of the relatively trivial tube theorem, let us prove a theorem which refers to two dimensions.

THEOREM. *Let $\mathfrak{T}_+$ be the forward tube in two dimensions and $\mathfrak{T}_- = P\mathfrak{T}_+$ the backward tube. Furthermore, let $\mathfrak{B}$ be a domain containing*

$\mathfrak{T}_+^n \cup \mathfrak{T}_-^n$ and an $L_+^\uparrow$-invariant neighborhood of the real points in $\mathfrak{T}_n'$. Then the holomorphy envelope of $\mathfrak{B}$ is $\mathfrak{T}_n'$.

REMARK. This is a simple case of a remarkable theorem of R. F. Streater referring to four dimensions (see next section).

PROOF. In the variables of §4, $\mathfrak{T}_+^n$ is expressed by $\operatorname{Im} u_k > 0, \operatorname{Im} v_k > 0$, $1 \leqq k \leqq n$, $\mathfrak{T}_-^n$ by $\operatorname{Im} u_k < 0, \operatorname{Im} v_k < 0, 1 \leqq k \leqq n$, and the real regularity points by $\sigma u_k > 0$, $\sigma v_k > 0$ with $\sigma^2 = 1$. Finally $L_+^\uparrow$ contains the transformations $\tilde{u}_k = \lambda u_k, \tilde{v}_k = \lambda v_k$ with $\lambda > 0$ real. We are evidently dealing with a situation where everything depends only on angles. The passage to logarithms is indicated:

$$\mu_k = \log u_k, \qquad \nu_k = \log v_k.$$

In these new variables, $\mathfrak{T}_+^n$ and $\mathfrak{T}_-^n$ are described by

$$C_+^n = \{0 < \operatorname{Im} \mu_k, \operatorname{Im} \nu_k < \pi\} \quad \text{and} \quad C_-^n = \{-\pi < \operatorname{Im} \mu_k, \operatorname{Im} \nu_k < 0\}$$

and the real points in $\mathfrak{T}_n'$ by $\operatorname{Im} \mu_k = \operatorname{Im} \nu_k = 0, 1 \leqq k \leqq n$, and $\operatorname{Im} \mu_k = \operatorname{Im} \nu_k = \pi$. We are clearly dealing with a tube, of which the basis contains the two cubes C_+^n and C_-^n, which are connected by the real points of $\mathfrak{T}_n'$, and their periodic repetition with period 2π.

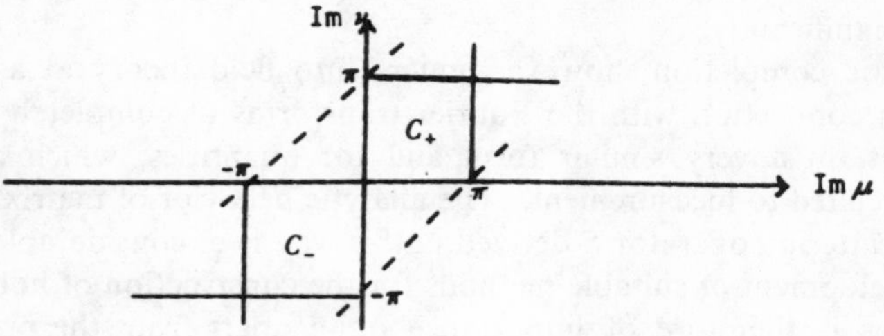

The envelope of holomorphy is the tube over the convex set generated by these cubes, i.e., the union of the cubes $\{\varphi < \operatorname{Im} \mu_k, \operatorname{Im} \nu_k < \varphi + \pi\}$ with arbitrary φ. If this tube is translated back to the old variables, the extended domain $\mathfrak{T}_n'$ is obtained.

We now come back to the problem referred to in the title. We already stated that for $n > 2$, $\mathfrak{S}_n^P$ is not a domain of holomorphy. The problem of analytic completion then immediately arises. This problem has been solved for $n = 3$ by Källén and Wightman [Kä 2]. Simplified derivations of their result are available [Ru 3] (making use essentially of a suitable generalization of the tube theorem). For larger values of n the problem of analytic completion (in more than two dimensions) seems to be very difficult.

This raises the question about the value to be attributed to the knowledge of the "true" domain of holomorphy for $\mathfrak{W}_n(z_1, \cdots, z_n)$. The word "true" is in quotation marks because we want to remind the reader and ourselves that we have for a long time dealt only with the linear restrictions on Wightman functions. As long as the nonlinear restrictions are ignored, we might conceive the rather unlikely situation that they extend the domain of holomorphy beyond $\mathscr{H}(\mathfrak{S}_n^P)$. Further spectral restrictions on the translation operator $T(a)$ will, however, not affect (within the "linear program") the analyticity behavior of $\mathfrak{W}_n(z_1, \cdots, z_n)$.

The original intention was to look at $\mathscr{H}(\mathfrak{S}_n^P)$ as an intermediate step towards finding a useful general representation of $\mathfrak{W}_n(z_1, \cdots, z_n)$ which would incorporate all linear restrictions, and to use this general representation later for the discussion of the nonlinear restrictions. Apart from the difficulty involved in constructing $\mathscr{H}(\mathfrak{S}_n^P)$ for $n > 3$ (which, to a large extent, legitimately, adds to the attraction of the problem), it is hard to foresee how it could lead, e.g., to a simple integral representation for the Wightman functions, because $\mathscr{H}(\mathfrak{S}_n^P)$ will probably not be an analytic polyhedron, the only case for which the Bergmann-Weil integral applies. The known envelope for the case $n = 3$, for which the Bergmann-Weil integral can be used, has so far failed (it seems to us) to increase our insight significantly.

Analytic completion, however, enters into field theory at a different place, in connection with the Fourier transforms of completely retarded functions, in a very similar form and for quantities, which are more closely related to measurement. The analytic behavior of matrix elements of the scattering operator S derived in this way is of considerable interest. The development of suitable methods for the construction of holomorphy envelopes is therefore of importance quite apart from the problem of Wightman functions (Chapter VII, §3).

We mention in this connection an elegant little theorem due to Ruelle [Ru 1], which, together with a remark of Steinmann, shows that $\mathfrak{S}_n^P$ for $n > 3$ and more than two dimensions is not a domain of holomorphy.

THEOREM. *All totally space-like points are in $\mathscr{H}(\mathfrak{S}_n^P)$.*

PROOF. It will be sufficient to treat only the time component as a complex variable and to keep the space variables real. Doing this we specify, of course, a coordinate system. Let us write t for $\operatorname{Im} z^0$. A point $(z_1, \cdots, z_n)$ is in $\mathfrak{S}_n^P$ if, for $k \neq l$, $t_k \neq t_l$. This is evident because ordering the points according to increasing values of t leads to a point in $\mathfrak{T}^{(n-1)}$. Possible singularities can therefore only occur if two values of t coincide. We now consider a point $(z_1, \cdots, z_n)$, of which the real part $(x_1, \cdots, x_n)$

is totally space-like: $(x_k - x_l)^2 < 0$ for $k \neq l$ and classify the dangerous points according to the number of t-values which coincide: For an m-point exactly m (independent) equations $t_k = t_l$ occur. We shall now show by induction that no singularity can occur for any m.

CASE $m = 1$. We assume again the points z_k to be ordered according to the values of t. The difference variables $\zeta_l = z_l - z_{l-1}$ are then all in $\mathfrak{T}$ with one exception, where the difference is real and space-like. But as we saw in the last section, such a point is in $\mathfrak{T}'_{(n-1)}$ and is therefore a point of regularity.

INDUCTION–ASSUMPTION. No singularities occur for $m < m_0$, $m_0 > 1$. Let $(z_1, \cdots, z_n)$ be an m_0-point, the z_l again ordered according to increasing t-values. Let ζ_k and ζ_l be two real difference variables. Let $\tau_k = t_k - t_{k-1}$ and $\tau_l = t_l - t_{l-1}$ be the imaginary parts of the time components of these difference variables for a neighborhood of our m_0-point. According to the definition of an m-point, there is a neighborhood of $\tau_k = \tau_l = 0$ (our m_0-point), e.g., $|\tau_k| < \epsilon$ and $|\tau_l| < \epsilon$, $\epsilon > 0$, in which no other m_0-point occurs. In this neighborhood $\tau_k = \tau_l = 0$ is the only possible singularity. Such a singularity is, however, removable (Kantensatz [Be 1*]).

But it remains to be shown that we have really performed an analytic completion. For this we point out a totally space-like point, which is not in $\mathfrak{S}_n^P$. Choose in three dimensions the points with the coordinates $(1 - \epsilon, 1, 1)$, $(1 - \epsilon, -1, -1)$, $(\epsilon - 1, 1, -1)$, $(\epsilon - 1, -1, 1)$ with $\epsilon > 0$ small. They are totally space-like and no permutation of them is an r-point.

B. ADDITIONAL REMARKS ON THE BHW-THEOREM. THE BHW-Theorem of §4 is only the first half of a dozen lemmas in the very important paper of Hall and Wightman [Hal 1]. It is the only result of this work which we shall use in this book. The remaining content is, however, important for other investigations. For this reason we want at least to describe the general ideas, and we do so in this subsection. In our exposition we shall follow to some extent two recent papers by K. Hepp [Hep 2, 3].

The following discussion is restricted to four dimensions. This restriction is made purely for reasons of convenience.

The Wightman function W_n is an $L_+(C)$-invariant function holomorphic in $\mathfrak{T}'_n$. One would like to write it in a manifestly invariant way, namely as a function of simple invariants like the scalar product $z_{ik} = (\zeta_i, \zeta_k)$. Such a representation, however, is not trivial.

In order to get some insight into the problems we want first to remind the reader of a similar but simpler situation in the classical theory of invariants. Here one deals with $L_+(C)$-invariant polynomials of n vector variables $\zeta_1, \cdots, \zeta_n$. Then the first main theorem of invariant theory states that every such polynomial is a polynomial in the following invariants:

$$z_{ik} = z_{ki} = (\zeta_i, \zeta_k), \qquad i \leqq k,$$
$$\Delta_{iklm} = \det \|\zeta_i, \zeta_k, \zeta_l, \zeta_m\|, \qquad i < k < l < m.$$

The determinants, of course, only appear if $n \geqq 4$. The total number of invariants is

$$r = \binom{n+1}{2} + \binom{n}{4}.$$

We shall denote them by $(I_1, \cdots, I_r) \equiv I$. They take values in $\mathbf{C}^r$. For $(\zeta_1, \cdots, \zeta_n)$ we again simply write ζ and for $\mathfrak{T}'_n$ use the symbol $\mathfrak{T}'$. Of fundamental importance for us is the mapping π: $\zeta \to I$. With this notation the content of the first main theorem can be stated as follows: to every $L_+(C)$-invariant polynomial $\mathfrak{p}$ of ζ corresponds a polynomial $\hat{\mathfrak{p}}$ in the variables I such that

(1) $$\mathfrak{p}(\zeta) = (\hat{\mathfrak{p}} \circ \pi)(\zeta).$$

The polynomial $\hat{\mathfrak{p}}$, however, is unique only in the simplest cases, namely if $n < 4$. In all other cases the invariants $I_1(\zeta), \cdots, I_r(\zeta)$ are not independent but satisfy certain polynomial identities. These identities are easy to find. First the rank of the matrix $\|z_{ik}\|$ does not exceed 4, i.e., all the $l \times l$ minors with $l > 4$ vanish.[3] Secondly

$$\Delta_{i_1 i_2 i_3 i_4} \Delta_{k_1 k_2 k_3 k_4} + \det \|z_{ik}\| = 0.^3$$

$\hat{\mathfrak{p}}$ is thus only defined modulo the ideal J generated by the finite number of polynomials which express the dependence between the invariants I.

We can state the situation in another way: The values $I(\zeta)$ do not in general cover the full $\mathbf{C}^r$ but lie on an algebraic variety defined by $J = 0$. Two polynomials $\hat{\mathfrak{p}}_1$ and $\hat{\mathfrak{p}}_2$ lead to the same invariant polynomial $\mathfrak{p}$ given by (1) if their difference vanishes on $\{J = 0\}$. But every specific polynomial $\hat{\mathfrak{p}}$ which satisfies (1) can be continued outside $\{J = 0\}$ into the whole space $\mathbf{C}^r$.

The aim must now be to prove the existence of a representation of the form (1) for Wightman functions. This is possible, but the difficulties encountered are considerable.

The first step in such a program concerns the mapping π. The first result is simple: the mapping π: $\zeta \to I$ is onto $\{J = 0\}$. To every point I^0 on $\{J = 0\}$ corresponds a vector ζ^0 such that $I^0 = \pi(\zeta^0)$.

---

[3] We do not claim that these identities are independent.

The second result is considerably deeper. We start with the trivial remark that on $\{J = 0\}$ a topology is induced by the neighborhoods in $\mathbf{C}^r$. The second result then states that to every $I^0 \in \{J = 0\}$ there is a point $\zeta^0 \in \pi^{-1}(I^0)$ such that every neighborhood of ζ^0 is mapped onto a neighborhood of I^0 (Lemma 3 in [Hal 1]). In general not every point in $\pi^{-1}(I^0)$ has this property, however.

The next step has to do with a decisive property of $\mathfrak{T}'$. $\mathfrak{T}'$ is saturated under π:

$$\mathfrak{T}' = \pi^{-1} \circ \pi(\mathfrak{T}'). \tag{2}$$

It is an easy consequence of the results quoted so far that there exists a function $\hat{W}$ continuous on $\pi(\mathfrak{T}')$ satisfying

$$W(\zeta) = (\hat{W} \circ \pi)(\zeta). \tag{3}$$

The function $\hat{W}$ is holomorphic in every regular point of $\{J = 0\}$, i.e., in every point of $\{J = 0\}$ in which locally the algebraic variety $\{J = 0\}$ is an algebraic manifold.

The representation (3) together with the properties of $\hat{W}$ mentioned form the principal result of the paper [Hal 1]. This result, however, is considerably weaker than the result obtained for invariant polynomials. There the polynomial could be extended beyond $\{J = 0\}$. According to Hepp a similar result can also, at least locally, be proved for $\hat{W}$ [Hep 2, 3]. To every point in $I^0 \in \pi(\mathfrak{T}')$ a neighborhood $N \in \mathbf{C}^r$ and a function $\check{W}'$ regular in N can be found such that $\hat{W}$ in $N \cap \pi(\mathfrak{T}')$ is the trace of $\check{W}'$. In other words, $\hat{W}$ is strongly holomorphic in $\pi(\mathfrak{T}')$.

The results quoted above follow from the slightly more general theorem:

THEOREM (BHW; HEPP). *Let the domain D in the variable ζ be π-saturated. Then every $L_+(C)$-invariant function F of the vectors ζ holomorphic in D allows the representation*

$$F(\zeta) = (\hat{F} \circ \pi)(\zeta) \tag{4}$$

and $\hat{F}$ is strongly holomorphic on $\pi(D)$.

The following theorem may be of some interest:

THEOREM (HEPP). *Let D be π-saturated and $\pi(D) = G \cap \{J = 0\}$, where G in $\mathbf{C}^r$ is holomorphically convex, then any function F holomorphic in D allows the representation* (4) *with a function $\hat{F}$ which is the trace of a function F' holomorphic in G.*

REMARKS. 1. The function F' is, of course, in general not uniquely defined since two different functions may agree on $\pi(D)$.

2. If in the above theorem $L_+(C)$ is replaced by $L(C)$ then the theorems stay correct if the invariants are restricted to the $\binom{n}{2}$ scalar products $z_{ik} = (\zeta_i, \zeta_k)$.

3. In theories which are reflection invariant, the Wightman functions are $L(C)$-invariant. Under this condition, the above theorem opens the possibility of extending the Wightman function of n four-vectors to a holomorphic $L^n(C)$-invariant function of n-vectors in an n-dimensional Minkowski space ($L^n(C)$: n-dimensional Lorentz group). This, however, is only possible if the extended tube of n-vectors in the n-dimensional Minkowski space is holomorphically convex. This is true for $n \leqq 4$ but unknown for $n > 4$.

We close this subsection with a few comments.

(a) The computation of the envelope of holomorphy of W_2 by Källén and Wightman [Kä 2] and by Ruelle [Ru 3] depends on the results of Hall and Wightman.

(b) For an analysis of the boundary of $\mathfrak{T}'_n$ we refer to [Kä 2, 5, 6; Jo 4; Wi 6; Mh 1].

(c) The geometry of the complex n-dimensional Minkowski space is analyzed in [Lo 1].

(d) We completely disregarded the extension of the above theory to covariant tensor fields. Important results have been found by Araki and Hepp [Hep 2, 3].

7. **The Theorem of Glaser and Streater.** As hinted at in the last section, V. Glaser and R. F. Streater [Str 1] discovered the following theorem, which sheds new light on the Bargmann-Hall-Wightman extended domain $\mathfrak{T}'_n$:

THEOREM (GLASER AND STREATER). *Let $\mathfrak{B}$ be an L_+-invariant domain, which contains $\mathfrak{T}^n$ and the real points J in $\mathfrak{T}'_n$. Then the envelope of holomorphy $\mathscr{H}(\mathfrak{B}) \supset \mathfrak{T}'_n$.*

PROOF.[4] Again we shall leave out the index n and write ζ for $(\zeta_1, \cdots, \zeta_n)$. Let $f(\zeta)$ be a function holomorphic in $\mathfrak{B}$. We want to show that it has a single-valued analytic extension into $\mathfrak{T}'$. We restrict ourselves to 4 dimensions.

1. Besides $\mathfrak{T}$, $\mathfrak{B}$ contains also $\mathfrak{T}_- = \{\zeta \mid -\zeta \in \mathfrak{T}\}$ because $\mathfrak{T}_- = R\mathfrak{T}$, where R is a reflection in L_+, e.g., the one represented by a diagonal

[4] I am indebted to Dr. H. Epstein, who pointed out to me that my original proof was wrong.

matrix with diagonal elements $(-1, -1, +1, +1)$. $f(\zeta)$ is therefore holomorphic both in $\mathfrak{T}$ and $\mathfrak{T}_-$. We begin with the discussion of the function $F(\chi; \zeta) = f(L(\chi)\zeta)$, where $\zeta \in \mathfrak{B}$ and $L(\chi)$ is an arbitrary (complex) Lorentz rotation in the (0, 1)-plane:

$$L(\chi) \equiv \begin{pmatrix} \mathrm{ch}\,\chi & \mathrm{sh}\,\chi & & 0 \\ \mathrm{sh}\,\chi & \mathrm{ch}\,\chi & & \\ & & 1 & \\ 0 & & & 1 \end{pmatrix}.$$

This function $F(\chi; \zeta)$ is defined for fixed ζ and holomorphic in "tubes" around $\mathrm{Im}\,\chi = m\pi$, $m = 0, \pm 1, \pm 2, \cdots$. Specifically, its domain of definition is given by $L(\chi)\zeta \in \mathfrak{T}$ and from the L_+-invariance of $\mathfrak{B}$, this is only a condition on the imaginary part of χ.

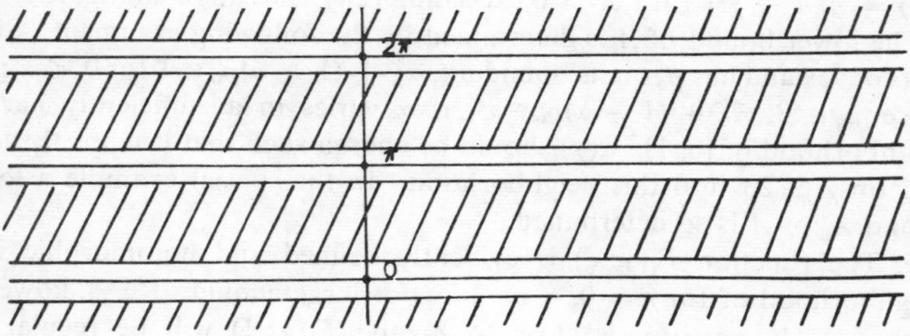

DOMAIN OF DEFINITION OF $F(\chi; \zeta)$. IN THE SHADED DOMAINS THE FUNCTION IS UNDEFINED.

2. There are even points $\zeta_0 \in \mathfrak{B}$, and therefore also neighborhoods of such points, for which $F(\chi; \zeta_0)$ is holomorphic for all values of χ. Examples of these are points in J for which the first component is larger than the absolute value of the zeroth component: $(\rho^0, \rho^1, \rho^2, \rho^3)$, such that $\rho^1 > |\rho^0|$, because such points are transformed by $L(i\varphi)$ either into points in $\mathfrak{T}$, $\mathfrak{T}_-$, or, for $\varphi = \pi$, in J (notice that J is invariant under L_+). Let us call these points ρ_0. The same is true for the application of $L(\chi)$ with arbitrary χ. Since the path $L(i\varphi)\rho_0$ is compact, we can also find a neighborhood of ρ_0 such that $L(i\varphi)$ applied to this neighborhood stays in $\mathfrak{B}$. The same then also holds for the application of $L(\chi)$ with arbitrary χ.

3. We have therefore the following typical situation: for certain values of ζ the function $F(\chi; \zeta)$ is holomorphic for all χ, e.g., in $0 \leqq \mathrm{Im}\,\chi \leqq 2\pi$, but as we vary ζ certain point sets appear, in which $F(\chi; \zeta)$ is no longer defined. If these sets (in the strip $0 \leqq \mathrm{Im}\,\chi \leqq 2\pi$) were, for suitable

values of ζ, contained in a compact set, we could easily extend the definition of $F(\chi; \zeta)$ to all values of χ (for these suitably chosen values ζ). Since this is not the case, we are forced to make a detour.

4. For this we discuss the function f in the points

$$L(\chi)[\alpha(\chi)\zeta + (1 - \alpha(\chi))\rho_0],$$

where χ is from now on restricted to $0 \leqq \operatorname{Im} \chi \leqq 2\pi$, and ζ is chosen from $\mathfrak{T}$. The resulting function of χ and ζ we call $F_1(\chi; \zeta)$. That is,

$$F_1(\chi; \zeta) = f(L(\chi)[\alpha(\chi)\zeta + (1 - \alpha(\chi))\rho_0]).$$

The function $\alpha(\chi)$ should be so chosen that it maps $\chi = \infty$ on the point $\alpha = 0$, the point $\chi = 0$ on $\alpha = 1$, and the strip $0 \leqq \operatorname{Im} \chi \leqq 2\pi$ into a suitable neighborhood of the segment [0, 1]. A simple choice is, e.g., $\alpha(\chi) = A[A + \chi^2]^{-1}$ for $A > 0$ exceeding $(2\pi)^2$ and large enough.

The lower bound of A is determined by the following argument. Since $\mathfrak{T}$ is convex and has ρ_0 on its boundary, $\alpha\zeta + (1 - \alpha)\rho_0 \in \mathfrak{T}$ for $0 < \alpha \leqq 1$. Since $\rho_0 \in \mathfrak{B}$, $\alpha\zeta + (1 - \alpha)\rho_0 \in \mathfrak{B}$, if α varies in a sufficiently narrow neighborhood of [0, 1]. $\alpha(\chi)$ should be chosen such that it maps the strip $0 \leqq \operatorname{Im} \chi \leqq 2\pi$ into this neighborhood. In the special example a lower bound A_0 of A is so determined.

5. The function $F_1(\chi; \zeta)$ is evidently defined and holomorphic in a neighborhood of $\operatorname{Im} \chi = 0$, π or 2π. For large enough $|\operatorname{Re} \chi|$, however, $\alpha(\chi) \cdot \zeta + (1 - \alpha(\chi))\rho_0$ is close to ρ_0 and $F_1(\chi; \zeta)$ will be regular for $0 \leqq \operatorname{Im} \chi \leqq 2\pi$. Hence the domain of definition of $F_1(\chi; \zeta)$ has the following general structure (Figure):

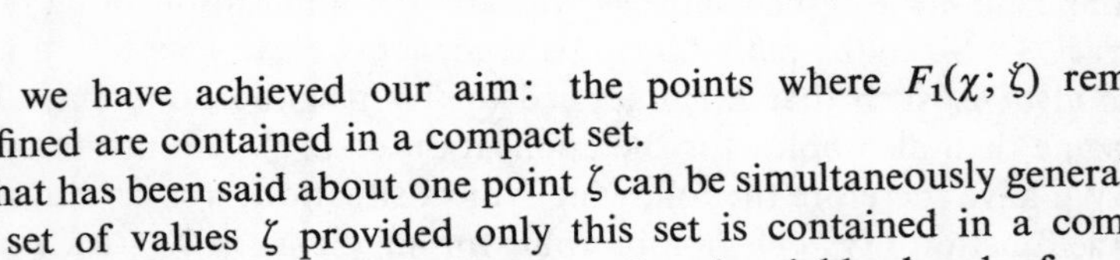

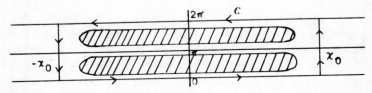

Domain of definition for $F_1(\chi; \zeta)$.

Thus we have achieved our aim: the points where $F_1(\chi; \zeta)$ remains undefined are contained in a compact set.

What has been said about one point ζ can be simultaneously generalized to a set of values ζ provided only this set is contained in a compact $\mathfrak{C}_0 \subset \mathfrak{T}$. We can even add to $\mathfrak{C}_0$ a closed neighborhood of ρ_0 and assume that the resulting union $\mathfrak{C}$ is connected.

6. Now we are ready to extend the definition of $F_1(\chi;\zeta)$ to $0 \leqq \text{Im}\,\chi \leqq 2\pi$ and arbitrary $\zeta \in \mathfrak{C} \cap \mathfrak{T}$. In fact, if $A > A_0$, the function $F_1(\chi;\zeta)$ will always be regular along the boundary of a rectangle bounded by the lines $\text{Re}\,\chi = \pm\chi_0$ and $\text{Im}\,\chi = 0, 2\pi$. The Cauchy integral

$$\tilde{F}_1(\chi;\zeta) = \frac{1}{2\pi i}\int_C \frac{F_1(\chi';\zeta)}{\chi' - \chi}\,d\chi' \tag{1}$$

therefore defines an analytic function of χ and ζ, which agrees with our old function, if ζ is close enough to ρ_0, such that $\tilde{F}_1(\chi;\zeta)$ is holomorphic throughout the rectangle, and, by analytic continuation, agrees with $F_1(\chi;\zeta)$ in all points of definition.

7. Nothing spectacular happens if we now formally go to the limit $A \to \infty$. Let us therefore ignore the details and immediately jump to the conclusion that it is possible to continue analytically the function $F(\chi;\zeta) = f(L(\chi)\zeta)$ to all the points $0 = \text{Im}\,\chi = 2\pi$, $\zeta \in \mathfrak{T}$, and that this continuation is single-valued.

8. The preceding discussion can immediately be generalized to the function, defined in $L_+(C) \times \mathfrak{T}$ by

$$F(\Lambda L(\chi);\zeta) \equiv f(\Lambda L(\chi)\zeta), \qquad \Lambda \in L_+^\uparrow.$$

For fixed Λ and ζ this function also allows a unique analytic continuation to arbitrary values of χ. Of special importance is the case $\chi = i\varphi$, φ real.

The function $F(\Lambda L(i\varphi);\zeta)$ is in fact single-valued in $L_+(C) \times \mathfrak{T}$ (wherever it is defined). This is so because

$$\Lambda' L(i\varphi') = \Lambda L(i\varphi)$$

implies $\Lambda' = \Lambda$ and $L(i\varphi') = L(i\varphi)$.

9. A slight change of notation is now required. From now on let $L_1(\chi) \equiv L(\chi)$ and let $L_k(\chi)$ be the corresponding Lorentz rotation in the $(0, k)$ 2-plane. Further, let $K_{lm}(\varphi)$, $0 < l < m$, be the one-parameter subgroup of $L_+(C)$ which rotates only the (l, m) 2-plane. We note the formula

$$K_{lm}(i\chi) = L_m(i\pi/2)L_l(\chi)L_m(-i\pi/2).$$

10. Next we discuss the function

$$F(\Lambda L_1(i\varphi)L_3(\chi);\zeta) \equiv F(\Lambda L_1(i\varphi); L_3(\chi)\zeta).$$

By a slight and obvious modification of the method described in 1–7 (a different choice of the point ρ_0 is necessary), this function can be extended to arbitrary values of χ; and we obtain as a special case the function

$$F(\Lambda L_1(i\varphi)L_3(i\pi/2);\ \zeta)$$

which is again one-valued in $L_+(C) \times \mathfrak{T}$.

The following extension is trivial (χ real)

$$F(\Lambda L_1(i\varphi)L_3(i\pi/2)L_2(\chi);\ \zeta) \equiv F(\Lambda L_1(i\varphi)L_3(i\pi/2);\ L_2(\chi)\zeta).$$

Slightly less trivial is the fact that it is single-valued in $L_+(C) \times \mathfrak{T}$. Let

$$\Lambda' L_1(i\varphi')L_3(i\pi/2)L_2(\chi') = \Lambda L_1(i\varphi)L_3(i\pi/2)L_2(\chi),$$

then

$$\Lambda^{-1}\Lambda' = L_1(i\varphi)K_{23}(i(\chi - \chi'))L_1(-i\varphi') = L_1(i(\varphi - \varphi'))K_{23}(i(\chi - \chi'))$$

and this is only possible (for $\Lambda, \Lambda' \in L_+^\uparrow$) if $\chi' = \chi$ and $L(i\varphi') = L(i\varphi)$.

11. Now

$$F(\Lambda L_1(i\varphi)L_3(i\pi/2)L_2(\chi)L_3(\chi');\ \zeta) \equiv F(\Lambda L_1(i\varphi)L_3(i\pi/2)L_2(\chi);\ L_3(\chi')\zeta)$$

is extended to $\chi' = -i\pi/2$, and we have $F(\Lambda L_1(i\varphi)K_{23}(i\chi);\ \zeta)$ single-valued in $L_+(C) \times \mathfrak{T}$.

A final trivial extension leads us to ($\Lambda_1 \in L_+^\uparrow$)

$$F(\Lambda L_1(i\varphi)K_{23}(i\chi)\Lambda_1;\ \zeta) \equiv F(\Lambda L_1(i\varphi)K_{23}(i\chi);\ \Lambda_1\zeta).$$

This last extension is again one-valued, if we restrict χ to *nonnegative* values, because we have from

$$\Lambda' L_1(i\varphi')K_{23}(i\chi')\Lambda_1' = \Lambda L_1(i\varphi)K_{23}(i\chi)\Lambda_1$$

first $L(i\varphi') = L(i\varphi)$ and $\chi = \chi'$ (uniqueness of the normal form, Appendix I, 3). One finds easily

$$\Lambda^{-1}\Lambda' L_2(2i\varphi)K_{23}(2i\chi) = L_2(2i\varphi)K_{23}(2i\chi)\Lambda^{-1}\Lambda'$$

and from this $[\Lambda^{-1}\Lambda',\ L_1(i\varphi)K_{23}(i\chi)] = 0$ and finally $\Lambda\Lambda_1 = \Lambda'\Lambda_1'$. We can therefore write

$$\begin{aligned} F(\Lambda' L_1(i\varphi')K_{23}(i\chi');\ \Lambda_1'\zeta) &= F(\Lambda L_1(i\varphi)K_{23}(i\chi)\Lambda^{-1}\Lambda';\ \Lambda_1'\zeta) \\ &= F(\Lambda L_1(i\varphi)K_{23}(i\chi);\ \Lambda_1\zeta). \end{aligned}$$

However, $\{\Lambda L_1(i\varphi)K_{23}(i\chi)\Lambda_1\}$ fills all of $L_+(C)$ apart from points in a lower-dimensional set, even for $\chi \geqq 0$. We thus have, by continuous extension into these exceptional points, a unique and analytic function $F(A;\ \zeta)$ defined on $A \in L_+(C)$, $\zeta \in \mathfrak{T}$. This function is an extension of $f(A\zeta)$.

12. It is a consequence of the last statement that

$$\Phi(B) \equiv F(AB^{-1};\ B\zeta)$$

is locally constant on $L_+(C)$. Its domain of definition is $\{B \mid B\zeta \in \mathfrak{T}, \zeta \in \mathfrak{T}\}$. Since this domain is connected [Hal 1; Jo 3], $\Phi(B)$ is globally constant and allows a one-valued analytic continuation into $L_+(C)$. Thus we are free to write

$$F(A;\zeta) = f_1(A\zeta)$$

and we have extended $f(\zeta)$ to $\mathfrak{T}'$.

This finishes the proof of the theorem.

REMARK. An interesting generalization states that we can leave out the requirement of L_+-invariance, if $\mathfrak{B}$ contains $\mathfrak{T}$, $\mathfrak{T}_-$ and J.

THEOREM (GLASER AND STREATER). *If $\mathfrak{B}$ is a domain which contains $\mathfrak{T}^n$, $\mathfrak{T}^n_-$ and J, then its envelope of holomorphy contains $\mathfrak{T}'_n$.*

The *proof* of this sharper form of Streater's theorem is based on the "Edge-of-the-Wedge" theorem [Bm 1; Dy 1; Ta 1; Gå 4; Ep 1], which, applied to the present situation, implies that the envelope of holomorphy of $\mathfrak{B}$ contains with every point $\rho \in J$ also a complex neighborhood of a universal size, which does not depend on $\mathfrak{B}$, except through the fact that $\mathfrak{B}$ contains $\mathfrak{T}^n$, $\mathfrak{T}^n_-$ and J. This leads us to the discussion of the set of all functions holomorphic in $\mathfrak{T}$, $\mathfrak{T}_-$ and J. All these functions will be (according to the above discussion) holomorphic in a universal neighborhood of J. Since, however, $\mathfrak{T}$, $\mathfrak{T}_-$ and J (again we have left out the index n) are an L_+-invariant set, the set of functions holomorphic in the union of these points is also L_+-invariant, as is the intersection of their domains of regularity. But this intersection contains the above-mentioned neighborhood of J and therefore contains an L_+-invariant domain $\mathfrak{B}_0$, which satisfies the requirements of the weaker form of Streater's theorem.

Combined with the "Edge-of-the-Wedge" theorem, the strong form of Streater's theorem then leads to the

THEOREM. *Let $f_+(\zeta_1, \cdots, \zeta_n)$ be holomorphic in $\mathfrak{T}^n$ and $f_-(\zeta_1, \cdots, \zeta_n)$ in $\mathfrak{T}^n_-$. Let $f_+(\zeta_1, \cdots, \zeta_n)$ and $f_-(\zeta_1, \cdots, \zeta_n)$ be such that the boundary values $f_+(\rho_1, \cdots, \rho_n)$ and $f_-(\rho_1, \cdots, \rho_n)$ exist as distributions.*

If now $f_+(\rho_1, \cdots, \rho_n) = f_-(\rho_1, \cdots, \rho_n)$ as distributions then f_+ and f_- have a (single-valued) analytic extension $f(\zeta_1, \cdots, \zeta_n)$ into $\mathfrak{T}'_n$.

8. **A theorem by Reeh and Schlieder and its application** [Re 1]. We have introduced in Chapters I, § 1C and III, § 4, the linear topological space

$$\underline{\mathscr{S}} = \bigoplus_{n=0}^{\infty} \mathscr{S}_n \tag{1}$$

of which the elements are sequences of test functions $\underline{\varphi} = (\varphi_0, \varphi_1, \varphi_2, \cdots)$

which almost all vanish. This space $\underline{\mathscr{S}}$ is mapped into operators over $\mathfrak{H}$ by

$$\underline{A}(\underline{\varphi}) = \sum_n \langle A^n, \varphi_n \rangle \tag{2}$$

and onto the dense set D by

$$\underline{\Phi}(\underline{\varphi}) = \underline{A}(\underline{\varphi})\Omega. \tag{3}$$

$\underline{\mathscr{S}}$ is a *-algebra and is mapped by (2) into an algebra $\mathfrak{A} = \{\underline{A}(\underline{\varphi})\}$ of operators defined on D. If we restrict $[\underline{A}(\underline{\varphi})]^*$ to D then the equation

$$[\underline{A}(\underline{\varphi})]^* = \underline{A}(\underline{\varphi}^*) \tag{4}$$

holds.

Now we are interested in subalgebras of $\underline{\mathscr{S}}$. Let $\mathfrak{B}$ be an open set in R^4; then we restrict φ_n by the condition supp $\varphi_n \subset \mathfrak{B}^{\times n}$ and define

$$\mathscr{S}_n(\mathfrak{B}) = \{\varphi_n \mid \varphi_n \in \mathscr{S}_n, \text{supp } \varphi_n \subset \mathfrak{B}^{\times n}\}. \tag{5}$$

Finally

$$\underline{\mathscr{S}}(\mathfrak{B}) = \bigoplus_{n=0}^{\infty} \mathscr{S}_n(\mathfrak{B}) \tag{6}$$

is a closed *-subalgebra of $\underline{\mathscr{S}}$.

$\underline{\mathscr{S}}(\mathfrak{B})$ is mapped by $\underline{A}$ into a subalgebra $\mathfrak{A}(\mathfrak{B})$ of $\mathfrak{A}$, and by $\underline{\Phi}$ into a subset $D(\mathfrak{B})$ of D.

The following remarkable theorem holds.

THEOREM [Re 1]. *$D(\mathfrak{B})$ is dense in $\mathfrak{H}$.*

PROOF. We have to show that $D(\mathfrak{B})^\perp = 0$. Now $\Psi \in D(\mathfrak{B})^\perp$ satisfies

$$(\Psi, \langle A^n, \varphi_n \rangle \Omega) = (\Psi, \Phi_n(\varphi_n)) = 0 \tag{7}$$

for all $\varphi_n \in \mathscr{S}_n(\mathfrak{B})$. Thus the distributions

$$(\Psi, \Phi_n(x_1, \cdots, x_n)) = F_n(\Psi)(x_1, \cdots, x_n) \tag{8}$$

vanish in $\mathfrak{B}^{\times n}$. These distributions, however, according to § 1, have analytic continuations $F_n(\Psi)(z_1, \cdots, z_n)$ into $\text{Im } z_1 \in V_+$, $\text{Im }(z_k - z_{k-1}) \in V_+$. Now the "Edge-of-the-Wedge" theorem allows an analytic continuation of $F_n(\Psi)$ through $\mathfrak{B}^{\times n}$ into $\text{Im } z_1 \in V_-$, $\text{Im }(z_k - z_{k-1}) \in V_-$ which is equal to zero. Thus $F_n(\Psi) = 0$ and $\Psi \in D^\perp = \{0\}$. Q.E.D.

Note that locality has not been used in the proof.

This theorem by Reeh and Schlieder allows a considerable generalization of a theorem by Ruelle derived in Chapter III, § 5B.

THEOREM. *Let $\mathfrak{B}$ be a domain invariant under a one-parameter time-like or light-like translation group:*

(9) $$x \in \mathfrak{B} \to x + \lambda a \in \mathfrak{B}, \qquad a \neq 0, a \in \bar{V}_+, -\infty < \lambda < +\infty.$$

Let $\mathfrak{A}(\mathfrak{B})$ be the corresponding ring of operators. A bounded operator C which satisfies

(10) $$(\Phi, C\underline{A}\Psi) = (\underline{A}^*\Phi, C\Psi)$$

for all $\underline{A} \in \mathfrak{A}(\mathfrak{B})$ and all $\Phi, \Psi \in D(\mathfrak{B})$ is a multiple of I.

PROOF. Let $T_\lambda = T(\lambda a) = \int e^{i\lambda a}\, dE_a(\lambda)$, and let $E_a(\Delta) = \int_\Delta dE_a(\lambda)$ for any Borel set Δ. Then $E_a([0, \infty)) = I$ and $E_a((-\infty, 0]) = E_0$, the projection on $\langle\Omega\rangle$. In exact analogy with the proof in Chapter III, § 5B we obtain from (10)

$$(\Omega, CE_1(\Delta)\underline{A}\Omega) = (\underline{A}^*\Omega, E_1(-\Delta)C\Omega),$$

where $-\Delta = \{\lambda \mid -\lambda \in \Delta\}$. By choosing $\Delta = [0, \infty)$ we obtain

(11) $$(\Omega, C\underline{A}\,\Omega) = (\Omega, C\Omega)(\Omega, \underline{A}\Omega)$$

for all $\underline{A} \in \mathfrak{A}(\mathfrak{B})$ and thus for all $\Phi \in D(\mathfrak{B})$

(12) $$(\Omega, C\Phi) = (\Omega, C\Omega)(\Omega, \Phi)$$

and finally, using (10) again, for all $\Phi, \Psi \in D(\mathfrak{B})$

(13) $$(\Psi, C\Phi) = (\Omega, C\Omega)(\Psi, \Phi)$$

and from $\overline{D(\mathfrak{B})} = \mathfrak{H}$ the result $C = (\Omega, C\Omega) \cdot I$. Q.E.D.

The theorem just proved is a special case of theorems proved by Borchers [Bo 2] and Araki [Ar 9].

If we combine the theorem by Reeh and Schlieder with locality, then the following useful criterion can be derived.

THEOREM. *Let $\underline{A} \in \mathfrak{A}(\mathfrak{B})$ and let $\mathfrak{B}$ be bounded, then*

(14) $$\underline{A}\Omega = 0$$

implies

(15) $$\underline{A}\Phi = 0 \quad \textit{for } \Phi \in D.$$

PROOF. If $\mathfrak{B}$ is bounded, then the domain $\mathfrak{B}'$ of points space-like with respect to $\overline{\mathfrak{B}}$:

(16) $$\mathfrak{B}' = \{x \mid (x - x_1)^2 < 0 \quad \forall x_1 \in \overline{\mathfrak{B}}\}$$

is not empty. Every operator $\underline{A}_1 \in \mathfrak{A}(\mathfrak{B}')$ commutes with $\underline{A}$. Thus we find from (14)

$$\underline{A}\underline{A}_1\Omega = \underline{A}_1\underline{A}\Omega = 0$$

and therefore

(18) $$\underline{A}\Phi' = 0 \quad \text{for all } \Phi' \in D(\mathfrak{B}').$$

Thus, since $\overline{D(\mathfrak{B}')} = \mathfrak{H}$, $\underline{A}^* = 0$ and finally $\underline{A}$ (which is the restriction of $\underline{A}^{**}$ to D) satisfies (15). Q.E.D.

CHAPTER V

The *TCP*-Theorem. Spin and Statistics

1. **Introductory remarks.** In this chapter we deal with two significant applications of the theory developed thus far. Both these applications treat problems which have been, and still are, widely discussed in Lagrangian field theory. The results are therefore by no means new. It seems to us, however, that the theory developed here gives a considerably deeper insight into the nature of these problems.

The *TCP*-Theorem states that any local field theory allows an additional discrete antilinear symmetry θ. This involution is in theories which are invariant under time inversion T, space reflection P and particle-antiparticle conjugation C represented by the product TCP. We shall prove this theorem only for the case of a real scalar field, i.e., for the theory defined in Chapter III.

The treatment of the connection between spin and statistics in this chapter is incomplete. An important addition will follow in Chapter VI. We treat here only the possible commutation relations between equal or different fields.

The result, combined with the Haag-Ruelle theory of asymptotic fields and particles (Chapter VI), leads to the statement that particles with integer spin, if they arise from a local field theory which satisfies the corresponding axioms, obey Bose-Einstein statistics, whereas particles with half integer spin obey Fermi-Dirac statistics.

For the treatment of spin and statistics we shall have to extend the axioms to the case of several fields with arbitrary transformation properties under the Lorentz group.

2. **The *TCP*-Theorem for one scalar field.** As already mentioned, the *TCP*-Theorem[1] states that any field theory satisfying all the axioms is invariant under an antiunitary involution θ. This transformation θ appears in special theories—namely those for which the operations T: time inversion, C: particle-antiparticle conjugation and P: space reflection are symmetries—as the product TCP.

The *TCP*-Theorem is remarkable because a discrete symmetry is shown

[1] See [Lü 1, 2; Pa 9; Sch 1; Jo 3; Gra 1].

to exist in theories which, to begin with, are only assumed to be invariant under connected continuous groups. As we shall see, it is intimately related to the fact that $L_+(C)$ contains as a real subgroup both sheets of L_+ and therefore the reflection PT.

Our analysis of the *TCP*-Theorem will go beyond its derivation. It will show in addition exactly how much of the axiom of locality is actually needed to insure the existence of the involution θ. In order to prepare the ground, we remember that any commutation relation of the form

$$(\Omega, A(r_0)A(r_1) \cdots A(r_n)\Omega) = (\Omega, A(r_{k_0}) \cdots A(r_{k_n})\Omega)$$

implies the extension of the Wightman function from its original domain $\mathfrak{S}'_n$ into $P\mathfrak{S}'_n$, where P is the permutation $(z_0, \cdots, z_n) \to (z_{k_0}, \cdots, z_{k_n})$. This is in general a true extension. For only two permutations does $\mathfrak{S}'_n = P\mathfrak{S}'_n$. These are the identity and the total inversion

$$(z_0, z_1, \cdots, z_n) \to (z_n, z_{n-1}, \cdots, z_0).$$

This can be seen as follows: if $(\zeta_1, \cdots, \zeta_n) \in \mathfrak{T}'_n$, then $(-\zeta_1, \cdots, -\zeta_n) \in \mathfrak{T}'_n$, because $\mathfrak{T}'_n$ is PT-invariant, but also $(-\zeta_n, -\zeta_{n-1}, \cdots, -\zeta_1) \in \mathfrak{T}'_n$, because the definition of $\mathfrak{T}'_n$ is symmetric in the difference variables. But $(-\zeta_n, -\zeta_{n-1}, \cdots, -\zeta_1)$ corresponds to the point $(z_n, z_{n-1}, \cdots, z_0)$. This naturally leads to the following

DEFINITION. (Dyson [Dy 1]). A field theory (of one neutral scalar field) is called weakly local, if for all n and all $(r_0, r_1, \cdots, r_n)$

$$(1) \qquad (\Omega, A(r_0)A(r_1) \cdots A(r_n)\Omega) = (\Omega, A(r_n)A(r_{n-1}) \cdots A(r_0)\Omega)$$

and if it satisfies all axioms except the fourth axiom.

REMARK. It has been shown before that locality implies weak locality. Now we have the

THEOREM. *Weak locality is* (*if all axioms except the axiom of locality hold*) *equivalent to the equations*

$$(2) \qquad \begin{aligned}(\Omega, A(x_0)A(x_1) \cdots A(x_n)\Omega) &= (\Omega, A(-x_n)A(-x_{n-1}) \cdots A(-x_0)\Omega) \\ &= \overline{(\Omega, A(-x_0)A(-x_1) \cdots A(-x_n)\Omega)}.\end{aligned}$$

PROOF. (1) *implies* (2). (1) expressed in W-functions reads

$$W(\rho_1, \rho_2, \cdots, \rho_n) = W(-\rho_n, -\rho_{n-1}, \cdots, -\rho_1)$$

and from the $L_+(C)$-invariance of W, and because $PT \in L_+(C)$ this yields

$$W(\rho_1, \cdots, \rho_n) = W(\rho_n, \cdots, \rho_1)$$

and by analytic continuation

$$W(\zeta_1, \cdots, \zeta_n) = W(\zeta_n, \cdots, \zeta_1).$$

Now we choose $(\zeta_1, \cdots, \zeta_n) \in \mathfrak{T}^n$, then also $(\zeta_n, \cdots, \zeta_1) \in \mathfrak{T}^n$.

After this we let the ζ_k approach real values, and obtain for the Wightman distributions

$$W(\xi_1, \cdots, \xi_n) = W(\xi_n, \cdots, \xi_1),$$

which, expressed in expectation values, reads

$$(\Omega, A(x_0) \cdots A(x_n)\Omega) = (\Omega, A(-x_n) \cdots A(-x_0)\Omega).$$

(2) *implies* (1). As we just saw (2) can be written as

$$W(\xi_1, \cdots, \xi_n) = W(\xi_n, \cdots, \xi_1).$$

This equation restricted to regularity points reads

$$W(\rho_1, \cdots, \rho_n) = W(\rho_n, \cdots, \rho_1).$$

Using the PT-invariance of the W-functions we find

$$W(\rho_1, \cdots, \rho_n) = W(-\rho_n, \cdots, -\rho_1)$$

which, translated into vacuum expectation values, is just (1).

TCP-THEOREM. *A weakly local theory possesses the antiunitary symmetry operation θ obtained by antilinear extension from*

$$\theta\Omega = \Omega, \qquad \theta\Phi_n(\varphi) = \Phi_n(\varphi^-),$$

where

$$\varphi^-(x_0, \cdots, x_n) = \bar{\varphi}(-x_0, \cdots, -x_n).$$

Conversely, if a theory is invariant under the above antiunitary involution, it is weakly local.

PROOF. According to the fifth axiom, θ is completely defined by the above conditions.

We then find for the scalar product

$$\begin{aligned}(\theta\Phi_n(\varphi), \theta\Phi_m(\psi)) &= (\Phi_n(\varphi^-), \Phi_m(\psi^-)) = \mathfrak{W}((\varphi^-)^* \otimes \psi^-) \\ &= \int \mathfrak{W}(x_0, \cdots, x_n, y_0, \cdots, y_m)\varphi(-x_n, \cdots, -x_0) \\ &\quad \times \overline{\psi}(-y_0, \cdots, -y_m)\, d(\underline{x})d(\underline{y})\end{aligned}$$

and for

$$\begin{aligned}&\overline{(\Phi_n(\varphi), \Phi_m(\psi))} \\ &\quad = (\Phi_m(\psi), \Phi_n(\varphi)) \\ &\quad = \int \mathfrak{W}(y_m, \cdots, y_0, x_n, \cdots, x_0)\overline{\psi}(y_0, \cdots, y_m)\varphi(x_n, \cdots, x_0)\, d(\underline{x})d(\underline{y}).\end{aligned}$$

These two quantities agree if and only if

$$\mathfrak{W}(x_0, \cdots, x_n, y_0, \cdots, y_m) = \mathfrak{W}(-y_m, \cdots, -y_0, -x_n, \cdots, -x_0);$$

but this is just equation (2). A similar discussion for the products $(\theta\Phi(\varphi), \Omega)$ leads to the conclusion that equation (2) is equivalent to the existence of θ. The first theorem then finishes the proof.

REMARKS ON THE *TCP*-THEOREM. 1. We stress once more that a local theory is also weakly local and therefore that θ exists for such a theory.

2. The following example shows however (if it were not already clear) that weak locality is really much weaker than strong locality.

EXAMPLE. Let $A(x)$ be a field which satisfies $(\Box + m^2)A(x) = 0$ and therefore allows the decomposition:

$$A(x) = (2\pi)^{-3/2} \int d^4p\delta(p^2 - m^2)[\theta(p)a(p)e^{-i(p,x)} + \theta(-p)a^*(-p)e^{i(p,x)}]$$

introduced in Chapter II, § 4, (6). But instead of the commutation relations (14) and (15) introduced there, we postulate now the anti-commutation relations

$$a(p)a^*(p') + a^*(p')a(p) = 2\omega(p)\delta(\vec{p} - \vec{p}')$$

and

$$a(p)a(p') + a(p')a(p) = a^*(p)a^*(p') + a^*(p')a^*(p) = 0.$$

This quantization together with the postulate of the existence of a vacuum state Ω, characterized by $a(p)\Omega = 0$, leads to fermions of spin zero. The theory is nonlocal: $A(x)$ and $A(y)$ do not commute for space-like separation nor do they anticommute as one sees from the relations

$$A(x)A(y) + A(y)A(x) = \Delta_1(x - y).$$

It allows, however, the antiunitary involution $\theta\Omega = \Omega$, $\theta A(x)\theta = A(-x)$, which leaves the field equation $(\Box + m^2)A(x) = 0$ and the commutation relations invariant. Written in terms of $a(p)$, θ takes a particularly simple form

$$\theta a(p)\theta = a(p), \qquad \theta a^*(p)\theta = a^*(p).$$

It then reduces in fact to the automorphism $z \to z^*$ of the complex numbers.

Now our corollary states that $A(x)$ satisfies the *normal* weak commutation relations:

$$(\Omega, A(r_0) \cdots A(r_n)\Omega) = (\Omega, A(r_n) \cdots A(r_0)\Omega).$$

These can be trivially checked for the two-point distribution

$$(\Omega, [A(x)A(y) - A(y)A(x)]\Omega) = i\Delta(x - y),$$

which vanishes for $(x - y)^2 < 0$, because it is an odd, $L_+^\uparrow$-invariant distribution.

3. Our present discussion of the *TCP*-Theorem fails to demonstrate the rôle of C. This is connected with the fact that it was illustrated only for *real scalar fields*. It is certainly evident what the necessary changes in the axioms would be if we were to adapt them to a *complex scalar field B*. The number of Wightman functions of course would increase, since not only $B(x)$ but also $B^*(x)$ can appear as a factor in the product of field operators. For real testing functions φ and $\Phi, \Psi \in D$ we would have, as defining relation between B and B^*:

$$\overline{(\Phi, B(\varphi)\Psi)} = (\Psi, B^*(\varphi)\Phi).$$

We could, of course, split the complex field B into two real fields A_1 and A_2 by $B = A_1 + iA_2$. This splitting is, however, devoid of any physical meaning in all cases where complex fields are legitimately introduced. This comes about through an additional requirement that, at least in the simplest case, the "gauge transformations" $e^{i\tau}B = B_1$ should be symmetries of the theory. In other words, there should exist a unitary group $V(\tau)$ of transformations, such that $V^{-1}(\tau)B(x)V(\tau) = e^{i\tau}B(x)$, $V(\tau)\Omega = \Omega$ and such that observables are invariant under $V(\tau)$. It is clear that the Hilbert space of states then splits according to the irreducible representations of the group $(e^{i\tau})$ and that no process will ever lead from one such subspace to another. This superselection rule will, however, not be discussed further [Wk 1].

For a free Dirac field, and in the general classical field theory, we have encountered the gauge group in connection with charge conservation. This connection is special: charge conservation is always connected with a gauge group, but there are gauge groups which are independent of charge conservation (in this sense also the "C" in *TCP* has to acquire the more general meaning of particle-antiparticle conjugation).

The weak commutation relations for a complex scalar field B read

$$(\Omega, B^{(\sigma_0)}(r_0)B^{(\sigma_1)}(r_1) \cdots B^{(\sigma_n)}(r_n)\Omega) = (\Omega, B^{(\sigma_n)}(r_n) \cdots B^{(\sigma_1)}(r_1)B^{(\sigma_0)}(r_0)\Omega),$$

where (σ_k) stands for a blank or for a $*$.

The first theorem in this case states that the equations

$$\begin{aligned}(\Omega, B^{(\sigma_0)}(x_0)&B^{(\sigma_1)}(x_1) \cdots B^{(\sigma_n)}(x_n)\Omega)\\ &= (\Omega, B^{(\sigma_n)}(-x_n) \cdots B^{(\sigma_1)}(-x_1)B^{(\sigma_0)}(-x_0)\Omega)\\ &= \overline{(\Omega, B^{(\sigma_0)*}(-x_0)B^{(\sigma_1)*}(-x_1) \cdots B^{(\sigma_n)*}(-x_n)\Omega)}\end{aligned}$$

are equivalent to the weak commutation relations.

The involution θ of the second theorem has the property

$$\theta B(x)\theta = B^*(-x), \qquad \theta B^*(x)\theta = B(-x)$$

and maps a state Φ, which transforms under $V(\tau)$ according to $e^{in\tau}$ into a state transforming according to $e^{-in\tau}$. If $n \neq 0$ these states are therefore different. If Φ belongs to a definite electric charge, the states Φ and $\theta\Phi$ have opposite charge.

The existence of θ therefore implies that to a state with a given charge, there always corresponds a state with opposite charge.

4. We have already had occasion to mention several times that the fundamental problem in general field theory is whether or not the axioms are compatible in a nontrivial way. It is interesting to remark that the replacement of the fourth axiom by the requirement of weak locality leads to a very wide and trivial framework [Jo 8].

5. Some very striking applications of the *TCP*-Theorem have been made by H. J. Borchers. We refrain from discussing them here. (See Chapter VII, §2.)

6. The generalization of our theorem to a finite number of different fields offers no difficulties and does not lead to significant new insights.

3. **Spin and statistics.** In this section we deal with a theory of an arbitrary but finite number of different fields. For reasons which will be explained in connection with the new formulation of the fourth axiom (locality) we shall require these fields to belong to irreducible, finite-dimensional *real* representations of the covering group of $L_+^\uparrow$. These irreducible real representations are in general reducible over the field of the complex numbers. In terms of the absolutely irreducible representations (k, l) introduced in Chapter I, §4, they are in fact given by $(k, l) \oplus (l, k)$ for $k \neq l$ and by (k, k). Only the last representations are irreducible over $\mathbf{C}$. In the representation space we choose a real basis. The matrices of the representations are therefore real. We do not, however, restrict the fields themselves to be real.

Our task is first to formulate the axioms for this more general case. A special emphasis lies on the fourth axiom (locality). This axiom allows several different formulations of which we choose one. It leaves a certain freedom for the commutation relations, a freedom in part restricted by the other axioms. These restrictions are completely described in two theorems (Burgoyne, Lüders and Zumino, Dell'Antonio) [Bu 1; Lü 3; De 2]. They refer to the commutation relations between one field and its adjoint and between a field with itself. The commutation relations in all the other cases are not restricted. They are, however, in general coupled to definite discrete additional symmetries of the theory (Araki) [Ar 5].

Only in one case, the case of the *normal commutation relations*, do such symmetries not occur. Normal commutation relations are defined as follows: tensor fields (belonging to one-valued representations of $L_+^\uparrow$) commute with themselves and with the spinor fields (belonging to two-valued representations of $L_+^\uparrow$) at space-like separation; spinor fields anti-commute at space-like separation.

It is a remarkable fact that in all abnormal cases new fields can be introduced with the help of the necessarily existing additional symmetries which obey normal commutation relations (O. Klein, Lüders, Araki) [Kl 1; Lü 4; Ar 5].

If we anticipate the results of the last chapter, where particles are introduced into a Wightman field theory, then the above results imply the law of the connection between spin and statistics: particles with integer spin obey Bose-Einstein statistics, particles with half integer spin obey Fermi-Dirac statistics.

The material of this section is quite complex. We shall therefore subdivide the section into subsections and even smaller parts.

A. THE WIGHTMAN AXIOMS AND THE WIGHTMAN DISTRIBUTIONS.

A1. *The axioms* [Wi 2]. We are dealing with a finite number of fields $\psi_1(x), \psi_2(x), \cdots, \psi_\Xi(x)$, each of which transforms according to a finite-dimensional real irreducible representation of the group $L_+^\uparrow$. The components of the field $\psi_k(x)$ are denoted by $\psi_{k,\alpha}(x)$. To each field a number $f(\psi_k) \equiv f_k$ is attributed, which takes the value $+1$ if ψ_k belongs to a two-valued representation of $L_+^\uparrow$, and 0 otherwise. A two-valued representation of $L_+^\uparrow$ is a true representation of the covering group $SL_2(C)$ of $L_+^\uparrow$. The elements of the covering group are denoted by Λ', the elements of $L_+^\uparrow$ as usual by Λ.[2]

The fields ψ_k are *not required* to be symmetric on the dense domain D. With each field ψ_k, however, the adjoint (possibly restricted to D) ψ_k^* is also a field. It belongs to the same representation as ψ_k.

We now review the axioms and indicate the necessary modifications.

The *zeroth axiom* stays unchanged.

The *first axiom* takes the new form: For each $\varphi \in \mathscr{S}$, $\psi_{k,\alpha}(\varphi)$ is a linear operator defined on the dense set D. For $\Phi \in D$ the vector $\psi_{k,\alpha}(\varphi)\Phi$ is linear and continuous in φ. $\psi_{k,\alpha}(\varphi)\, D \subset D$. For $\Phi, \Psi \in D$:

$$(\Phi, \psi_{k,\alpha}(\varphi)\Psi) = (\psi_{k,\alpha}^*(\bar{\varphi})\Phi, \Psi).$$

[2] We depart here from the notation of Chapter I, §4.

The *second axiom* takes the new form: There exists a unitary (continuous) representation $U(a, \Lambda')$ of the universal covering group of the restricted inhomogeneous Lorentz group satisfying

$$U(a, \Lambda')\psi_k(x)U^{-1}(a, \Lambda') = S_k(\Lambda'^{-1})\psi_k(\Lambda x + a) \tag{1}$$

and $U(a, \Lambda')D \subset D$.

$\Lambda = \Lambda(\Lambda')$ is the homogeneous Lorentz transformation corresponding to the element Λ' of the universal covering group. S_k is the (real) irreducible representation to which the field ψ_k belongs. The matrix elements $S_k(\Lambda')_\alpha^{\alpha'}$ are real.

The *third axiom* remains unchanged.

The *fourth axiom* is replaced by another axiom which, even when restricted to the case of a single real scalar field, is more general.

Fourth axiom. If $x - y$ is space-like and if $\psi_{k,\alpha}$ and $\psi_{l,\beta}$ are components of the same or different fields, then

$$\psi_{k,\alpha}(x)\psi_{l,\beta}(y) = \sigma_{kl}\psi_{l,\beta}(y)\psi_{k,\alpha}(x), \tag{2}$$

where σ_{kl} does not depend on the special components α and β and equals either $+1$ or -1. Equation (2) is only required to hold on the domain D.

Fifth axiom. The state Ω is cyclic with respect to all field operators.

A2. *Discussion of the fourth axiom.* We repeat that (2) has to be interpreted in the well-known way as an equation for distributions. In addition, (2) is only required to hold on the domain D.

We have said that the commutation relations (2) do not depend on the components α and β. A more general situation could be envisaged in which the commutation relations (2) are replaced by

$$\psi_{k,\alpha}(x)\psi_{l,\beta}(y) = \sum_{\gamma,\delta} M_{kl,\alpha\beta}{}^{\gamma\delta}\, \psi_{l,\delta}(y)\psi_{k,\gamma}(x). \tag{2'}$$

The matrix M_{kl} has to satisfy certain properties in order to be compatible with the second axiom. One easily verifies the following necessary and sufficient conditions:

$$S_k(\Lambda') \otimes S_l(\Lambda')M_{kl} = M_{kl}S_k(\Lambda') \otimes S_l(\Lambda'), \tag{3}$$

where again S_k and S_l are the representations corresponding to the fields ψ_k and ψ_l. Of course, M_{kl} must satisfy additional restrictions which originate in *other* axioms than the second. (3) is satisfied if M_{kl} is a multiple of the identity. In general, however, other choices are also possible. We do not go into these matters further. The following theorem by W. Schneider is relevant in this context [Sn 1].

THEOREM 1. *If the matrix M_{kl} in the basis indicated by* (2') *is diagonal, with diagonal elements ± 1, then it is a multiple of the identity.*

PROOF. Clearly $(I_{kl} \pm M_{kl})/2 = P_{\pm}$ are two diagonal projections, which commute with the representation $S_k \otimes S_l$. If both are nontrivial, then the matrices $(S_k(\Lambda') \otimes S_l(\Lambda'))_{\alpha\beta,\gamma\delta}$ are reduced. There exists at least one matrix element $(\alpha_0\beta_0, \gamma_0\delta_0)$ which vanishes identically:

$$S_k(\Lambda')_{\alpha_0\gamma_0} S_l(\Lambda')_{\beta_0\delta_0} = 0 \tag{4}$$

for all elements $\Lambda' \in SL_2(C)$. Since the matrix elements of S_k and S_l are real analytic functions on the group $SL_2(C)$ and thus belong to a ring without zero divisors, either $S_{k,\alpha_0\gamma_0}(\Lambda') = 0$ or $S_{l,\beta_0\delta_0}(\Lambda') = 0$ for all Λ'. Let us assume that $S_{k,\alpha_0\gamma_0}(\Lambda') = 0$. If we apply the matrices $S_k(\Lambda')$ on the vectors which have only a γ_0-component different from zero, the resulting vectors span a true real invariant subspace, namely a subspace of vectors with vanishing α_0-component. Thus S_k is reducible over the field of real numbers in contrast to the assumptions.

A special comment is required as a justification for the introduction of complex (nonsymmetrical) fields. It is true that we can split any field ψ_k into its real part $(\psi_k + \psi_k^*)/2$ and its imaginary part $(\psi_k - \psi_k^*)/2$. This split is, however, unphysical in all cases where a gauge group exists. We say that a gauge group exists if the theory is invariant under the transformation (τ real)

$$\psi_{k'} \to e^{i\tau}\psi_{k'}, \quad \psi_{k'}^* \to e^{-i\tau}\psi_{k'}^*, \quad \Omega \to \Omega \tag{5}$$

$\{k'\}$ a subset of $\{1, 2, \cdots, \Xi\}$.[3] The splitting of the fields $\psi_{k'}$ into their real and imaginary parts is not invariant under the group (5). The corresponding commutation relations of the form (2) can therefore violate gauge invariance. We only introduce complex fields if a gauge group exists.

At a later stage of our analysis we shall split the fields into real and imaginary parts. This will only be done after we have made sure that gauge invariance is not lost (theorem of Dell'Antonio).

The whole discussion arises because (2) is a nonlinear condition for the single fields. It is therefore not invariant under linear transformations of fields with identical transformation character. The choice of the irreducible fields ψ_k satisfying (2) has to be made on dynamical grounds, i.e., on reasons lying beyond the general axioms of Wightman.

A3. *The Wightman distributions.* The definition of the Wightman distributions remains unchanged: they are still the vacuum expectation values of products of field operators. Their properties change or stay the

[3] We do not claim that all gauge groups are of this kind. The gauge groups discussed here are however the only ones relevant to our problem.

same in an evident way. They are in general not scalar distributions. Their transformation properties are defined by the transformation properties of their factors:

$$(6)\quad \begin{aligned}&(\Omega, \psi_{k_1}(\Lambda x_1 + a), \cdots, \psi_{k_n}(\Lambda x_n + a)\Omega)\\ &\qquad = S_{k_1}(\Lambda') \otimes \cdots \otimes S_{k_n}(\Lambda')(\Omega, \psi_{k_1}(x_1) \cdots \psi_{k_n}(x_n)\Omega).\end{aligned}$$

If the representation $S_{k_1} \otimes \cdots \otimes S_{k_n}$ is a two-valued representation of $L_+^\uparrow$ then (6) implies that the Wightman distribution vanishes. This leads to the

LEMMA 1. *The Wightman distributions having an odd number of spinor fields and an arbitrary number of tensor fields vanish.*

The only Wightman distributions different from zero thus transform under the inhomogeneous Lorentz group like covariant tensor fields.

Again the axioms imply that the Wightman distributions are boundary values of Wightman functions regular in $\mathfrak{S}_n$. A slight modification in the proof of the BHW-Theorem leads to the extension of the domain of regularity into $\mathfrak{S}_n'$. In $\mathfrak{S}_n'$ the Wightman functions are covariant tensor fields under the complex inhomogeneous Lorentz group:

$$(7)\qquad \mathfrak{W}(Az + \alpha) = S(A)\mathfrak{W}(z)$$

for $A \in L_+(C)$. The extension of the representation

$$S(\Lambda) = S_{k_1}(\Lambda') \otimes \cdots \otimes S_{k_n}(\Lambda')$$

from $L_+^\uparrow$ to $L_+(C)$ is trivial, since $S(\Lambda)$ is, as a tensor representation, a polynomial in the matrix elements of Λ if $\mathfrak{W}(z)$ differs from zero. The fact that $PT \in L_+(C)$ is once more of principal importance to us (theorem of Burgoyne, Lüder and Zumino).

B. THE THEOREMS OF DELL'ANTONIO AND OF BURGOYNE, LÜDERS AND ZUMINO.

In this subsection we shall exclude certain commutation relations. We use the word exclude in order to indicate that the commutation relations under discussions are compatible with the axioms only if at least one of the fields in them vanishes.

As a simple tool we need the following

LEMMA 2. *If a field ψ_k annihilates Ω, then it vanishes.*

PROOF. The assumption clearly means that for any $\varphi \in \mathcal{S}$ the operator $\psi_k(\varphi)$ satisfies $\psi_k(\varphi)\Omega = 0$. We discuss a Wightman distribution containing ψ_k as a factor. In a real regularity point, ψ_k can, by at most changing the sign of the vacuum expectation value, be moved to the extreme right, where it acts directly on Ω. Such a Wightman distribution thus vanishes in the real regularity points and thus, by analytic continuation, identically. The fifth axiom then implies $\psi_k = 0$. Another proof follows from the theorem of Reeh and Schlieder (Chapter IV, §8).

B1. *The theorem of Dell'Antonio* [De 2].

THEOREM 2. *If* $\psi_l \neq 0$ *then the commutation relations*

$$\psi_k(x)\psi_l(y) = \sigma\psi_l(y)\psi_k(x) \tag{8}$$

and

$$\psi_k^*(x)\psi_l(y) = -\sigma\psi_l(y)\psi_k^*(x) \tag{9}$$

valid for $(x - y)^2 < 0$ *imply* $\psi_k = 0$.

PROOF. We discuss the following Wightman distribution

$$(\Omega, \psi_{l,\alpha}^*(x_1)\psi_{l,\alpha}(x_2)\psi_{k,\beta}(y_1)\psi_{k,\beta}^*(y_2)\Omega) \tag{10}$$

which under the assumption $(x_r - y_s)^2 < 0$, $r, s = 1, 2$, equals, according to (8) and (9),

$$-(\Omega, \psi_{l,\alpha}^*(x_1)\psi_{k,\beta}(y_1)\psi_{k,\beta}^*(y_2)\psi_{l,\alpha}(x_2)\Omega). \tag{10$'$}$$

Now let φ_1 and φ_2 be two real-valued test functions with compact support and let a be space-like. We define $\varphi_{2,\lambda}(x) = \varphi_2(x - \lambda a)$ for $\lambda > 0$, such that

$$\begin{aligned}(\Omega, \psi_{l,\alpha}^*(\varphi_1)\psi_{l,\alpha}(\varphi_1)T(\lambda a)\psi_{k,\beta}(\varphi_2)\psi_{k,\beta}^*(\varphi_2)\Omega)&\\ = (\Omega, \psi_{l,\alpha}^*(\varphi_1)\psi_{l,\alpha}(\varphi_1)\psi_{k,\beta}(\varphi_{2,\lambda})\psi_{k,\beta}^*(\varphi_{2,\lambda})\Omega)&\end{aligned} \tag{11}$$

and if λ is big enough, according to (10) and (10')

$$\begin{aligned}&= -(\Omega, \psi_{l,\alpha}^*(\varphi_1)\psi_{k,\beta}(\varphi_{2,\lambda})\psi_{k,\beta}^*(\varphi_{2,\lambda})\psi_{l,\alpha}(\varphi_1)\Omega)\\ &= -\|\psi_{k,\beta}^*(\varphi_{2,\lambda})\psi_{l,\alpha}(\varphi_1)\Omega\|^2.\end{aligned} \tag{11$'$}$$

But as $\lambda \to \infty$, from Chapter III, §6, the first term in (11) tends to the value

$$\begin{aligned}(\Omega, \psi_{l,\alpha}^*(\varphi_1)\psi_{l,\alpha}(\varphi_1)\Omega)(\Omega, \psi_{k,\beta}(\varphi_2)\psi_{k,\beta}^*(\varphi_2)\Omega)&\\ = \|\psi_{l,\alpha}(\varphi_1)\Omega\|^2\,\|\psi_{k,\beta}^*(\varphi_2)\Omega\|^2.&\end{aligned} \tag{12}$$

From the assumption $\psi_l \neq 0$, (11') and (12) imply $\psi_k^* = 0$ and $\psi_k = 0$. Q.E.D.

As already indicated, Theorem 2 allows us to split all fields into real and imaginary parts, without conflicting with the presence of gauge groups. We shall denote the new fields by the same letters $\psi_k(x)$, k

$= 1, 2, \cdots, \Xi'$. We hope that this does not lead to any confusion. $\psi_k^*(x) = \psi_k(x)$ from now on. The commutation relations keep the form (2). Real and imaginary part of one original field have the same commutation relations among each other as the single parts have themselves.

B2. *The theorem of Burgoyne, Lüders and Zumino* [Bu 1; Lü 3]. We come to the last step in the first part of our program, the exclusion of certain commutation relations.

THEOREM 3. *The commutation relations*

$$\psi_k(x)\psi_k(y) = -(-1)^{f_k^2}\psi_k(y)\psi_k(x) \tag{13}$$

for $(x - y)^2 < 0$ *are excluded.*

REMARKS. 1. We remind the reader that $f_k = 1$ for "two-valued" fields (spinor fields) and $f_k = 0$ for "single-valued" fields (tensor fields).

2. By this theorem the constants σ_{kk} in

$$\psi_k(x)\psi_l(y) = \sigma_{kl}\psi_l(y)\psi_k(x) \tag{14}$$

are determined: $\sigma_{kk} = (-1)^{f_k^2}$. The same is true for the corresponding constants in (2) (before the split of the fields into real and imaginary parts).

PROOF. Here we are forced to split the real irreducible representation to which ψ_k belongs into its absolutely irreducible parts. This is, of course, unnecessary for those fields which transform, to begin with, according to absolutely irreducible representations. Since this latter case allows an even simpler treatment, we keep to the more complicated case, where the representation S_k splits into two complex representations (k_k, l_k) and (l_k, k_k). The field which, after this decomposition transforms according to the representation (k_k, l_k) will be denoted by χ_k. The part which transforms according to (l_k, k_k) is then equal to χ_k^*. χ_k belongs to the Pauli character (σ_1, σ_2), χ_k^* to the Pauli character (Chapter I, §4) (σ_2, σ_1). The quantity $(-1)^{f_k^2}$ equals $\sigma_1\sigma_2$. The assumption (13) now implies

$$\chi_{k,\alpha}(x)\chi^*_{k,\alpha}(y) = -\sigma_1\sigma_2\chi^*_{k,\alpha}(y)\chi_{k,\alpha}(x) \tag{14}$$

for $(x - y)^2 < 0$. We discuss the pair of Wightman distributions

$$\mathfrak{W}_1(x_0, x_1) = (\Omega, \chi_{k,\alpha}(x_0)\chi^*_{k,\alpha}(x_1)\Omega) \tag{15}$$

and

$$\mathfrak{W}_2(x_0, x_1) = (\Omega, \chi^*_{k,\alpha}(x_0)\chi_{k,\alpha}(x_1)\Omega). \tag{15'}$$

They both belong to the Pauli character $(\sigma_1\sigma_2, \sigma_1\sigma_2)$. According to (14), in the real regularity points they satisfy the relation

$$\mathfrak{W}_1(r_0, r_1) = -\sigma_1\sigma_2\mathfrak{W}_2(r_1, r_0). \tag{16}$$

In addition, both $\mathfrak{W}_1(z_0, z_1)$ and $\mathfrak{W}_2(z_0, z_1)$ transform covariantly with respect to $L_+(C)$ and therefore with respect to PT. We find therefore

$$\mathfrak{W}_2(-r_0, -r_1) = \sigma_1\sigma_2\mathfrak{W}_2(r_0, r_1). \tag{17}$$

(16) and (17) lead, by analytic continuation, to

$$\mathfrak{W}_1(z_0, z_1) = -\mathfrak{W}_2(-z_1, -z_0). \tag{18}$$

If we go on both sides of (17) to the physical boundary values in $\mathfrak{S}_2$ then we find

$$\mathfrak{W}_1(x_0, x_1) = -\mathfrak{W}_2(-x_1, -x_0) \tag{19}$$

for all values of x_0 and x_1. Multiplication of both sides of (19) by $\bar{\varphi}(-x_1)\varphi(-x_0)$ and integration leads, with (15) and (15′), to

$$\|\chi^*_{k,\alpha}(\varphi^-)\Omega\|^2 = -\|\chi_{k,\alpha}(\varphi)\Omega\|^2 \tag{20}$$

with $\varphi^-(x) = \varphi(-x)$. Thus from Lemma 2 both $\chi_{k,\alpha}$ and $\chi^*_{k,a}$ vanish since both of them annihilate Ω.

C. THE THEOREM OF ARAKI AND THE KLEIN TRANSFORMATIONS [Ar 5].

In this section we shall analyze the nature of a theory with abnormal commutation relations. Such theories can exist and we shall find for them a complete characterization in terms of certain symmetries. Once these symmetries are uncovered it will be easy to relate the abnormal theories to normal ones. The basis of our discussion is now a set of real fields ψ_k, $k = 1, 2, \cdots, \Xi'$, satisfying the commutation relations

$$\psi_k\psi_l = (-1)^{f_k f_l}(-1)^{\eta_{kl}}\psi_l\psi_k. \tag{21}$$

In ψ_k and ψ_l arguments with a space-like difference are tacitly assumed. The numbers $\eta_{kl} = \eta_{lk}$ are restricted to the values 0 and 1. They satisfy the crucial equations

$$\eta_{11} = \eta_{22} = \cdots = \eta_{\Xi'\Xi'} = 0 \tag{22}$$

and thus form a symmetric matrix η with vanishing diagonal elements.

For normal commutation relations $\eta = 0$. There are certain restrictions on the matrix η for those real fields obtained from splitting original complex fields. If ψ_{k_0} and ψ_{l_0} are real and imaginary parts of one complex field, then

$$\eta_{k_0 l} = \eta_{l_0 l}$$

for all values l. As a special case $\eta_{k_0 l_0} = 0$.

Apart from such restrictions the matrix η is arbitrary.

C1. *The monomials and their commutation relations.* A monomial is a product of field (or field components). The set of arguments of the single factors are assumed to be totally space-like: the difference between any two different arguments is space-like. We denote monomials by the letter M. The product of two monomials M_1 and M_2 is again a monomial

$M = M_1M_2$. We assume that the arguments in M_1 and M_2 are so chosen that the arguments of M are totally space-like. Under these conditions, monomials satisfy definite commutation relations:

$$M_1M_2 = \sigma(M_1, M_2)M_2M_1, \tag{23}$$

where $\sigma^2 = 1$. $\sigma(M_1, M_2)$ is uniquely defined by (21). It does not depend on the order of factors in M_1 or M_2. It only depends on the number of times each field ψ_k enters into M_1 and M_2. Only the rest class modulo 2 of these numbers matters. This leads us in a natural way to a mapping of the monomials M into a Ξ'-dimensional vector space $\mathfrak{B}$ over the field consisting of the two numbers 0 and 1 (prime field characteristic 2) with the following rules of computation:

$$0 + 0 = 0, \quad 0 + 1 = 1 + 0 = 1, \quad 1 + 1 = 0,$$
$$0 \cdot 0 = 0, \quad 0 \cdot 1 = 1 \cdot 0 = 0, \quad 1 \cdot 1 = 1.$$

Each M is mapped on a vector

$$m = (m^1, \cdots, m^{\Xi'}) \quad \text{in } \mathfrak{B}.$$

$m^k = 1$ if the field ψ_k enters an odd number of times into M, $m^k = 0$ otherwise. To each vector m we attribute the value $F = \sum m^k f_k$ of a linear form. With these notations we write the commutation relations (23) in the form

$$M_1M_2 = (-1)^{F_1F_2}(-1)^{(m_1,m_2)}M_2M_1 \tag{24}$$

where of course $m_i = m(M_i)$ and $F_i = (f, m_i)$, $i = 1, 2$. (24) introduces the symmetrical function (m_1, m_2) of two vectors. This function is bilinear in the factors m_1 and m_2. This is seen as follows:

$$\begin{aligned} M_1M_2M_3 &= (-1)^{F_1F_2}(-1)^{(m_1,m_2)}M_2M_1M_3 \\ &= (-1)^{F_1(F_2+F_3)}(-1)^{(m_1,m_2)+(m_1,m_3)}M_2M_3M_1 \\ &= (-1)^{F_1(F_2+F_3)}(-1)^{(m_1,m_2+m_3)}M_2M_3M_1. \end{aligned} \tag{25}$$

The last equation follows from $m(M_2M_3) = m(M_2) + m(M_3)$. Thus $(m_1, m_2 + m_3) = (m_1, m_2) + (m_1, m_3)$. The linearity in the first factor follows from the symmetry $(m_1, m_2) = (m_2, m_1)$. An explicit expression for (m_1, m_2) is now easily found to be (always in the prime field of characteristic 2)

$$(m_1, m_2) = \sum \eta_{kl} m_1^k m_2^l. \tag{26}$$

We summarize the results and round them out in the following

Lemma 3. *The commutation relations between monomials are given by*

$$M_1M_2 = (-1)^{F_1F_2}(-1)^{(m_1,m_2)}M_2M_1, \tag{27}$$

where $F_i = \sum f_k m_i^k$, $i = 1, 2$, *and* $(m_1, m_2) = \sum \eta_{kl} m_1^k m_2^l$. *The scalar product* (m_1, m_2) *has the properties*

$$(m_1, m_2) + (m_2, m_1) = 0 \tag{28}$$

and

$$(m, m) = 0 \quad \textit{for all } m \in \mathfrak{B}. \tag{29}$$

It therefore induces a symplectic structure in $\mathfrak{B}$ [At 1*].

PROOF. (28) is trivial, since $(m_1, m_2) = (m_2, m_1)$ and thus $(m_1, m_2) + (m_2, m_1) = (m_1, m_2) + (m_1, m_2) = 0$. (29) is crucial. It is a consequence of (22) because

$$\begin{aligned}(m, m) &= \sum_{k<l} \eta_{kl} m^k m^l + \sum_{k>l} \eta_{kl} m^k m^l \\ &= \sum_{k<l} \eta_{kl} m^k m^l + \sum_{k<l} \eta_{kl} m^k m^l = 0.\end{aligned} \tag{30}$$

C2. *The vacuum expectation values.* The usefulness of the scalar product (m_1, m_2) rests on the following

LEMMA 4. *If* $(m_1, m_2) = 1$ *then*

$$(\Omega, M_1\Omega)(\Omega, M_2\Omega) = 0. \tag{31}$$

PROOF. Let φ_1 and φ_2 be test functions having as compact support only real regularity points of $(\Omega, M_1\Omega)$ and $(\Omega, M_2\Omega)$. Let α be space-like and λ positive. If λ is big enough, then

$$\begin{aligned}&M_1(\varphi_1)[T(\lambda a)M_2(\varphi_2)T(-\lambda a)] \\ &\qquad = (-1)^{F_1F_2}(-1)^{(m_1,m_2)}[T(\lambda a)M_2(\varphi_2)T(-\lambda a)]M_1(\varphi_1)\end{aligned} \tag{32}$$

and thus

$$\begin{aligned}&(\Omega, M_1(\varphi_1)T(\lambda a)M_2(\varphi_2)\Omega) \\ &\qquad = (-1)^{F_1F_2}(-1)^{(m_1,m_2)}(\Omega, M_2(\varphi_2)T(-\lambda a)M_1(\varphi_1)\Omega).\end{aligned} \tag{33}$$

As $\lambda \to \infty$, we find according to Chapter III, §6, Corollary,

$$\begin{aligned}&(\Omega, M_1(\varphi_1)\Omega)(\Omega, M_2(\varphi_2)\Omega) \\ &\qquad = (-1)^{F_1F_2}(-1)^{(m_1,m_2)}(\Omega, M_2(\varphi_2)\Omega)(\Omega, M_1(\varphi_1)\Omega).\end{aligned} \tag{34}$$

Since $(m_1, m_2) = 1$ we either have $F_1F_2 = 1$ or

$$(\Omega, M_1(\varphi_1)\Omega)(\Omega, M_2(\varphi_2)\Omega) = 0.$$

However $F_1F_2 = 1$ only if $F_1 = 1$ and $F_2 = 1$. In this case Lemma 1 leads to $(\Omega, M_1(\varphi_1)\Omega) = 0$ and $(\Omega, M_2(\varphi_2)\Omega) = 0$. In both cases analytic continuation leads to (31).

C3. *The vector space* $\mathfrak{V}_0$. All elementary notions of affine and metric geometry [At 1*] (and others will not be needed) are true for our vector space $\mathfrak{V}$, despite the discrete nature of its ground-field $\{0, 1\}$. The fact that $\mathfrak{V}$ is a symplectic space may at first sight seem rather unusual to the physicist. It is not, as we shall illustrate presently, and it is very welcome, since orthogonal geometry over a field of characteristic 2 shows very special features, in contrast to symplectic geometry. The physicist knows symplectic geometry from analytical dynamics. The linear forms in phase space represent a vector space. The Poisson brackets [La 1*] induce in this vector space a symplectic structure. The momenta $p_1, \cdots, p_f$ and the conjugate coordinates $q_1, \cdots, q_f$ form a *canonical basis*. They satisfy $\{p_k, p_l\} = \{q_k, q_l\} = 0$ and $\{p_k, q_l\} = \delta_{kl}$. A similar basis for $\mathfrak{V}$ will turn out to be useful to us. We start with a few

DEFINITIONS. Two vectors m_1, m_2 are orthogonal if $(m_1, m_2) = 0$. A vector m is orthogonal to a linear subspace $\mathfrak{V}_1$, if m is orthogonal to all vectors in $\mathfrak{V}_1$. All the vectors orthogonal to $\mathfrak{V}_1$ form another subspace, denoted by $\mathfrak{V}_1^{\perp}$. The intersection $\mathfrak{V}_1 \cap \mathfrak{V}_1^{\perp}$ is the *radical* of $\mathfrak{V}_1$. If $\mathfrak{V}_1 \cap \mathfrak{V}_1^{\perp} = \mathfrak{V}_1$, then $\mathfrak{V}_1$ is isotropic: any two vectors in $\mathfrak{V}_1$ are orthogonal. The radical of $\mathfrak{V}$ itself will be denoted by $\mathfrak{R}$:

$$\mathfrak{R} = \mathfrak{V} \cap \mathfrak{V}^{\perp}.$$

If the monomial M_1 is mapped into $\mathfrak{R}$ then, by definition of $\mathfrak{R}$, we have with any other monomial M the commutation relations

$$MM_1 = (-1)^{FF_1} M_1 M. \tag{35}$$

Differently phrased: the monomials which belong to the radical $\mathfrak{R}$ already have normal commutation relations. Since we are interested here in the abnormal commutation relations (and want to transform *them* into normal ones) we are not interested in such monomials and we shall suppress them by going to the *factor space* $\mathfrak{V}_0 = \mathfrak{V}/\mathfrak{R}$.

The symplectic structure of $\mathfrak{V}$ uniquely determines a symplectic structure in $\mathfrak{V}_0$: a scalar product (m_1, m_2) with the properties (28) and (29) is defined in $\mathfrak{V}_0$. Its value equals the unique value of the scalar product of any vector from the coset of m_1 with any vector from the coset of m_2. $\mathfrak{V}_0$ has, however, the trivial radical $\{0\}$; it is nonsingular. From now on we shall work only in $\mathfrak{V}_0$. We shall construct a special canonical basis of $\mathfrak{V}_0$. Such a basis can of course easily be completed by adding a set of linearly independent vectors from $\mathfrak{R}$ to a basis of $\mathfrak{V}$.

The following lemma, which is a consequence of elementary theorems on linear equations, will be useful:

LEMMA 5. *If* $\mathfrak{V}_1$ *is a subspace of* $\mathfrak{V}_0$ *then*

$$\dim \mathfrak{V}_1 + \dim \mathfrak{V}_1^{\perp} = \dim \mathfrak{V}_0. \tag{36}$$

C4. *Construction of the basis in* $\mathfrak{B}_0$.

LEMMA 6. *The set of vectors* $\mathfrak{U} \subset \mathfrak{B}_0$ *belonging to monomials with nonvanishing vacuum expectation values form an isotropic subspace*: $\mathfrak{U} = \langle a_1, a_2, \cdots, a_r \rangle$, $\{a_k\}$ *linearly independent*, $(a_k, a_l) = 0$.

PROOF. (a) We first show that $m_1 \in \mathfrak{U}$, $m_2 \in \mathfrak{U}$ implies $m_1 + m_2 \in \mathfrak{U}$. Let $m_k = m(M_k)$ and $(\Omega, M_k\Omega) \neq 0$ for $k = 1, 2$. Then, as $(a, a) \to -\infty$

$$(\Omega, M_1T(a)M_2\Omega) \to (\Omega, M_1\Omega)(\Omega, M_2\Omega)$$

(Chapter III, §6, Corollary), thus

$$(\Omega, M_1M_2'\Omega) = (\Omega, M_1T(a)M_2T(-a)\Omega) \neq 0 \tag{37}$$

for a suitably chosen value of a. Finally $m(M_1M_2') = m_1 + m_2$.

Since $m_1 + m_1 = 0$, $\mathfrak{U}$ contains the zero vector and with any two vectors also their sum. It is therefore a subspace.

(b) Now we show that $\mathfrak{U}$ is isotropic. Choose m_k and M_k, $k = 1, 2$, as in (a). Assume $(m_1, m_2) = 1$, then according to Lemma 4 we have $(\Omega, M_1\Omega)(\Omega, M_2\Omega) = 0$ in contradiction to the choice of M_1 and M_2. This finishes the proof of Lemma 6.

In general $\mathfrak{U}^\perp$ contains $\mathfrak{U}$ as a true subspace. If this is the case then $a_{r+1} \in \mathfrak{U}^\perp$ and $a_{r+1} \notin \mathfrak{U}$ exists and can be used to imbed $\mathfrak{U}$ into a larger isotropic subspace $\langle a_1, \cdots, a_{r+1} \rangle$. Proceeding in this manner leads finally to a *maximal* isotropic subspace $\langle a_1, a_2, \cdots, a_s \rangle = \mathfrak{U}_1$, which satisfies $\mathfrak{U}_1^\perp = \mathfrak{U}_1$ and thus, according to Lemma 5, 2 dim $\mathfrak{U}_1 = 2s =$ dim $\mathfrak{B}_0$.

The set of vectors $\{a_1, \cdots, a_s\}$ can easily be completed to a canonical basis of $\mathfrak{B}_0$ by the addition of vectors $\{b_1, \cdots, b_s\}$ again generating a maximal isotropic subspace, and such that the scalar products satisfy $(a_k, b_l) = \delta_{kl}$. Thus we have

LEMMA 7. $\mathfrak{B}_0$ *possesses a canonical basis* $a_1, \cdots, a_s, b_1, \cdots, b_s$, *which satisfies*

$$(a_k, a_l) = (b_k, b_l) = 0, \qquad (a_k, b_l) = \delta_{kl} \tag{1}$$

for $k, l = 1, \cdots, s$.

$$(\Omega, M_1\Omega) = 0 \tag{2}$$

if $m_1 = m(M_1)$ *satisfies for at least one value* k: $(a_k, m_1) = 1$.

PROOF OF THE STATEMENT (2). If $(a_k, m_1) = 1$ then $m_1 \notin \langle a_1, \cdots, a_s \rangle$ and thus $m_1 \notin \mathfrak{U}$. The definition of $\mathfrak{U}$ leads to $(\Omega, M_1\Omega) = 0$.

C5. *The symmetries and the Klein transformations.* Each field ψ_k is itself a monomial and therefore mapped on a vector in $\mathfrak{B}_0$. We write for this vector e_k

$$e_k = m(\psi_k). \tag{38}$$

THEOREM 4. *The transformations θ_k defined by*

$$\theta_k\Omega = \Omega, \tag{39}$$

$$\theta_k \psi_l \theta_k^{-1} = (-1)^{(a_k, e_l)} \psi_l \tag{40}$$

are unitary symmetries of the theory. They satisfy $\theta_k^2 = I$ and are therefore involutions.

PROOF. 1. The transformations are clearly involutions. We therefore write $\theta_k \psi_l \theta_k$ instead of $\theta_k \psi_l \theta_k^{-1}$.

2. We have to show that (39) and (40) define a unitary transformation. From the main theorem in Chapter III, §4, it is sufficient to prove that the fields $\psi_l' = \theta_k \psi_l \theta_k$ have the same Wightman distributions as the original fields. From (40) it follows that

$$M' = \theta_k M \theta_k = (-1)^{(a_k, m)} M, \tag{41}$$

and thus, with (39)

$$(\Omega, \theta_k M \theta_k \Omega) = (-1)^{(a_k, m)} (\Omega, M\Omega). \tag{42}$$

In order that

$$(\Omega, M'\Omega) = (\Omega, M\Omega) \tag{43}$$

it is necessary and sufficient that $(\Omega, M\Omega) = 0$ whenever $(a_k, m) = 1$. This is, however, guaranteed by Lemma 7.

Theorem 4 gives us a complete insight into the structure of a theory with abnormal commutation relations. It allows us to prove the final theorem.

THEOREM 5 (ARAKI). *The new fields, defined by*

$$\psi_k' = \prod_t (i)^{(a_t, e_k)(b_t, e_k)} \psi_k \prod_t \theta_t^{(b_t, e_k)} \tag{44}$$

are again real and satisfy normal commutation relations:

$$\psi_k' \psi_l' = (-1)^{f_k f_l} \psi_l' \psi_k'. \tag{45}$$

PROOF. 1. Reality of ψ_k':

$$\begin{aligned} \psi_k'^* &= \prod_t (-i)^{(a_t, e_k)(b_t, e_k)} \prod_t \theta_t^{(b_t, e_k)} \psi_k \prod_t \theta_t^{(b_t, e_k)} \prod_t \theta_t^{(b_t, e_k)} \\ &= \prod_t (-i)^{(a_t, e_k)(b_t, e_k)} (-1)^{(b_t, e_k)(a_t, e_k)} \psi_k \prod_t \theta_t^{(b_t, e_k)} = \psi_k'. \end{aligned} \tag{46}$$

2. The commutation relations: For the verification of (45) the first factor in (44) (power of i) is clearly immaterial. We therefore introduce

$$\psi_k'' = \psi_k \prod_t \theta_t^{(b_t, e_k)} \tag{47}$$

and calculate

$$\psi_k''\psi_l'' = \psi_k\psi_l \prod_t (-1)^{(b_t,e_k)(a_t,e_l)} \prod_t \theta_t^{(b_t,e_k+e_l)} \tag{48}$$

and

$$\psi_l''\psi_k'' = \psi_k\psi_l(-1)^{\eta_{kl}}(-1)^{f_k f_l} \prod_t (-1)^{(b_t,e_l)(a_t,e_l)} \prod_t \theta_t^{(b_t,e_k+e_l)} \tag{49}$$

thus

$$\begin{aligned} \psi_k''\psi_l'' &= \psi_l''\psi_k''(-1)^{f_k f_l}(-1)^{\eta_{kl}} \prod_t (-1)^{[(a_t,e_l)(b_t,e_k)+(b_t,e_l)(a_t,e_k)]} \\ &= (-1)^{f_k f_l}\psi_l''\psi_k'' \end{aligned} \tag{50}$$

because, according to the definition of a canonical basis:

$$\sum_t [(a_t, e_k)(b_t, e_l) + (a_t, e_l)(b_t, e_k)] = (e_k, e_l) = \eta_{lk}. \tag{51}$$

Remarks. 1. Transformations of the type (44) were first discovered by O. Klein [Kl 1]. Here they are called Klein transformations.

2. The importance of the vector space $\mathfrak{B}$ was first realized by G. Lüders [Lü 4]. Lüders has solved the problem of subsection C in conventional Lagrangian field theory.

D. An example of abnormal commutation relations.

Theorems 4 and 5 can be used for the construction of theories with abnormal commutation relations. The simplest example is given here.

We start with a normal theory of two real scalar fields A and B. We assume that all Wightman functions with an odd number of fields B vanish. The theory then possesses the symmetry θ which satisfies

$$\theta B \theta = -B \quad \text{and} \quad \theta A \theta = A. \tag{52}$$

Now we introduce the new fields

$$A' = A\theta \quad \text{and} \quad B' = B. \tag{53}$$

The commutation relations between A' and B' are then abnormal:

$$A'B' = A\theta B = -AB\theta = -BA\theta = -B'A'. \tag{54}$$

CHAPTER VI

The Haag-Ruelle Theory of Asymptotic Fields and Particles

1. **Introductory remarks.** As we have stressed several times, the axioms of Wightman do not introduce the notion of a particle. The particle notion is, however, of crucial importance if any connection of the theory with the realities of physics is to be achieved. The principal observable of elementary particle physics is the scattering matrix (S-matrix) [Hei 5]. It describes the result of scattering experiments by relating the state of the particles before the collision to the state of the particles after the collision. Since we want to stress in this book mostly the formal and mathematical aspects of the theory we do not here go any further into discussion of the S-matrix and its connection with experiments. We refer the reader to the excellent article by Brenig and Haag [Br 1] for further discussions of the physical background. For us it suffices that the S-matrix depends essentially on the possibility of defining asymptotic incoming and outgoing states, which themselves can be described by free particles and their corresponding free fields.

It is highly gratifying that, under natural conditions, a Wightman field theory allows the precise definition of such asymptotic fields. This was proved by D. Ruelle [Ru 4] in an admirable analysis on which this chapter is based. Ruelle proved that assumptions of Haag [Ha 2, 3, 4] which were introduced for the purpose of defining asymptotic free particles can in fact be rigorously derived.

2. **The special assumptions on the field theory.** In his theory, Ruelle [Ru 4] has to make some natural additional assumptions which go beyond the axioms of Wightman. This is not astonishing. It is easily seen that in a theory which allows a complete particle interpretation the spectrum of the energy momentum vector must have special properties.

We shall not present the general theory in this chapter. The special case to which we shall restrict ourselves, however, shows most of the interesting aspects of the general case. We shall try to indicate in what way our assumptions differ from Ruelle's. It is characterized by a set of increasingly restrictive assumptions given below.

The *first assumption* is our usual one, that we are dealing with one real scalar field $A(x)$ alone. This assumption is special. Ruelle treats the general case of at most countably many irreducible tensor and spinor fields.

Our *second assumption* refers to the spectrum of the energy momentum operator P. *This is supposed to be identical with the corresponding spectrum of a free field of mass m.* It has therefore the following components: $\{p \mid p = 0\}$, the vacuum; $\{p \mid p_0 > 0, (p, p) = m^2\}$, the one-particle hyperboloid; and the continuum $\bar{V}_+^{2m}$.

The *third assumption* refers to the Hilbert space $\mathfrak{H}_1$, corresponding to the one-particle hyperboloid. $\mathfrak{H}_1$ is Lorentz invariant. The representation $U(a, \Lambda)$ of the inhomogeneous Lorentz group reduces in $\mathfrak{H}_1$ to a representation $U_1(a, \Lambda)$. *This representation is supposed to be irreducible and to have spin* 0. It clearly belongs to mass m.

In the general case treated by Ruelle one has to assume the existence of discrete representations in the direct integral decomposition of $\mathfrak{H}$. It is reasonable to assume that, unless additional symmetries enforce a degeneracy, the corresponding representations of the inhomogeneous Lorentz group are irreducible. The spins of the representations, however, are arbitrary. In our case, of course, only integer values could occur.

The *last assumption* is connected to the spin assignment in the third assumption. It requires essentially that the field A should have nonvanishing matrix elements between Ω and $\mathfrak{H}_1$. In addition a certain normalization of the field A is assumed. Let P_1 be the projection on $\mathfrak{H}_1$ then we require

(1) $$(\Omega, A(x)P_1A(y)\Omega) = i\Delta_+(m^2; x - y).$$

Another formulation of this assumption is more suitable for our later work. Let h be a testing function such that $h(\lambda) = 1$ in a neighborhood of $\lambda = m^2$, $h(\lambda) = 0$ for $|\lambda - m^2| > m^2/2$, $0 \leqq u(\lambda) \leqq 1$. The field B defined by its Fourier transform

(2) $$\tilde{B}(p) \equiv \tilde{A}(p)h((p, p))$$

satisfies all axioms except locality and completeness. $B(\varphi)\Omega \in \mathfrak{H}_1$. (1) then states

(3) $$(\Omega, B(x)B(y)\Omega) = i\Delta_+(m^2; x - y).$$

The special nature of the fourth assumption is evident. From completeness follows only the existence of a polynomial in the field operator A having transitions between Ω and $\mathfrak{H}_1$. This polynomial replaces the field B in the general case. *If the one-particle hyperboloid is submerged in the continuum*, the existence of a polynomial in the fields has to be assumed of which the only transitions from Ω lead to the corresponding one-particle states. The existence of such a polynomial may be assured by selection rules.

3. **The results.** The proofs of the following results are rather long, so we shall just state the theorems in this section and give the proofs afterwards. Comments will be in part contained in the last section of this chapter.

The field $B(x)$ introduced by §2, (2) has the special property of being smooth in the variable $x^0 = t$: if φ is a test function from $\mathscr{S}$ of the three-vector $\mathfrak{x} = (x^1, x^2, x^3)$ then

$$B_\varphi(t) = \int B(t, \mathfrak{x})\varphi(\mathfrak{x})\, d^3x \tag{1}$$

is defined on D. $B_\varphi(t)\Phi$ with $\Phi \in D$ is C_∞ in t and continuous in φ.

We call a solution of the Klein-Gordon equation

$$(\Box + m^2)f = 0 \tag{2}$$

smooth, if it is of the form

$$f(x) = (2\pi)^{-3/2}\int \delta(p^2 - m^2)[e^{-i(p,x)}\theta(p)g_+(\mathfrak{p}) + e^{i(p,x)}\theta(p)g_-(\mathfrak{p})]\, d^4p \tag{3}$$

and $g_\pm \in \mathscr{D}$ as functions of the three-vector $\mathfrak{p} = (p^1, p^2, p^3)$. An arbitrary derivative of a smooth solution is again a smooth solution.

The quantities

$$B_f(t) = i\int_{x^0=t} \bar{f}\,\overleftrightarrow{\partial}_0 B\, d^3x \tag{4}$$

thus exist as operators on D.

Our principal aim is to prove the following theorems.

THEOREM 1. *The states*

$$\Phi(t) = B_{f_0}(t)B_{f_1}(t)\cdots B_{f_n}(t)\Omega \tag{5}$$

satisfy $\|\Phi(t_1) - \Phi(t_2)\| \to 0$ *as* $t_1, t_2 \to -\infty$ (*or* $t_1, t_2 \to +\infty$). *They have therefore a strong limit as* $t \to -\infty$ (*or* $t \to +\infty$). *This limit does not* (*within the restricted Lorentz group*) *depend on the special coordinate system in which* (4) *is defined.*

DEFINITIONS. A state $\lim_{t\to-\infty} \Phi(t)$ is called an incoming state Φ^{in}, a state $\lim_{t\to+\infty} \Phi(t)$ an outgoing state Φ^{out}. $\mathfrak{H}_{\substack{\text{in}\\\text{out}}}$ is the Hilbert space spanned by the $\binom{\text{incoming}}{\text{outgoing}}$ states. The symbol "ex" stands for either "in" or "out".

We write

$$\Phi^{\substack{\text{in}\\\text{out}}}(\underline{f}) = \Phi^{\substack{\text{in}\\\text{out}}}(f_0, f_1, \cdots, f_n) \tag{6}$$
$$= \lim_{t\to\mp\infty} B_{f_0}(t)B_{f_1}(t)\cdots B_{f_n}(t)\Omega.$$

THEOREM 2. *The operators defined by linear extension from*

$$A_f^{\text{ex}}\Phi^{\text{ex}}(f_0, f_1, \cdots, f_n) = \Phi^{\text{ex}}(f, f_0, f_1, \cdots, f_n) \tag{7}$$

define two free real scalar fields $A^{\text{ex}}(x)$ satisfying (*Chapter* II, §§3, 4)

$$A_f^{\text{ex}} = i\int_{x^0=t} \bar{f}\,\overleftrightarrow{\partial}_0 A^{\text{ex}}\, d^3x, \tag{8}$$

$$U(a, \Lambda)A^{\text{ex}}(x)U^{-1}(a, \Lambda) = A^{\text{ex}}(\Lambda x + a) \tag{9}$$

and

$$\theta A^{\text{in}}(x)\theta = A^{\text{out}}(-x), \tag{10}$$

where θ is the "TCP" operator $\theta A(x)\theta = A(-x)$ (*Chapter* V, §2).

At this point one has to introduce a new postulate, in order to assure a complete particle interpretation of the theory.

Axiom of completeness of the incoming states [Ru 4]. It is expressed by

$$\mathfrak{H}_{\text{in}} = \mathfrak{H}. \tag{11}$$

(10) implies that $\theta\mathfrak{H}_{\text{in}} = \mathfrak{H}_{\text{out}}$. Since $\theta\mathfrak{H} = \mathfrak{H}$, (11) has the consequence

$$\mathfrak{H} = \mathfrak{H}_{\text{in}} = \mathfrak{H}_{\text{out}}. \tag{12}$$

$A^{\text{in}}(x)$ and $A^{\text{out}}(x)$ now act on the same Hilbert space and are unitarily equivalent. Thus there exists a unitary operator S uniquely defined by

$$A^{\text{out}}(x) = S^{-1}A^{\text{in}}(x)S \tag{13}$$

and

$$S\Omega = \Omega. \tag{14}$$

S is the scattering matrix. It gives the transition probabilities between incoming and outgoing states. (9), (10) together with the irreducibility of the free field and (14) lead to

$$U(a, \Lambda)SU^{-1}(a, \Lambda) = S \tag{15}$$

and

$$\theta S\theta = S^*. \tag{16}$$

4. Smooth solutions of the Klein-Gordon equation. The proofs of Theorems 1 and 2 depend on two auxiliary theorems of which one is concerned with smooth solutions of the Klein-Gordon equation and the other with certain properties (space-like asymptotic conditions) of the TVEV of the field A.

We start by discussing the smooth positive frequency solutions

$$f(x) = (2\pi)^{-3/2} \int e^{-i(p,x)} \theta(p) \delta(p^2 - m^2) g(\mathfrak{p})\, d^4p, \tag{1}$$

where the function g of the three-vector variable $\mathfrak{p} = (p^1, p^2, p^3)$ is a test function from $\mathscr{D}$ (Chapter I, §1A). All our results will be true, however, for arbitrary smooth solutions, i.e., an arbitrary sum of a smooth positive frequency solution and the conjugate complex of another positive frequency solution.

$f(x)$ appears as the Fourier transform of a function with compact support. It is therefore an entire analytic function and thus C_∞. We now split x into its time part $x^0 = t$ and space part $\mathfrak{x}$. Then

$$f(t, \mathfrak{x}) = (2\pi)^{-3/2} \int d^3p e^{-i\mathfrak{p}\cdot\mathfrak{x}} \left[\frac{1}{2\omega(\mathfrak{p})} e^{-i\omega t} g(\mathfrak{p})\right] \tag{2}$$

with $\omega(\mathfrak{p}) = \sqrt{(m^2 + \mathfrak{p}^2)}$. The function in square brackets is an element of $\mathscr{D}$. Thus $f(t, \mathfrak{x})$ is, for fixed t, an element from $\mathscr{S}$ in the variable $\mathfrak{x}$. The same is clearly true for any time derivative of f. Thus we can write

First property. $f(t, \mathfrak{x})$ is for fixed t a test function from $\mathscr{S}$.

Next we are interested in the behavior of $f(t, \mathfrak{x})$ as a function of t. It is best to begin by finding how $f(x)$ behaves radially, that is how $f(\lambda u)$ behaves as a function of λ for u a fixed four-vector. To make uniform estimates in all directions, we restrict u to the euclidean unit sphere $\|u\|^2 = (u^0)^2 + (u^1)^2 + (u^2)^2 + (u^3)^2 = 1$. Then

$$f(\lambda u) = \int e^{-i\lambda s} \varphi_u(s)\, ds \tag{3}$$

with

$$\varphi_u(s) = (2\pi)^{-3/2} \int \delta(p^2 - m^2) \theta(p) \delta((p, u) - s) g(\mathfrak{p})\, d^4p. \tag{4}$$

$\varphi_u(s)$ is the integral of $(2\pi)^{-3/2}\delta(p^2 - m^2)\theta(p)g(\mathfrak{p})$ over the plane $(p, u) = s$. The behavior of φ_u, as a function of s, critically depends on whether one of the planes $(p, u) = s$, $-\infty < s < +\infty$ is a tangent plane to $(p, p) = m^2$ in a point of the support of $\delta(p^2 - m^2)\theta(p)g(\mathfrak{p})$. This can clearly only happen for $(u, u) > 0$. $(p, u) = s$ is tangent to $p^2 = m^2$ if $s = s_0 = m(u, u)^{1/2}$ and the point of contact is

$$\hat{p} = m(u, u)^{-1/2} u.$$

Let $\mathfrak{C}$ be the (closed) set $\{u \mid \pm\hat{p} \in \operatorname{supp} \delta(p^2 - m^2)\theta(p)g(\mathrm{p})\}$ and $\mathfrak{C}_\pm = \mathfrak{C} \cap V_\pm$. Let $\mathfrak{C}'$ be the complement of $\mathfrak{C}$. Finally we introduce $\mathfrak{D} \subset V_+ \cup V_-$ (and $\mathfrak{D}_\pm = \mathfrak{D} \cap V_\pm$) as an open set on $\|u\| = 1$, which contains $\mathfrak{C}$. Its complement $\mathfrak{D}'$ is closed. $\overline{\mathfrak{D}}$ is the closure of $\mathfrak{D}$. We may choose for $\mathfrak{D}$ a set $\{u \mid \|\vec{u}\| < \rho|u^0|\}$ for some suitable value $0 < \rho < 1$.

In any case φ_u has compact support as a function of s. As one easily sees it is C_∞ and thus a test function from $\mathscr{S}$, as long as $u \in \mathfrak{C}'$. $f(\lambda u)$ therefore decreases strongly for $|\lambda| \to \infty$ and one finds the

Second property. For $u \in \mathfrak{C}'$, and any integer M

$$|\lambda^M f(\lambda u)| < C_M(u), \tag{5}$$

where $C_M(u)$ is uniformly bounded in any compact subset of $\mathfrak{C}'$. In $\mathfrak{D}'$ we thus have

$$|\lambda^M f(\lambda u)| < C_M. \tag{6}$$

The situation is quite different for $u \in \mathfrak{C}_+$ (or $u \in \mathfrak{C}_-$). Then $\varphi_u(s)$ is of the following form:

$$\varphi_u(s) = \theta(s - s_0)\sqrt{(s^2 - s_0^2)}\chi_u(\sqrt{(s^2 - s_0^2)}) \tag{7}$$

(or $\varphi_u(s) = \theta(s_0 - s)\sqrt{(s^2 - s_0^2)}\chi_u(\sqrt{(s^2 - s_0^2)})$).

$\chi_u(\tau)$ has compact support and is C_∞ for $0 \leqq \tau < \infty$. However, it does not vanish in general for $\tau = 0$. Instead of (7) we may also write (treating the case $u \in \mathfrak{C}_+$ only):

$$\varphi_u(s) = \theta(s - s_0)\sqrt{(s - s_0)}\hat{\chi}_u(\sqrt{(s - s_0)}), \tag{7'}$$

where $\hat{\chi}_u(\tau)$ is again C_∞ on the closed half line.

Then we obtain

$$f(\lambda u) = \int_0^\infty e^{-i\lambda(v+s_0)}\sqrt{v}\hat{\chi}_u(\sqrt{v})\,dv \tag{8}$$

or

$$f(\lambda u) = 2\int_0^\infty e^{-i\lambda(\tau^2+s_0)}\hat{\chi}_u(\tau)\tau^2\,d\tau. \tag{9}$$

If we split $\hat{\chi}_u(\tau) = \hat{\chi}_u(0)e^{-\tau^2} + (\hat{\chi}_u(\tau) - \hat{\chi}_u(0)e^{-\tau^2})$, then the contribution of the first (leading) term can be explicitly calculated, the contribution from the second can be estimated, and one verifies that

$$|\lambda|^{3/2}\,|f(\lambda u)| < C(u), \tag{10}$$

where $C(u)$ is uniformly bounded on $\mathfrak{C}$. Of course exactly the same procedure can be applied to $\overline{\mathfrak{D}}_+$ or $\overline{\mathfrak{D}}_-$ or even to all vectors u.

Third property. For $u \in \overline{\mathfrak{D}}$ we have

$$|\lambda|^{3/2}|f(\lambda u)| < C. \tag{11}$$

If C is suitably chosen, this statement is even true for all vectors u.

We are now prepared for the

FIRST AUXILIARY THEOREM [Ru 4]. *A smooth solution $f(t, \mathfrak{x})$ of the Klein-Gordon equation has the following properties*:

It is for fixed t a testing function from $\mathscr{S}$ in the variable $\mathfrak{x}$;

There is a constant Γ, depending on f, such that

$$|t|^{3/2} \max_{|\mathfrak{x}|} |f(t, \mathfrak{x})| < \Gamma; \tag{12}$$

$$\int |f(t, \mathfrak{x})|\, d^3x < \Gamma(1 + |t|^{3/2}); \tag{13}$$

$$|t|^{1/2} \max \|\mathfrak{x}\|\, |f(t, \mathfrak{x})| < \Gamma. \tag{14}$$

PROOF. (12) and (14) follow from (11) which states

$$(\sqrt{(t^2 + \mathfrak{x}^2)})^{3/2}\, |f(t, \mathfrak{x})| < C. \tag{15}$$

(13) follows from (6) and (11). For some $0 < \rho < 1$ and $|\mathfrak{x}| > \rho|t|$, (6) implies

$$|f(t, \mathfrak{x})| < \frac{C_4}{(\sqrt{(t^2 + \|\mathfrak{x}\|^2)})^4}. \tag{16}$$

(16) together with (15) leads to the estimate

$$\int |f(t, \mathfrak{x})|\, d^3x < 4\pi\left[\int_0^{\rho|t|} \frac{Cr^2}{(\sqrt{(t^2 + r^2)})^{3/2}}\, dr + \int_{r > \rho|t|} \frac{C_4 r^2}{(t^2 + r^2)^2}\, dr\right]. \tag{17}$$

The first term in the square bracket is proportional to $|t|^{3/2}$, the second one is proportional to $|t|^{-1}$. Since the left-hand side of (17) is bounded for any value of t, a majorization of the type (13) exists.

Since any derivative of a smooth solution is smooth, the theorem also applies to any time derivative of $f(t, \mathfrak{x})$ although of course in general the value of Γ will be different.

One last remark: the first auxiliary theorem is also valid if the functions $g_\pm$ in §3, (3), or the function g in §4, (1), are only restricted to being elements of $\mathscr{S}$, but we shall not need to use this fact.

5. **Space-like asymptotic property of TVEV's.** The truncated vacuum expectation values were introduced in Chapter III, §5, C. We use the same notation as there

$$\mathfrak{W}^T(x_0, \cdots, x_n) = (\Omega, A(x_0) \cdots A(x_n)\Omega)^T. \tag{1}$$

The $(n + 1)$-tuple of points $(x_0, x_1, \cdots, x_n)$ will, however, be abbreviated by $\underline{x}$. $\mathfrak{a}$ denotes in the following a four-vector of the form $(0, a^1, a^2, a^3)$ *and* the corresponding three-vector (a^1, a^2, a^3). $\underline{\mathfrak{a}}$ stands for an $(n + 1)$-tuple of four or three vectors: $(\mathfrak{a}_0, \mathfrak{a}_1, \cdots, \mathfrak{a}_n)$. The quantity under discussion will be

$$\Phi(\underline{\mathfrak{a}}) = \int \mathfrak{W}^T(\underline{x} + \underline{\mathfrak{a}})\varphi(\underline{x})\, d\underline{x}, \qquad \varphi \in \mathscr{S}(R^{4(n+1)}), \tag{2}$$

where $d\underline{x}$ denotes $d^{4(n+1)}x$. From the translational invariance of $\mathfrak{W}^T(\underline{x})$, $\Phi(\underline{\mathfrak{a}})$ is a function of the variables $\vec{\alpha}_k = \mathfrak{a}_k - \mathfrak{a}_0$ only. We write $\underline{\vec{\alpha}}$ for $(\vec{\alpha}_1, \cdots, \vec{\alpha}_n)$.

Ruelle, by an extremely ingenious application of the axiom of locality and the spectral condition, was able to prove the following

SECOND AUXILIARY THEOREM [Ru 4; Ar 8]. Φ *defined by* (2) *is as a function of* $\underline{\vec{\alpha}}$ *a testing function from* $\mathscr{S}$.

REMARKS. 1. Φ is clearly C_∞.

2. Any derivative of Φ is again of the form (2). Thus we only have to prove that any Φ is fast decreasing as a function of $\underline{\vec{\alpha}}$.

3. If D^m is an arbitrary derivative monomial in $\underline{x}$, then

$$\begin{aligned} \Phi_1(\mathfrak{a}) &= \int (D^m\mathfrak{W}^T)(\underline{x} + \underline{\mathfrak{a}})\varphi(\underline{x})\, d\underline{x} \\ &= (-1)^{|m|} \int \mathfrak{W}^T(\underline{x} + \underline{\mathfrak{a}})(D^m\varphi)(\underline{x})\, d\underline{x} \end{aligned} \tag{3}$$

is again of the form (2). If therefore we replace some fields $A(x_k)$ in (1) by derivatives, the statement of the second auxiliary theorem stays true.

The proof of the second auxiliary theorem is long and complicated. We try to reproduce it here, cut up in smaller, sometimes even minute, parts. We start with a few elementary geometric definitions and observations.

DEFINITION 1. (Chapter I, §1A, (1) and Chapter I, §2, (4)). If $\xi = (\xi^0, \xi^1, \xi^2, \xi^3)$ is a four-vector, then

$$\|\xi\|^2 = (\xi^0)^2 + (\xi^1)^2 + (\xi^2)^2 + (\xi^3)^2.$$

Similarly $\|\underline{x}\|^2 = \sum_i \|x_i\|^2$.

DEFINITION 2. The diameter $d(\underline{\mathfrak{a}})$ is defined by

$$d(\underline{\mathfrak{a}}) = \max_{i,k} \|\mathfrak{a}_i - \mathfrak{a}_k\|. \tag{4}$$

DEFINITION 3. If X is the subset $(i_0, \cdots, i_k)$ of the indices $(0, 1, \cdots, n)$, all the indices taken in natural order, then $X' = (i'_0, \cdots, i'_{k'})$ is the complement of X, the indices again taken in natural order. We define

$$\delta(X) = \delta(X') = \min_{i \in X, i' \in X'} \| \mathfrak{a}_i - \mathfrak{a}_{i'} \|. \tag{5}$$

LEMMA 1. *To any configuration* $\underline{\mathfrak{a}}$ *there exists a partition* X, X' *such that*

$$n\delta(X) \geqq d(\underline{\mathfrak{a}}). \tag{6}$$

PROOF. Let $d(\underline{\mathfrak{a}}) = \|\mathfrak{a}_k - \mathfrak{a}_l\|$. We interpret $(\mathfrak{a}_0, \mathfrak{a}_1, \cdots, \mathfrak{a}_n)$ as points in a three-dimensional euclidean space. The planes through $\mathfrak{a}_k$ and $\mathfrak{a}_l$ orthogonal to the vector $\mathfrak{a}_k - \mathfrak{a}_l$ are supporting planes of the convex set generated by the points $\{\mathfrak{a}_i\}$. The planes orthogonal to $\mathfrak{a}_k - \mathfrak{a}_l$ and passing through the points $\mathfrak{a}_i$ thus cut the segment $(\mathfrak{a}_k, \mathfrak{a}_l)$ and decompose it in at most n intervals of total length d. At least one of the intervals must have a length which is not shorter than d/n. The corresponding planes through the end points of such an interval define a partition X, X' satisfying (6).

LEMMA 2. *Let* X, X' *be the partition of Lemma* 1.

If $\|\underline{x}\| < d/2n$, *then* $(x_i + \mathfrak{a}_i) - (x_{i'} + \mathfrak{a}_{i'})$ *is a space-like vector for any* $i \in X, i' \in X'$.

PROOF. Since $\|\underline{x}\| < d/2n$ we certainly have

$$\|x_i\|^2 + \|x_{i'}\|^2 < \frac{d^2}{4n^2} \leqq \frac{1}{4} \min_{k \in X, k' \in X'} \|\mathfrak{a}_k - \mathfrak{a}_{k'}\|^2 \leqq \frac{1}{4} \|\mathfrak{a}_i - \mathfrak{a}_{i'}\|^2.$$

But $\|x_i - x_{i'}\|^2 + \|x_i + x_{i'}\|^2 = 2\|x_i\|^2 + 2\|x_{i'}\|^2$. This gives with the above inequality

$$\|x_i - x_{i'}\|^2 < \tfrac{1}{2}\|\mathfrak{a}_i - \mathfrak{a}_{i'}\|^2.$$

We put $\xi = x_i - x_{i'}$ and $\vec{\alpha} = \mathfrak{a}_i - \mathfrak{a}_{i'}$, then the last inequality says that

$$(\xi^0)^2 + \|\vec{\xi}\|^2 < \tfrac{1}{2}\|\vec{\alpha}\|^2$$

and thus implies

$$2|\xi^0| \, \|\vec{\xi}\| < \tfrac{1}{2}\|\vec{\alpha}\|^2$$

which has the consequence that $(|\xi^0| + \|\vec{\xi}\|)^2 < \|\vec{\alpha}\|^2$ or

$$|\xi^0| < \|\vec{\alpha}\| - \|\vec{\xi}\|.$$

But $\|\vec{\alpha} + \vec{\xi}\| \geqq \|\vec{\alpha}\| - \|\vec{\xi}\|$ and thus $|\xi^0| < \|\vec{\alpha} + \vec{\xi}\|$ or, finally: $\xi + \vec{\alpha}$ is space-like. But $\xi + \vec{\alpha} = (x_i + \mathfrak{a}_i) - (x_{i'} + \mathfrak{a}_{i'})$.

DEFINITION 4. Let π be the permutation

$$\pi(0, 1, \cdots, n) = (k_0, \cdots, k_n).$$

Then we define

$$\mathfrak{W}^T_\pi(\underline{x}) = \mathfrak{W}^T(x_{k_0}, \cdots, x_{k_n}) \tag{7}$$

and

$$\Phi_\pi(\underline{\mathfrak{a}}) = \int \mathfrak{W}^T_\pi(\underline{x} + \underline{\mathfrak{a}})\varphi(\underline{x})\, d\underline{x}. \tag{8}$$

This definition already begins the analytic part of proving the second auxiliary theorem. The first step in this part makes use of locality.

LEMMA 3. *If the configuration* $\underline{\mathfrak{a}}$ *separates in such a way that, for a fixed partition* X, X', *we always have* $n\delta(X) \geqq d(\mathfrak{a})$. *Then, for any natural number* M, *we find, uniformly in* $\underline{\mathfrak{a}}$

$$d^M(\Phi - \Phi_\pi) \to 0 \tag{9}$$

as $d \to \infty$. *Here* $\pi(0, 1, \cdots, n) = (i_0, \cdots, i_k, i'_0, \cdots, i'_{k'})$.

PROOF.

$$\Phi - \Phi_\pi = \int [\mathfrak{W}^T(\underline{x} + \underline{\mathfrak{a}}) - \mathfrak{W}^T_\pi(\underline{x} + \underline{\mathfrak{a}})]\varphi(\underline{x})\, d\underline{x}. \tag{10}$$

Since both Φ and Φ_π are translation invariant, we can without restriction choose $\mathfrak{a}_0 = 0$. Then

$$\|\underline{\mathfrak{a}}\| \leqq d\sqrt{n}. \tag{11}$$

From locality, those points in $\underline{x}$-space for which $(x_i + \mathfrak{a}_i) - (x_{i'} + \mathfrak{a}_{i'})$ is space-like for any $i \in X$, $i' \in X'$ do not contribute to the integral (10). According to Lemma 2 this is the case if $\|\underline{x}\| < d/2n$.

Now $\mathfrak{W}^T - \mathfrak{W}^T_\pi$ is a tempered distribution and as such the derivative of a continuous function with at most polynomial increase [Sw 2*] (Chapter I, § 1C, Example 2)

$$\mathfrak{W}^T - \mathfrak{W}^T_\pi = D^m\, \mathfrak{V} \tag{12}$$

with

$$|\mathfrak{V}(\underline{x})| < C(1 + \|\underline{x}\|^2)^{\alpha/2} \tag{13}$$

for a suitable constant C and a natural number α. Substitution of (13) into (10) gives

$$\Phi - \Phi_\pi = (-1)^{|m|} \int_{\|\underline{x}\| \geqq d/2n} \mathfrak{V}(\underline{x} + \underline{\mathfrak{a}}) D^m \varphi(\underline{x})\, d\underline{x} \tag{14}$$

or, writing $(-1)^{|m|} D^m \varphi = \varphi_1$,

$$\Phi - \Phi_\pi = \int_{\|\underline{x}\| \geqq d/2n} \mathfrak{V}(\underline{x} + \underline{\mathfrak{a}}) \varphi_1(\underline{x})\, d\underline{x}. \tag{15}$$

This almost finishes the proof, because $\varphi_1(\underline{x})$ decreases faster than any polynomial. All we need are a few estimates. First

$$(16)\quad |\mathfrak{V}(\underline{x} + \underline{\mathfrak{a}})| < C(1 + \|\underline{x} + \underline{\mathfrak{a}}\|^2)^{\alpha/2} < C(1 + 2\|\underline{x}\|^2)^{\alpha/2}(1 + 2\|\underline{\mathfrak{a}}\|^2)^{\alpha/2}$$

and secondly, for any natural number M, we can find a constant C_1, such that

$$(17)\qquad |\varphi_1(\underline{x})| < C_1 \|x\|^{-(M+\alpha+4n+5)}(1 + 2\|\underline{x}\|^2)^{-\alpha/2}.$$

With these estimates it follows from (15) and (11) that

$$(18)\qquad |\Phi - \Phi_\pi| < S_n \cdot C \cdot C_1(1 + 2nd^2)^{\alpha/2} \int_{d/2n}^{\infty} \|\underline{x}\|^{-M-\alpha-2}\, d\|\underline{x}\|,$$

where S_n is the surface of the $4(n+1)$-dimensional unit sphere. (9) follows from (18).

REMARK ON LEMMA 3. Let π' be the permutation

$$\pi'(0, 1, \cdots, n) = (i'_0, \cdots, i'_{k'}, i_0, \cdots, i_k).$$

It is clear that, under the conditions of Lemma 3

$$(19)\qquad \lim_{d\to\infty} d^M(\Phi_\pi - \Phi_{\pi'}) = 0.$$

Now we use the spectral condition. We recall (Chapter III, § 5, Theorem) that, as a result of the truncation, points in the support of $\widetilde{\mathfrak{W}}^T$ satisfy $\sum_{l=s}^n p_l \in \bar{V}_+^\mu$ for $1 \leqq s \leqq n$ and $p_0 + p_1 + \cdots + p_n = 0$. The last condition of course represents translation invariance.

Correspondingly all points in the support of $\widetilde{\mathfrak{W}}_\pi^T$ satisfy

$$P' = \sum_{i'\in X'} p_{i'} \in \bar{V}_+^\mu$$

and therefore $P = \sum_{i\in X} p_i = -P' \in \bar{V}_-^\mu$. The points in the support of $\widetilde{\mathfrak{W}}_{\pi'}^T$, however, satisfy $P' \in \bar{V}_-^\mu$ and $P \in \bar{V}_+^\mu$. This leads us to

LEMMA 4. *A function $h_1 \in \mathcal{O}_M$* [Sw 2*] (*Chapter* I, §1C, *Example* 1) *exists such that*

$$(20)\qquad h_1\widetilde{\mathfrak{W}}_\pi^T = \widetilde{\mathfrak{W}}_\pi^T \quad \textit{and} \quad h_1\widetilde{\mathfrak{W}}_{\pi'}^T = 0.$$

PROOF. It suffices to choose a function h_1 of P_0 alone. Let $h_1(P_0) = 1$ for $P_0 < -\mu/2$, $h_1(P_0) = 0$ for $P_0 > 0$ and $h_1 \in \mathcal{O}_M$ then (20) is satisfied.

LEMMA 5. *Under the conditions of Lemma 3 we have for any natural number M uniformly in $\underline{\mathfrak{a}}$:*

$$(21)\qquad \lim_{d\to\infty} d^M \Phi = 0.$$

PROOF. Let $\tilde{\psi} = h_1 \tilde{\varphi}$ and

$$(22)\qquad \begin{aligned} \Psi_\pi(\underline{\mathfrak{a}}) &= \int \mathfrak{W}^T_\pi(\underline{x} + \underline{\mathfrak{a}})\psi(\underline{x})\, d\underline{x}, \\ \Psi_{\pi'}(\underline{\mathfrak{a}}) &= \int \mathfrak{W}^T_{\pi'}(\underline{x} + \underline{\mathfrak{a}})\psi(\underline{x})\, d\underline{x}. \end{aligned}$$

(20) implies $\Phi_\pi = \Psi_\pi$ and $\Psi_{\pi'} = 0$. (19) stays correct if we substitute $\Psi_{\pi,\pi'}$ for $\Phi_{\pi,\pi'}$. Thus $d^M \Psi_\pi = d^M \Phi_\pi \to 0$ as $d \to \infty$, and according to Lemma 3 $d^M \Phi \to 0$. Phrased a little bit differently, from estimates of the kind (18) we have the following

RESULT. For any natural number M and any configuration $\underline{\mathfrak{a}}$

$$(23)\qquad d^M(\underline{\mathfrak{a}})\, |\Phi(\underline{\mathfrak{a}})| < C_M(X),$$

where (X, X') is the partition of Lemma 1.

Since there are, however, only a finite number of partitions (X, X'), $C_M = \max_X C_M(X)$ exists and satisfies

$$(24)\qquad d^M(\underline{\mathfrak{a}})\, |\Phi(\underline{\mathfrak{a}})| < C_M.$$

(24) together with the second remark on the auxiliary theorem proves this theorem.

Comment on the second auxiliary theorem. In the proof of the second auxiliary theorem we used locality (proof of Lemma 3). It appears, however, that this lemma and the second auxiliary theorem hold under more general conditions. A suitably strong decrease of the commutator of two fields for space-like separation is sufficient. The Haag-Ruelle theory therefore presumably holds also in certain nonlocal theories.

6. **The proofs of Theorems 1 and 2.** § 4 of this chapter was completely independent of any field theory. § 5 depended only on the temperedness of the TVEV, their translation invariance, the support properties of their Fourier transforms and locality. Nowhere did we make use of the special assumptions of § 2. In this section we shall assume these restrictive properties.

We start with a property of $B(t, \mathfrak{x})$ which was needed in § 3.

LEMMA 6. *For $\varphi \in \mathscr{S}$ the operator*

$$(1)\qquad \int B(t, \mathfrak{x})\varphi(\mathfrak{x})\, d^3x = B_\varphi(t)$$

is defined on D, C_∞ in t and continuous in φ.

PROOF.

(2) $$B_\varphi(t) = \int \tilde{A}(p)h((p, p))\tilde{\varphi}(\mathfrak{p})e^{ip_0t}\, d^4p.$$

The function $h((p, p))\tilde{\varphi}(\mathfrak{p})e^{ip_0t}$ is a testing function from $\mathscr{S}(R^4)$ as are all its time derivatives. It converges to zero as $\tilde{\varphi} \to 0$.

Lemma 6 allows the definitions of equal-time VEV and equal-time TVEV of products of B-fields and their time derivatives:

(3) $$\begin{aligned}\mathfrak{F}(\underline{\mathfrak{x}}) &= \mathfrak{F}(\mathfrak{x}_0, \mathfrak{x}_1, \cdots, \mathfrak{x}_n) = F(\underline{\vec{\xi}}) = F(\vec{\xi}_1, \cdots, \vec{\xi}_n)\\ &\equiv (\Omega, B(t, \mathfrak{x}_0)B(t\, \mathfrak{x}_1) \cdots\ B(t, \mathfrak{x}_n)\Omega),\end{aligned}$$

where $\vec{\xi}_k = \mathfrak{x}_k - \mathfrak{x}_0$. $\mathfrak{F}^T$ and F^T are defined by the ordinary truncation procedure. Similar expressions arise if some of the fields $B(t, \mathfrak{x}_i)$ are replaced by time derivatives. Since the transformation properties of such TVEV do not matter for us, we shall again denote such expressions by $\mathfrak{F}^T$ and F^T, respectively. The proofs of the following lemmas will only be given for the expression (3). The proofs for the corresponding statements in the general case are identical.

LEMMA 7. *For any $\varphi \in \mathscr{S}$ the function*

(4) $$\Phi(\underline{\vec{\alpha}}) = \int \mathfrak{F}^T(\underline{\mathfrak{x}} + \underline{\mathfrak{a}})\varphi(\underline{\mathfrak{x}})\, d\underline{\mathfrak{x}}, \qquad \vec{\alpha}_k = \mathfrak{a}_k - \mathfrak{a}_0,$$

is an element from $\mathscr{S}$.

PROOF. It follows from the definition of B and $\mathfrak{F}^T$ that

(5) $$\Phi(\underline{\vec{\alpha}}) = \int \mathfrak{W}^T(\underline{x} + \underline{\mathfrak{a}})\psi(\underline{x})\, d\underline{x}$$

with

(6) $$\tilde{\psi}(p_0, \cdots, p_n) = \prod_{k=0}^{n} h((p_k, p_k))\tilde{\varphi}(\mathfrak{p}_0, \cdots, \mathfrak{p}_n).$$

Obviously $\tilde{\psi}(\underline{p}) \in \mathscr{S}$, thus $\psi(\underline{x}) \in \mathscr{S}$.

Application of the second auxiliary theorem leads to the statement.

Another useful way of stating Lemma 7 is obtained with the help of a theorem by L. Schwartz [Sw 2*, p. 100, Théorème IX] (Chapter I, § 1C, Example 4, Theorem).

LEMMA 8. $\mathfrak{F}^T(0, \vec{\xi}_1, \cdots, \vec{\xi}_n) = F^T(\underline{\vec{\xi}})$ *is a finite sum of derivatives of continuous functions absolutely bounded by expressions of the form* $C\prod_{k=1}^{n}(1 + \|\vec{\xi}_k\|^2)^{-2}$.

Technically speaking $F^T(\underline{\vec{\xi}}) \in \mathscr{O}'_C$ [Sw 2*] (Chapter I, § 1C, Example 4).

LEMMA 9. *Let $\{f_k \mid k = 0, 1, \cdots, n\}$ be an arbitrary set of smooth solutions of the Klein-Gordon equation.*

Let

$$B_{f_k}(t) = i \int_{x^0=t} \bar{f}_k \overleftrightarrow{\partial}_0 B \, d^3x; \tag{7}$$

then, for $n \geqq 1$,

$$|(\Omega, B_{f_0}(t) B_{f_1}(t) \cdots B_{f_n}(t)\Omega)^T| \, |t|^{3(n-1)/2} \tag{8}$$

is bounded in t. The same is true if some of the operators $B_{f_k}(t)$ are replaced by arbitrary time derivatives.

PROOF. The proof is based on Lemma 8 and on the first auxiliary theorem. The expression (8) is of the form

$$\left| \sum \int \mathfrak{F}^T(0, \mathfrak{x}_1, \cdots, \mathfrak{x}_n) f_0'(t, \mathfrak{x}_0) f_1'(t, \mathfrak{x}_1) \prod_{k=2}^{n} t^{3/2} f_k'(t, \mathfrak{x}_k) \, d\underline{\mathfrak{x}} \right|, \tag{9}$$

where $\sum$ denotes a finite sum and the prime on $f_l(t, \mathfrak{x}_l)$ means a possible time derivative. Using the decomposition of Lemma 8 we get a bound for the expression (9) in the form of a finite sum of terms of the sort

$$\begin{aligned} &C(1 + |t|^{3/2})^{-1} \int (1 + |t|^{3/2}) \, |f_0''(t, \mathfrak{x}_0)| \, d^3x \\ &\times \max_{\mathfrak{x}_1} |f_1''(t, \mathfrak{x}_1)| \prod_{k=2}^{n} |t|^{3/2} \max_{\mathfrak{x}_k} |f_k''(t, \mathfrak{x}_k)| \left[\int \frac{d^3x}{(1 + \|\mathfrak{x}\|^2)^2} \right]^n, \end{aligned} \tag{10}$$

where the double primes now mean possible space-time derivatives. All the expressions (10) are bounded, according to the first auxiliary theorem.

The following lemma is a trivial consequence of the definition of $B(t, \mathfrak{x})$ and the assumption of § 2.

LEMMA 10. *If $f(t, \mathfrak{x})$ is a smooth solution of the Klein-Gordon equation and $B_f(t)$ is defined by*

$$B_f(t) = i \int_{x^0=t} \bar{f} \overleftrightarrow{\partial}_0 B \, d^3x \tag{11}$$

then the vector $B_f(t)\Omega$ is time independent.

PROOF (CHAPTER II, §3, (11)). $B(x)\Omega$ is a vector solution of the Klein-Gordon equation. This follows from $B(\varphi)\Omega \in \mathfrak{H}_1$ and the properties of $\mathfrak{H}_1$.

LEMMA 11 (THEOREM 1, FIRST PART) [Ha 3; Ru 4]. *Let $B_{f_k}(t)$ again be defined by* (7). *The vector*

$$\Phi(t) = B_{f_0}(t) B_{f_1}(t) \cdots B_{f_n}(t)\Omega \tag{12}$$

converges strongly for $t \to -\infty$ and $t \to +\infty$.

PROOF (HAAG). We expand $\|d\Phi(t)/dt\|^2$ in products of TVEV's of the form $(\Omega, B'_{f_{k_0}}(t), \cdots, B'_{f_{k_r}}(t)\Omega)^T$, where the prime denotes a possible time derivative. There will be terms which contain exclusively TVEV's quadratic in the fields B_{f_k}. Two factors in such a term will contain time derivatives and be of the form

$$\left(\Omega, B_f \frac{d}{dt} B_{f'}\Omega\right) \quad \text{or} \quad \left(\frac{d}{dt} B_f^* \Omega, B_{f'}\Omega\right).$$

They vanish according to Lemma 11. The rest of the terms contain either two cubic factors of TVEV's or one factor of higher than third degree. From Lemma 9, these terms are bounded by $C_i\,|t|^{-3}$. Thus

$$\left\| \frac{d\Phi(t)}{dt} \right\| < \frac{1}{2} C\,|t|^{-3/2} \tag{13}$$

and we have for $t_2 < t_1 < 0$:

$$\left\| \Phi(t_2) - \Phi(t_1) \right\| \leqq \int_{t_2}^{t_1} \left\| \frac{d\Phi(t)}{dt} \right\| dt < C\{|t_2|^{-1/2} - |t_1|^{-1/2}\} \tag{14}$$

and therefore convergence of $\Phi(t)$ as $t \to -\infty$.

The same is true for $t \to +\infty$.

LEMMA 12 (THEOREM 1, SECOND PART). *The limit for $t \to -\infty$ ($t \to +\infty$) of the vector* (12) *is, within the restricted Lorentz group, independent of the Lorentz frame.*

PROOF. If we introduce for $\Lambda \in L_+^\uparrow$ the functions $f_{k,\Lambda}(x) = f_k(\Lambda^{-1}x)$, the operator $B_\Lambda(x) = B(\Lambda^{-1}x)$,

$$B_{f_k}^\Lambda(t) = i \int_{x^0=t} \bar{f}_{k,\Lambda} \overleftrightarrow{\partial}_0 B_\Lambda \, d^3x \tag{15}$$

and finally

$$\Phi_\Lambda(t) = B_{f_0}^\Lambda(t) \cdots B_{f_n}^\Lambda(t)\Omega \tag{16}$$

then we have to show that

$$\|\Phi_\Lambda(t) - \Phi(t)\| \to 0 \tag{17}$$

for $t \to \mp\infty$. (The invariance with respect to translations is trivial.)

Since all quantities involved are smooth, we can freely operate with infinitesimal Lorentz transformations. As rotational invariance is again trivial, we restrict ourselves to infinitesimal transformations $x^s\partial_0 - x^0\partial_s$, $1 \leqq s \leqq 3$. Such a transformation leads to the following change of $B_f(t)$:

$$dB_f(t) = i \int_{x^0=t} x^s \bar{f}\,(\Box + m^2) B \, d^3x. \tag{18}$$

From (18) we conclude that

$$dB_f(t)\Omega = 0 \tag{19}$$

since $B(x)\Omega$ is a solution of the Klein-Gordon equation. Next we expand $\|d\Phi(t)\|^2$ in TVEV. From (19), the product of quadratic TVEV again does not contribute. All the other terms behave for $|t| \to \infty$ at least as $|t|^{-1/2}$. Thus $\|d\Phi(t)\| \to 0$ for $|t| \to \infty$.

The reader should remember the definitions of $\mathfrak{H}_{\text{in}}$, $\mathfrak{H}_{\text{out}}$, and $\mathfrak{H}_{\text{ex}}$ in § 3 and the additional notation:

$$\Phi^{\substack{\text{in}\\ \text{out}}}(f) = \Phi^{\substack{\text{in}\\ \text{out}}}(f_0, f_1, \cdots, f_n) = \lim_{t \to \mp\infty} B_{f_0}(t) \cdots B_{f_n}(t)\Omega. \tag{20}$$

LEMMA 13 (THEOREM 2) [Ru 4]. *The scalar products* $(\Phi^{\text{ex}}(\underline{f}), \Phi^{\text{ex}}(\underline{g}))$ *agree with the corresponding scalar products of a free real scalar field. The equations*

$$A_f^{\text{ex}}\Phi^{\text{ex}}(f_0, \cdots, f_n) = \Phi^{\text{ex}}(f, f_0, \cdots, f_n) \tag{21}$$

define, by linear extension, two free real scalar fields $A^{\text{in}}(x)$ *and* $A^{\text{out}}(x)$. *These fields satisfy*

$$U(a, \Lambda)A^{\text{ex}}(x)U^{-1}(a, \Lambda) = A^{\text{ex}}(\Lambda x + a) \tag{22}$$

and

$$\theta A^{\text{in}}(x)\theta = A^{\text{out}}(-x). \tag{23}$$

PROOF. (a) The scalar product of the vectors

$$B_{f_0}(t) \cdots B_{f_n}(t)\Omega \quad \text{and} \quad B_{g_0}(t) \cdots B_{g_m}(t)\Omega$$

is expanded in TVEV. From the by now familiar estimates, it follows that all terms vanish in the limit $t \to -\infty$ $(t \to +\infty)$ except those containing exclusively quadratic TVEV. From assumption § 2, (3), the sums of these remaining terms agree exactly with the corresponding scalar product in a free scalar neutral field theory.

(b) From (a) it follows that A_f^{ex} defined by (21) allows the representation

$$A_f^{\text{ex}} = i\int_{x^0=t} f\overleftrightarrow{\partial}_0 A^{\text{ex}}\, d^3x,$$

where $A^{\text{ex}}(x)$ is a free scalar neutral field.

(c) The behavior (22) of $A^{\text{ex}}(x)$ follows from Lemma 12.

(d) The behavior of $A^{\text{in}}(x)$ under the *TCP*-transformation θ follows from $\theta A(x)\theta = A(-x)$.

7. **Discussion of the results, concluding remarks.** We have given a detailed description of the Haag-Ruelle theory of asymptotic states and particles for a special case. The procedure in the general case, though

possibly not completely clear to the reader, may be extrapolated with sufficient clarity for the purposes of the following general discussion.

We have learned that, under natural restrictions on the spectrum of P and on certain polynomials in the field operators, asymptotic free fields can be defined. These free fields necessarily satisfy normal commutation relations if the original fields do so. The corresponding particles thus satisfy the correct connection between spin and statistics. Together with the results of Chapter V, § 2, a considerable understanding of this fundamental law of nature has been achieved.

There is no indication of an intimate connection between the fields of a theory and the corresponding asymptotic particles, apart from the trivial restriction that asymptotic particles with half integer spin can only occur in a theory containing at least one spinor field.

A theory with a small number of fields and a large number of stable particles seems to be possible, but we must remember that the problem of the compatibility of the axioms with a scattering matrix $S \neq I$ is completely unsolved.

Nothing is known about the opposite problem: whether to any stable particle a corresponding Wightman field can be newly introduced in such a way, that the field has nonvanishing matrix elements between Ω and the one-particle states. In the framework of LSZ this problem has successfully been analyzed by W. Zimmermann [Zi 1].

The additional postulate of the completeness of the incoming states, introduced in § 3, seems to me to be of great significance. For its discussion we shall restrict ourselves to the special model defined by the assumptions of § 2. The postulate $\mathfrak{H}_{\text{in}} = \mathfrak{H}$ implies the zeroth axiom. This axiom thus becomes superfluous. It also implies, and even sharpens, the third axiom, except for the requirement $\Omega \in D$. Furthermore, the representation $U(a, \Lambda)$ in the second axiom is uniquely determined by the field $A^{\text{in}}(x)$. Only the conditions $U(a, \Lambda)A(x)U^{-1}(a, \Lambda) = A(\Lambda x + a)$ and $U(a, \Lambda)D \subset D$ remain of this axiom. The only axioms which stay completely unaffected are the first and the fourth ones. The fifth axiom is a consequence of $\mathfrak{H} = \mathfrak{H}_{\text{in}}$ and our fourth assumption.

Thus we see that the postulate $\mathfrak{H} = \mathfrak{H}_{\text{in}}$ undermines to a considerable extent the seemingly well-founded structure of Wightman. It also undermines the usefulness of the main tool, the Wightman distributions. At least it does not seem possible, without further restrictive assumptions (from which one should not shrink back, since it is in any case unknown whether or not the axioms describe only trivial models), to express the completeness postulate as a property of Wightman functions.

In this connection the S-matrix theory in the sense of LSZ has to be mentioned. In such a theory (restricted to the simplest case of only neutral spin 0 particles) the primary quantities are $A^{\text{in}}(x)$, $A^{\text{out}}(x)$ and the unitary transformation S which satisfies $S^{-1}A^{\text{in}}(x)S = A^{\text{out}}(x)$. The field $A(x)$ itself enters as an interpolating field between A^{in} and A^{out}. The most delicate part of the theory lies in the exact definition of in what sense $A(x)$ has the limits $A^{\text{in; out}}(x)$ for $t \to \mp\infty$. This convergence does not specify $A(x)$ uniquely, but the condition that at least one local interpolating field exists is a most interesting and essential restriction on the S-matrix. The specific LSZ asymptotic condition allows us to make use of the completeness axiom.

Recent and forcefully advertised "pure S-matrix theories" in the sense of G. F. Chew which eliminate the notion of fields completely cannot be discussed here. They form in a completely different sense, than the Wightman theory, a framework only: their structure is not mathematically defined. They can absorb almost any possibly useful idea. One can always express the hope that such an idea could be a consequence of some "fundamental assumption" of the type quoted in the Introduction (No. 18). They can best be characterized in German "als ein Medium des freien Werdens".

CHAPTER VII

Things Not Treated

We give in this last chapter a short, very uneven and superficial review of topics not well treated in this book. Despite the superficiality, for which we apologize, the reader will get some impression of the incompleteness of our selection.

1. **Models.** We had very compelling reasons for not mentioning any models except free fields. No interesting models are known. This is to some extent a disturbing fact since it leaves wide open the important existence question: Are the Wightman axioms compatible with an S-matrix different from unity? It is clear from our discussion, however, that no cheap models can exist. A nontrivial model is necessarily extremely complex at least if formulated in terms of Wightman functions. The fact that the Wightman axioms allow only "realistic" nontrivial models, if any, speaks in favor of them.

Let us now mention a few models.

A. From any free real scalar field $A_0(x)$ new fields (satisfying the Wightman axioms) can be obtained by the following (formal) procedure.

Let $\{\mathfrak{p}_m(\lambda)\}$ be a finite set of real polynomials in the variable λ, then A is defined by

$$A(x) = \sum_m (\mathfrak{p}_m(\Box) \colon A_0^m \colon)(x).$$

For exact definitions see [Wi 3]. If $\mathfrak{p}_0 = 0$ and $\mathfrak{p}_1(-m^2) = 1$, the field defines asymptotic states and satisfies the completeness postulate. The S-matrix is trivial ($S = I$). If $\mathfrak{p}_0 = 0$ and $\mathfrak{p}_1(-m^2) = 0$ then no asymptotic states (and no S-matrix) can be defined.

B. We discussed the generalized free fields extensively in Chapter II, § 6. In a heuristic way, such fields can be interpreted as superpositions of free fields [Li 1]. The following characterizations of generalized free fields are interesting.

THEOREM [Li 1]. *If the real scalar Wightman field $A(x)$ satisfies on D the commutation relations*

$$[A(x), A(y)] = i \int \Delta(m^2, x - y)\, d\rho(m^2) \tag{1}$$

with some polynomial bounded by positive measure $d\rho(m^2)$ *having support in* $0 < m^2 < \infty$, *then* $A(x)$ *is a generalized free field.*

We remark that the commutator (Chapter II, § 6, (33)) can of course be written in the form (1).

THEOREM (ROBINSON, GREENBERG [Ro 1; De 3]). *If the Fourier transform* $\tilde{A}$ *of a real scalar Wightman field vanishes in the neighborhood of a space-like vector* p_0, *then* A *is a generalized free field.*

This is a most remarkable theorem. The next theorem discusses, in a sense, the support of A for time-like vectors:

THEOREM (BORCHERS AND GREENBERG [Gr 2]). *If the Fourier transform of the two-point function* $\tilde{W}_1$ *vanishes for* $p^2 > M^2 > 0$ *then the field* A *is a generalized free field.*

For still another characterization see Licht and Toll [Li 1].

2. **Application of the *TCP*-Theorem.** An interesting application of θ-invariance was made by Borchers [Bo 1]: Let A be the real scalar Wightman field introduced in Chapter III, § 2, and $\{B_k\}$ a family of operator-valued distributions defined on D. Let $B_k(\varphi)D \subset D$ and $U(a, \Lambda)B_k(x)U^{-1}(a, \Lambda) = B_k(\Lambda x + a)$. Then the following notions can be introduced.

DEFINITION. B_k is local relative to A if

$$[A(x)B_k(y) - B_k(y)A(x)]\Phi = 0$$

for $(x - y)^2 < 0$ and all $\Phi \in D$.

B_k is weakly local relative to A if

$$(\Omega, A(r_0) \cdots A(r_{s-1})B_k(r_s)A(r_{s+1}) \cdots A(r_n)\Omega) = (\Omega, A(r_n) \cdots A(r_{s+1})B_k(r_s)A(r_{s-1}) \cdots A(r_0)\Omega)$$

for all $0 \leqq s \leqq n$, all n and all real regularity points.

Now we can formulate two theorems by Borchers.

THEOREM. *If all the fields of the family* $\{B_k\}$ *are local (weakly local) relative to* A, *then the fields* B_k *are local (weakly local) relative to each other.*

THEOREM. *Let the field* A *satisfy the requirements of Chapter* VI *including the completeness postulate. Let* B *be a real scalar field, defined on* D, *and possessing an asymptotic field* B^{in} *which satisfies*

$$A^{\text{in}}(x) = B^{\text{in}}(x).$$

If A and B are weakly local relative to each other then they belong to the same S-matrix and vice versa.

REMARK. This last theorem clearly allows almost automatic generalizations to more complicated situations with several in-fields, etc.

DEFINITION. The class of real scalar fields B_k defined on D and local relative to A is called the Borchers class of A.

The fields in § 1A belong to the Borchers class of the free field A_0. Recently Schroer [Sr 1] and Epstein [Ep 2] independently gave a complete characterization of the Borchers class of a free field. It essentially agrees with the models in § 1A.

3. **τ- and r-functions, analytic properties in p-space.** In the LSZ-formalism [LSZ 1, 2; GLZ 1] one assumes the existence of time-ordered products and retarded products of the field operator. Their vacuum expectation values are the τ- and r-distributions (about the existence see [Ste 3]). These distributions play a similar role to the Wightman distributions in a Wightman field theory. The r-distributions are, in the simplest case, Lorentz invariant distributions

$$r(x_0, x_1, \cdots, x_n) = r_1(x_0 - x_1, x_0 - x_2, \cdots, x_0 - x_n),$$

$$r_1(\xi_1, \cdots, \xi_n) = 0$$

if, for one l, $\xi_l \notin V_+$. r_1 therefore has similar properties to the Fourier transform $\tilde{W}$ of a Wightman distribution. The essential results of Chapter IV, §§ 2, 3, 4 are applicable to the Fourier transforms $\tilde{r}_1$. In momentum space, the $\tilde{r}_1$-distributions are the boundary values of analytic $\tilde{r}_1$-functions regular in extended tubes $\mathfrak{T}'_n$. The spectral conditions for P imply an extension of the domain of regularity which we shall not describe here. It is somewhat similar to the extension that follows from locality in the case of the W-functions. As before, the resulting domain for all interesting cases is not a domain of regularity. Its envelope of holomorphy is unknown except for a very special situation [Kä 2] where it coincides with the Källén-Wightman domain (Chapter IV, § 6).

The situation is, however, considerably more involved. As discovered by O. Steinmann [Ste 1] certain linear relations between four boundary values of $\tilde{r}_1$-functions have to be satisfied if Wightman functions satisfying all linear properties a1 to a4 in Chapter III, § 3 are to exist. For $n > 2$, these relations lead to an *additional* extension of the domain of holomorphy [Ste 1].

This rather complicated situation is analyzed in papers [Ste 1, 2; Ru 5, 2; Ar 4, 6].

The main interest in analytic continuation of the $\tilde{r}_1$-functions stems from the fact that they are intimately related to certain elements of the scattering matrix S [LSZ 1, 2]. The complete domain of regularity of $\tilde{r}_1$ can thus lead to statements about possible analytic continuations of elements of the S-matrix.

Results about analyticity properties for the elastic two-particle scattering amplitude have been obtained by many authors [Bog 1*; Sy 1; Le 1, 2]. There is a disturbing result about the vertex function in [Jo 3]. The most complete results were found by Lehmann [Le 1, 2] using a certain integral representation for the matrix elements of the commutator of local fields [Jo 1; Dy 2]. This integral representation and related techniques have proved to be fruitful also in other domains [Ar 8, 9; Bro 1; Gr 2; Ro 1]. Mandelstam [Ma 3], for a special case, succeeded in finding a domain of regularity in both variables (energy and momentum transfer) for an elastic two-particle scattering amplitude.

The results mentioned so far depend only on assumptions corresponding to the linear restrictions on the Wightman distributions. It is interesting to know that the nonlinear restrictions lead to an extension of the domains of regularity mentioned above [Ma 3] (continuation across a cut: see [Zi 2; Gu 1; Oe 1]).

It has been emphasized before that the forward pion-nucleon dispersion relations, derived from analyticity of the corresponding scattering amplitude, have been experimentally confirmed [Noy 1].

We shall not discuss the interesting though incomplete results on analytic properties of scattering amplitudes derived from perturbation theory in Lagrangian field theory [Ma 1, 2]. Nor can we go, due to a large extent to lack of knowledge on our side, into a remarkable and difficult program of K. Symanzik [Sy 2, 3, 4].

4. Canonical commutation relations. In the discussion of free fields we encountered the formal commutation relations

$$[a_k, a_l^*]_{\mp} = \delta_{kl}$$

for a denumerable set of commuting operators a_k and their adjoints. The only representation we used was characterized by the existence of a state Ω satisfying $a_k\Omega = 0$ for all k.

Much work [Gå 2; Wi 7; Se 1; Ar 1; Fu 1; Ge 1*; Lew 1] has been done in (a) rigorizing and generalizing the formal commutation relations mentioned above and the formulation of well-defined mathematical problems, and (b) in the analysis of these problems. The monumental thesis of Lew contains an excellent account of this work besides contributing to it.

This work was in part motivated by a theorem of Haag [Ha 1] for which we refer the reader to the literature [Hal 1; Jo 4; Fe 1]. The relation between inequivalent cyclic representations of the canonical commutation relations and the Hamiltonian of a Lagrangian field theory is analyzed in [Ar 1].

5. **Rings of operators.** For every open set $\mathfrak{B}$ in space-time R^4 a certain von Neumann algebra [Dix 1*] $\mathfrak{A}(\mathfrak{B})$ can be defined. We denote by $\mathfrak{A}'(\mathfrak{B})$ the set of bounded operators O such that for all $\Phi, \Psi \in D$ and $\varphi \in \mathscr{S}$ with support in $\mathfrak{B}$, the relation

$$(O\Psi, A(\varphi)\Phi) = (A(\varphi^*)\Psi, O^*\Phi)$$

holds. $\mathfrak{A}(\mathfrak{B})$ is defined as the commutant of $\mathfrak{A}'(\mathfrak{B})$. $\mathfrak{A}(\mathfrak{B})$ is a von Neumann algebra [Bo 2; Ar 9].

From Chapter III, § 5 we find that for $\mathfrak{B} = R$, $\mathfrak{A}'(R^4) = \{\lambda I\}$, and thus $\mathfrak{A}(R^4)$ equals the set of all bounded operators on $\mathfrak{H}$.

The algebra $\mathfrak{A}(\mathfrak{B})$ is of considerable interest, but its physical significance is still obscured by the fact that only very little is known about the self-adjoint extensions of $A(\varphi)$ for real $\varphi \in \mathscr{S}$. It is, for instance, unknown whether or not an extension of $A(\varphi)$ exists for which the spectral measure belongs to $\mathfrak{A}(\mathfrak{B})$.

The following theorem, intuitively very appealing, is due to Borchers [Bo 2].

THEOREM. *Let* $\mathfrak{B} = \{x \mid |x^0| < T, |\mathfrak{x}| < \epsilon\}$ *and*

$$\hat{\mathfrak{B}} = \{x \mid |x^0| < T, |\mathfrak{x}| < \epsilon + T - |x^0|\},$$

then

$$\mathfrak{A}(\mathfrak{B}) = \mathfrak{A}(\hat{\mathfrak{B}}).$$

COROLLARY. *If* $\mathfrak{B} = \{x \mid |\mathfrak{x}| < \epsilon\}$ *then* $\mathfrak{A}(\mathfrak{B}) = \mathfrak{A}(R^4)$.

A more general theorem and simultaneously an alternative proof of Borchers' theorem was given by Araki [Ar 9].

The real significance of rings of operators attributed to open sets in R^4 may, however, lie much deeper. Recently, R. Haag and H. Araki [Ar 10] constructed a very interesting and impressively complete theory, in which rings of operators, belonging to open space-time regions, form the primary objects. They are restricted by a set of natural axioms. It may be that if the notion of local fields has to be sacrificed, the theory of Araki and Haag will be a suitable framework for a more successful theory. For reasons mentioned above (ignorance about the selfadjoint extensions of fields), the connection between the theory of Haag and Araki and the general theory of quantized fields is not well understood. It seems to us to be an important task for the future to clear up these problems.

APPENDIX I

1. **Normal forms of Lorentz transformations.** It is the principal aim of this appendix to find a normal form for a complex Lorentz transformation. Such a normal form is motivated by the following reasoning. Let A be an isometric mapping of two complex Lorentz spaces. We want to simplify the matrix representing A by choosing suitable *real* coordinate systems in the two complex spaces. This leads to

DEFINITION 1. Two complex Lorentz transformations A and B are equivalent relative to $L_+^\uparrow$ if $A = \Lambda_1 B \Lambda_2$ and $\Lambda_1, \Lambda_2 \in L_+^\uparrow$. We then write $A \sim B$.

LEMMA 1. *If $A \sim B$, then $M = \bar{A}^{-1}A$ and $N = \bar{B}^{-1}B$ are related by a similarity transformation*

$$M = \Lambda_2^{-1} N \Lambda_2, \qquad \Lambda_2 \in L_+^\uparrow.$$

They satisfy in addition

$$M\bar{M} = N\bar{N} = I.$$

PROOF. Follows trivially from the definition.

DEFINITION 2. A complex Lorentz transformation satisfying $M\bar{M} = I$ is called purely imaginary. The real significance of the purely imaginary transformations appears only within the pseudo-unitary geometry defined by the scalar product $[\zeta, \eta] = \bar{\zeta}^T G \eta$. The adjoint of a matrix C within this geometry is defined by $C^+ = G\bar{C}^T G$. A pseudo-unitary transformation corresponds to a matrix for which $U^+ = U^{-1}$. A real pseudo-unitary transformation is simultaneously a real Lorentz transformation: $\Lambda^+ = \Lambda^{-1}$, $\bar{\Lambda} = \Lambda$. A purely imaginary Lorentz transformation, however, satisfies $M^+ = M$ and $\bar{M} = M^{-1}$. M is therefore *selfadjoint*. The connection between real unitary transformations Λ and selfadjoint transformations M is given by the following

LEMMA 2 (HEPP). *If M is selfadjoint and satisfies $\bar{M} = M^{-1}$ and if ϵ is not a proper value of M and satisfies $\epsilon^2 \neq 1$, $|\epsilon| = 1$, then*

$$\Lambda = (1 - \epsilon M)(M - \epsilon)^{-1} \tag{1.1}$$

is real unitary and satisfies $\det \Lambda = \det M$.

If Λ *is real unitary and* $\epsilon^2 \neq 1$, $|\epsilon| = 1$ *is such that* $-\epsilon$ *is not a proper value of* Λ, *then*

$$M = (1 + \epsilon\Lambda)(\Lambda + \epsilon)^{-1} \tag{1.2}$$

is selfadjoint and satisfies $\bar{M} = M^{-1}$ *and* $\det \Lambda = \det M$.

PROOF. 1. $\Lambda^+ = (1 - \epsilon^{-1}M^+)(M^+ - \epsilon^{-1})^{-1} = (\epsilon - M)(\epsilon M - 1)^{-1} = \Lambda^{-1}$ since $M^+ = M$.

2.
$$\begin{aligned}\bar{\Lambda} &= (1 - \epsilon^{-1}\bar{M})(\bar{M} - \epsilon^{-1})^{-1} = (\epsilon - M^{-1})(\epsilon M^{-1} - 1)^{-1}\\ &= (1 - \epsilon M)(M - \epsilon)^{-1} = \Lambda\end{aligned}$$
because $\bar{M} = M^{-1}$.

3.
$$\begin{aligned}\det \Lambda/\det M &= \det (M^{-1} - \epsilon)/\det (M - \epsilon)\\ &= \det G(M^T - \epsilon)G/\det (M - \epsilon) = 1\end{aligned}$$

since $M^{-1} = GM^TG$ and $G^2 = I$.

4. $M^+ = (1 + \epsilon^{-1}\Lambda^+)(\Lambda^+ + \epsilon^{-1})^{-1} = (\epsilon\Lambda + 1)(\epsilon + \Lambda)^{-1} = M$ since $\Lambda^+ = \Lambda^{-1}$.

5. $\bar{M} = (1 + \epsilon^{-1}\Lambda)(\Lambda + \epsilon^{-1})^{-1} = (\epsilon + \Lambda)(1 + \epsilon\Lambda)^{-1} = M^{-1}$ from $\bar{\Lambda} = \Lambda$.

6. $\det \Lambda = \det M$ follows as above. Q.E.D.

The classification problem for purely imaginary Lorentz transformations relative to $L_+^\uparrow$ is therefore identical with the classification problem of real Lorentz transformations relative to $L_+^\uparrow$.

2. The normal form of a restricted Lorentz transformation. Let $\Lambda \in L_+^\uparrow$ and $\chi(\lambda) = \det (\Lambda - \lambda I)$ the corresponding characteristic polynomial.

LEMMA 3. *If* $\chi(\lambda_0) = 0$ *then* $\chi(\lambda_0^{-1}) = 0$. *If* $\chi(\lambda_0) = 0$ *and* $\bar{\lambda}_0 \neq \lambda_0$, *then* $\lambda_0^{-1} = \bar{\lambda}_0$.

PROOF. 1.
$$\begin{aligned}\chi(\lambda) &= \det(\Lambda - \lambda I) = \det G(\Lambda^T - \lambda I)G\\ &= \det(\Lambda^{-1} - \lambda I) = (-\lambda)^N \det(\Lambda - \lambda^{-1}I)\end{aligned}$$

from which the first statement follows.

2. Now let $\bar{\lambda} \neq \lambda$ and $\Lambda\zeta = \lambda\zeta$, then $(\Lambda\zeta, \Lambda\zeta) = \lambda^2(\zeta, \zeta) = (\zeta, \zeta) = 0$ since $\lambda^2 \neq 1$. Furthermore, $\Lambda\bar{\zeta} = \bar{\lambda}\bar{\zeta}$ and $(\zeta, \bar{\zeta}) = \lambda\bar{\lambda}(\zeta, \bar{\zeta})$. However, $(\zeta, \bar{\zeta}) = 0$ is impossible since otherwise Re ζ and Im ζ would span a two-dimensional isotropic subspace. Since $\lambda \neq \bar{\lambda}$, ζ and $\bar{\zeta}$ are linearly independent. Thus $\lambda\bar{\lambda} = 1$. Q.E.D.

LEMMA 4. *The vector space $\mathfrak{V}$ splits into invariant orthogonal subspaces $\mathfrak{V}_0$ and $\mathfrak{V}_0^\perp$, where $\mathfrak{V}_0$ is time-like and Λ restricted to $\mathfrak{V}_0$ is a proper restricted Lorentz transformation with real eigenvalues and exclusively time-like or light-like real eigenvectors. Λ restricted to $\mathfrak{V}_0^\perp$ is a proper orthogonal transformation Λ_0.*

PROOF. Let $\lambda = e^{i\varphi}$ be a complex eigenvalue and $\zeta = \epsilon_1 + i\epsilon_2$ the corresponding eigenvector. Since $(\epsilon_1, \epsilon_1) = (\epsilon_2, \epsilon_2)$ and $(\epsilon_1, \epsilon_2) = 0$ the space $\langle \epsilon_1, \epsilon_2 \rangle$ is space-like. If $(\epsilon_1, \epsilon_1) = (\epsilon_2, \epsilon_2) = -1$, Λ restricted to $\langle \epsilon_1, \epsilon_2 \rangle$ has the canonical form

$$K(\varphi) = \begin{pmatrix} \cos \varphi & -\sin \varphi \\ \sin \varphi & \cos \varphi \end{pmatrix}.$$

$\langle \epsilon_1, \epsilon_2 \rangle^\perp$ is time-like, and since $\det K(\varphi) = 1$, Λ restricted to $\langle \epsilon_1, \epsilon_2 \rangle^\perp$ is proper and orthochronous.

By iteration we end up with a proper Lorentz transformation Λ_1 having only real eigenvalues. The *space-like* eigenvectors now belong to real eigenvalues of modulus $+1$. They span a subspace $\mathfrak{V}_1$ in which Λ_1 induces an involution. In $\mathfrak{V}_1^\perp$, Λ_1 induces an *orthochronous* Lorentz transformation with real eigenvalues and time-like or light-like eigenvectors. The eigenvalues are therefore necessarily positive. Thus the involution in $\mathfrak{V}_1$ has determinant $+1$ and is therefore a proper orthogonal transformation. Q.E.D.

We turn now to the analysis of Λ_0 and distinguish several cases.

CASE (1). Λ_0 has a time-like eigenvector. Then $\mathfrak{V}_0$ is one-dimensional and Λ_0 is the identity. We obtain the following normal forms for the complete Lorentz transformation

$$\Lambda \approx \begin{pmatrix} 1 & & & & & & \\ & K(\varphi_1) & & & & & \\ & & K(\varphi_2) & & & & \\ & & & \cdot & & & \\ & & & & \cdot & & \\ & & & & & \cdot & \\ & & & & & & K(\varphi_r) \end{pmatrix} \quad \text{for odd dimensions,}$$

$$\Lambda \approx \begin{pmatrix} L(0) & & & & & \\ & K(\varphi_1) & & & & \\ & & \cdot & & & \\ & & & \cdot & & \\ & & & & \cdot & \\ & & & & & K(\varphi_r) \end{pmatrix} \quad \text{for even dimensions,}$$

where

$$L(\chi) = \begin{pmatrix} \text{Ch}\,\chi & \text{Sh}\,\chi \\ \text{Sh}\,\chi & \text{Ch}\,\chi \end{pmatrix}.$$

CASE (2). Λ_0 has a light-like eigenvector α with an eigenvalue $\lambda = e^{\chi}$, $\chi \neq 0$. Then Λ_0 has a second eigenvalue $\lambda = e^{-x}$ which belongs to a linearly independent light-like vector β. $\mathfrak{V}_0 = \langle \alpha, \beta \rangle$ is two-dimensional and if we write

$$\alpha = \epsilon_0 + \epsilon_1 \quad \text{and} \quad \beta = \epsilon_0 - \epsilon_1; \qquad (\epsilon_0, \epsilon_0) = -(\epsilon_1, \epsilon_1) = 1, (\epsilon_0, \epsilon_1) = 0,$$

then Λ_0 becomes in this basis

$$L(\chi) = \begin{pmatrix} \text{Ch}\,\chi & \text{Sh}\,\chi \\ \text{Sh}\,\chi & \text{Ch}\,\chi \end{pmatrix}.$$

For Λ the canonical form reads

$$\Lambda \approx \begin{pmatrix} L(\chi) & & & & & \\ & K(\varphi_1) & & & & \\ & & \cdot & & & \\ & & & \cdot & & \\ & & & & \cdot & \\ & & & & K(\varphi_r) & \\ & & & & & (1) \end{pmatrix},$$

where (1) appears only for odd dimension.

CASE (3). Λ_0 has only the eigenvalue 1 and one light-like eigenvector α (if it had two it would be the identity). The metric in $\langle \alpha \rangle^{\perp}$ is singular. $\langle \alpha \rangle^{\perp}$ has the one-dimensional radical $\langle \alpha \rangle$. The factor space $\langle \alpha \rangle / \langle \alpha \rangle^{\perp}$ is euclidean and Λ_0 induces the identity on it. Therefore if $\xi \in \langle \alpha \rangle^{\perp}$ then, $\Lambda\xi = \xi + (l, \xi)\alpha$, where $l \in \langle \alpha \rangle^{\perp}$ is defined modulo $\langle \alpha \rangle$ and therefore $l \in \langle \alpha \rangle^{\perp} / \langle \alpha \rangle$. Since $l \neq 0$ we find that $\langle \alpha \rangle^{\perp} / \langle \alpha \rangle$ is at least one-dimensional. It cannot be more than one-dimensional since otherwise Λ_0 would have space-like eigenvectors. Thus $\langle \alpha \rangle^{\perp}$ is two-dimensional and $\mathfrak{V}_0$ three-dimensional.

Let $\mathfrak{V}_0 = \langle e_0, e_1, e_2 \rangle$ in an orthonormal basis such that

$$\alpha = e_0 + e_1, \qquad \langle \alpha \rangle^{\perp} = \langle \alpha, e_2 \rangle, \qquad \langle \alpha \rangle^{\perp} / \langle \alpha \rangle = \langle e_2 \rangle,$$

then Λ_0 takes the form

$$M(\tau) = \begin{pmatrix} 1 + \frac{1}{2}\tau^2 & -\frac{1}{2}\tau^2 & -\tau \\ \frac{1}{2}\tau^2 & 1 - \frac{1}{2}\tau^2 & -\tau \\ -\tau & \tau & 1 \end{pmatrix}, \qquad \tau \neq 0.$$

The normal form of Λ reads

$$\Lambda \approx \begin{pmatrix} M(\tau) & & & & & \\ & K(\varphi_1) & & & & \\ & & \cdot & & & \\ & & & \cdot & & \\ & & & & \cdot & \\ & & & & & K(\varphi_r) \\ & & & & & & [1] \end{pmatrix},$$

where the [1] appears for even dimensions.

Thus we have found all normal forms for $\Lambda \in L_+^\uparrow$. The normal forms for $\Lambda \in L_+^\downarrow$ are obtained by the following changes of signs:

CASE ($2^\downarrow$).

$$\Lambda \approx \begin{pmatrix} -L(\chi) & & & & & \\ & K(\varphi_1) & & & & \\ & & \cdot & & & \\ & & & \cdot & & \\ & & & & \cdot & \\ & & & & & K(\varphi_r) \\ & & & & & & (1) \end{pmatrix}.$$

CASE ($3^\downarrow$).

$$\Lambda \approx \begin{pmatrix} -M(\tau) & & & & & & \\ & -1 & & & & & \\ & & K(\varphi_1) & & & & \\ & & & \cdot & & & \\ & & & & \cdot & & \\ & & & & & \cdot & \\ & & & & & & K(\varphi_r) \\ & & & & & & & (1) \end{pmatrix},$$

where in both cases the (1) appears only for odd dimensions.

REMARKS. 1. $K(\varphi)$, $L(\chi)$, and $M(\tau)$ are one-parameter groups: e.g. $M(\tau_1 + \tau_2) = M(\tau_1)M(\tau_2)$.

2. These normal forms simultaneously describe the classes of $L_+^\uparrow$. A normal subgroup of $L_+^\uparrow$ is therefore characterized by the normal forms it contains. It is easy to prove, using the normal forms, that $L_+^\uparrow$ has no nontrivial normal subgroups. $L_+^\uparrow$ is therefore a simple group.

3. The three normal forms in three dimensions

$$\begin{pmatrix} 1 & \\ & K(\varphi) \end{pmatrix}, \qquad \begin{pmatrix} L(\chi) & \\ & 1 \end{pmatrix}, \qquad M(\tau)$$

have a simple significance in two-dimensional noneuclidean geometry [Kl 1*, p. 105].

3. **The normal form of a complex Lorentz transformation.** Lemma 2 now allows us to classify first all imaginary proper Lorentz transformations

$$M = \frac{1 + \epsilon\Lambda}{\Lambda + \epsilon}, \qquad |\epsilon| = 1 \text{ and } \det(\Lambda + \epsilon) \neq 0. \tag{3.1}$$

We are only interested in transformations for which $\det M = +1$. Since the transformation $(1 + \epsilon w)/(w + \epsilon)$ maps the real axis into the unit circle and the unit circle into the real axis, the normal forms for M are obtained by substituting imaginary values for χ and φ_ν in the normal forms obtained in § 2 for the Cases (1) and (2). The same is, however, also true for the parameter τ which appears in the exceptional Case (3) as variable in $M(\tau)$. This follows either directly or from the fact that $M(\tau)$ is a limiting case of transformations in three dimensions which belong to the normal forms mentioned in remark 3 above. The fact that all parameters φ, χ and τ have to be replaced by purely imaginary values justifies the name, purely imaginary Lorentz transformations, for M.

The purely imaginary Lorentz transformations in which we are interested however are, according to § 1, the transformations $M = \bar{A}^{-1}A$. These transformations have special properties: the hermitian form $(\bar{\zeta}, M\zeta)$ has the same index of inertia as $(\bar{\zeta}, \zeta)$ itself. This follows from $(\bar{\zeta}, M\zeta) = (\bar{A}\bar{\zeta}, A\zeta)$. This leaves us with the following normal forms.

CASE (1′). Odd dimensions:

$$M \approx \begin{pmatrix} 1 & & & & \\ & K(i\varphi_1) & & & \\ & & \cdot & & \\ & & & \cdot & \\ & & & & \cdot \\ & & & & & K(i\varphi_r) \end{pmatrix}.$$

Even dimensions:

$$M \approx \begin{pmatrix} L(i\chi) & & & & \\ & K(i\varphi_1) & & & \\ & & \cdot & & \\ & & & \cdot & \\ & & & & \cdot \\ & & & & & K(i\varphi_r) \end{pmatrix} \quad \text{with } \chi = 0 \text{ or } \chi = \pi.$$

CASE (2′).

$$M \approx \begin{pmatrix} L(i\chi) & & & & \\ & K(i\varphi_1) & & & \\ & & \cdot & & \\ & & & \cdot & \\ & & & & \cdot \\ & & & & & K(i\varphi_r) \end{pmatrix}_{(1)} \quad \text{with } |\chi| \leqq \pi.$$

CASE (3′).

$$M \approx \begin{pmatrix} M(i\tau) & & & & \\ & K(i\varphi_1) & & & \\ & & \cdot & & \\ & & & \cdot & \\ & & & & \cdot \\ & & & & & K(i\varphi_r) \end{pmatrix}_{[1]} \quad \text{with } \tau \neq 0 \text{ real.}$$

It is now easy to solve our initial problem. Let $A \in L_+(C)$ and $M = \bar{A}^{-1}A$, let $M_0 = \Lambda^{-1}M\Lambda$, $\Lambda \in L_+^\uparrow$ be the corresponding normal form. These are the forms exhibited above. All the constituents $L(i\chi)$, $M(i\tau)$, $K(i\varphi)$ allow a purely imaginary square root: $L(i\chi/2)$, $M(i\tau/2)$, $K(i\varphi/2)$. Thus $\sqrt{M_0} = N_0$ is purely imaginary and in $L_+(C)$, so $A_0 = \Lambda^{-1}A\Lambda$ satisfies $\bar{A}_0^{-1}A_0 = N^2$, where $\bar{N}N = I$ or

$$A_0\bar{N} = \bar{A}_0 N = \Lambda_1 \in L_+.$$

If $\Lambda_1 \in L_+^\uparrow$ then $A \sim A_0 = N\Lambda_1 \sim N$ and N is already in the normal form we want. It will look like one of the Cases (1′), (2′), (3′) above. If $\Lambda_1 \in L_+^\downarrow$ then N has to be multiplied from the right by some suitable fixed reflection $R \in L_+^\downarrow$ such that $A_0 = (NR)(R\Lambda)$ and NR is the desired normal form. Up to the choice of $\tau \neq 0$ and R, all normal forms are unique.

This procedure leads exactly to the statement made in Chapter IV, § 3.

APPENDIX II

Uniqueness of $W(\zeta)$ in $\bigcup_\pi \mathfrak{T}'_\pi$

The content of this Appendix is exclusively due to D. Ruelle (private communication).

The basis of the argument is the following

THEOREM. *Let π be a permutation of the points $z_0, z_1, \cdots, z_n$ and also the induced linear transformation on the difference variables $\zeta_k \equiv z_k - z_{k-1}$. Let $W(\zeta_1, \cdots, \zeta_n)$ be $L_+(C)$-invariant, single-valued and analytic in $\mathfrak{T}'_n$, let $W_\pi(\zeta_1, \cdots, \zeta_n)$ be $L_+(C)$-invariant, analytic and single-valued in $\pi\mathfrak{T}'_n$. Further, assume the existence of the boundary values $W_\pi(\rho_1, \cdots, \rho_n)$ as distributions.*

If

$$W(\rho_1, \cdots, \rho_n) = W_\pi(\rho_1, \cdots, \rho_n), \tag{1}$$

then W_π is a unique analytic continuation of W into the domain $\mathfrak{T}'_n \cup \pi\mathfrak{T}'_n$.

PROOF. 1. We use the simplified notation: $\zeta \equiv (\zeta_1, \cdots, \zeta_n)$,

$$\mathfrak{T}' \equiv \mathfrak{T}'_n, \qquad \mathfrak{T} \equiv \mathfrak{T}^n, \qquad \mathfrak{T}_\pi = \pi\mathfrak{T}.$$

2. We rule out the trivial cases of π being the identity or total inversion. Then ρ is a boundary point of $\mathfrak{T}_\pi$.

3. From equation (1), W_π is holomorphic in ρ, and in all the points $A\rho$, $A \in L_+(C)$ where it has the value $W_\pi(A\rho) = W_\pi(\rho)$. Therefore we have

$$W(A\rho) = W_\pi(B\rho) \quad \text{for } A, B \in L_+(C). \tag{1'}$$

4. Starting from (1) and (1′) we have to show that

$$W(\zeta) = W_\pi(\zeta) \quad \text{for } \zeta \in \mathfrak{Q} \equiv \mathfrak{T}' \cap \mathfrak{T}'_\pi.$$

Now as a consequence of $\zeta \in \mathfrak{Q}$ there exist two Lorentz transformations A and B with $\zeta \in A\mathfrak{T} \cap B\mathfrak{T}_\pi$. By a continuity argument we rule out the exceptional classes for A and B. The intersection $\mathfrak{Q}_0 \equiv A\mathfrak{T} \cap B\mathfrak{T}_\pi$ is again convex and therefore connected. It is therefore sufficient to show the identity of W and W_π in the neighborhood of *one* point in $\mathfrak{Q}_0$.

5. We first consider the case where B is the identity and A a normal form N. The interesting case $N\mathfrak{T} \cap \mathfrak{T}_\pi \neq \emptyset$ only occurs for

$$N = \begin{pmatrix} L(i\varphi) & & & & \\ & K(i\chi_1) & & & \\ & & \cdot & & \\ & & & \cdot & \\ & & & & \cdot \\ & & & & K(i\chi_r) \end{pmatrix} \quad (1)$$

with $\varphi \neq 0, \pi$. Then $\sin \varphi \neq 0$ and N applied to the point

$$\zeta_1 = \zeta_2 = \cdots = \zeta_n = (i, -\text{ctg}\,\varphi, 0 \cdots 0)$$

gives $\rho_1 = \rho_2 = \cdots = \rho_n = (0, -(\sin\varphi)^{-1}, 0 \cdots 0)$. Therefore $N\mathfrak{T}$ also contains real points of $\mathfrak{T}'$. To these boundary points ρ of $\mathfrak{T}_\pi$ equation (1) applies: W and W_π are regular in a neighborhood of ρ and coincide there and so in $N\mathfrak{T} \cap \mathfrak{T}_\pi$.

6. Finally we can reduce the general case $A\mathfrak{T} \cap B\mathfrak{T}_\pi \neq \emptyset$ to the foregoing argument: Since we have $B^{-1}A = \Lambda_1 N \Lambda_2$, $\Lambda_i \in L_+^\uparrow$, and since $B^{-1}A\mathfrak{T} = \Lambda_1 N\mathfrak{T}$ contains, just as does $N\mathfrak{T}$, a real point ρ of $\mathfrak{T}'$, $A\mathfrak{T}$ contains $B\rho$ which lies on the boundary of $B\mathfrak{T}_\pi$. Here according to (1′) W and W_π are identical in a complex neighborhood.

Application. As a direct consequence of this theorem we see that in a local theory $\mathfrak{W}(z_0, z_1, \cdots, z_n)$ can be uniquely continued into $\mathfrak{S}_n^P$, where the complete symmetry, in the arguments $(z_0, z_1, \cdots, z_n)$ enters through the real regularity points $(r_0, r_1, \cdots, r_n)$. Since for $n \geqq 2$, $\mathfrak{S}_n^P$ is not a domain of holomorphy, there nevertheless exists the possibility that the envelope of holomorphy of $\mathfrak{S}_n^P$ is no longer schlicht. Yet this complication does not arise for $n = 2$.

Generalization. Up to now we have assumed the existence of the boundary values $W_\pi(\rho)$. This condition can be weakened if the dimension is greater than two. One only postulates that W and W_π are identical in the intersection of the real points of $\mathfrak{T}'$ and $\mathfrak{T}'_\pi$. Then the equation (1) follows by analytic continuation. This results from the following properties, the proofs of which are left to the reader:

(a) The intersection $\mathfrak{T}' \cap \mathfrak{T}'_\pi$ contains real points, if the dimension of $\mathfrak{B}$ is greater than two, and therefore a real neighborhood.

(b) The set of the real points in $\mathfrak{T}'$ is connected, again if the dimension of $\mathfrak{B}$ is greater than two.

Bibliography

A. Original Publications

[Ar 1] Araki, H., J. Mathematical Phys. **1**(1960), 492.
[Ar 2] ———, Ann. Physics **11**(1960), 260.
[Ar 3] Araki, H. and N. Burgoyne, Nuovo Cimento **8**(1960), 342.
[Ar 4] Araki, H., J. Mathematical Phys. **2**(1961), 163.
[Ar 5] ———, J. Mathematical Phys. **2**(1961), 267.
[Ar 6] ———, Progr. Theoret. Phys. Suppl. **18**(1961), 83.
[Ar 7] Araki, H., R. Haag and B. Schroer, Nuovo Cimento **19**(1961), 90.
[Ar 8] Araki, H., K. Hepp and D. Ruelle, Helv. Phys. Acta **35**(1962), 164.
[Ar 9] Araki, H., Helv. Phys. Acta **36**(1963), 132.
[Ar 10] ———, *Einführung in die axiomatische Quantenfeldtheorie*. I, II, Lecture notes, ETH, Zürich, 1961/62.

[Ba 1] Bargmann, V. and E. P. Wigner, Proc. Nat. Acad. Sci. U.S.A. **34**(1946), 211.
[Ba 2] Bargmann, V., Ann. of Math. (2) **59**(1954), 1.
[BR 1] Bohr, N. and L. Rosenfeld, Mat.-Fys. Medd. Danske Vid. Selsk. **12**(1933), no. 8.
[BR 2] ———, Phys. Rev. **78**(1950), 794.
[Bo 1] Borchers, H. J., Nuovo Cimento **15**(1960), 784.
[Bo 2] ———, Nuovo Cimento **19**(1960), 787.
[Bo 3] ———, Nuovo Cimento **24**(1962), 214.
[Bn 1] Born, M., W. Heisenberg and P. Jordan, Z. Physik **35**(1926), 557.
[Bm 1] Bremermann, H., R. Oehme and J. G. Taylor, Phys. Rev. **109**(1958), 2178.
[Br 1] Brenig, W. and R. Haag, Fortschr. Physik **7**(1959), 183.
[Bro 1] Bros, J., A. Messiah and R. Stora, J. Mathematical Phys. **2**(1961), 639.
[Bu 1] Burgoyne, N., Nuovo Cimento **8**(1958), 607.

[Co 1] Cook, J. M., Trans. Amer. Math. Soc. **74**(1953), 222.
[Cor 1] Corinaldesi, E., Nuovo Cimento Suppl. **10**(1953), 83.

[Db 1] Debye, P., Ann. Physik (4) **33**(1910), 1427.
[De 1] Dell'Antonio, G. F. and P. Gulmanelli, Nuovo Cimento **12**(1959), 38.
[De 2] Dell'Antonio, G. F., Ann. Physics **16**(1961), 153.
[De 3] ———, J. Mathematical Phys. **2**(1961), 759.
[Di 1] Dirac, P. A. M., Proc. Roy. Soc. Ser. A **114**(1927), 243.
[Di 2] ———, Rapport du 7e Conseil Solvay de Physique (1934), p. 203.
[Dy 1] Dyson, F. J., Phys. Rev. **110**(1958), 579.
[Dy 2] ———, Phys. Rev. **110**(1958), 1460.

[Ep 1] Epstein, H., J. Mathematical Phys. **1**(1960), 524.
[Ep 2] ———, Nuovo Cimento **27**(1963), 886.

[Fe 1] Federbush, P. G. and K. A. Johnson, Phys. Rev. **120**(1960), 1926.
[Fi 1] Fierz, M., Helv. Phys. Acta **12**(1939), 3.
[Fo 1] Fock, V., Z. Physik **75**(1932), 622.
[Fu 1] Fukutome, H., Progr. Theoret. Phys. **23**(1960), 989.

[Gå 1] Gårding, L., Proc. Nat. Acad. Sci. U.S.A. **33**(1947), 331.
[Gå 2] Gårding, L. and A. S. Wightman, Proc. Nat. Acad. Sci. U.S.A. **40**(1954), 617, 622.
[Gå 3] Gårding, L. and J. L. Lions, Nuovo Cimento Suppl. **14**(1959), 9.
[GLZ 1] Glaser, V., H. Lehmann and W. Zimmermann, Nuovo Cimento **6**(1957), 1122.
[Gra 1] Grawert, G., G. Lüders and H. Rollnik, Fortschr. Physik **7**(1959), 291.
[Gr 1] Greenberg, O. W., Ann. Physics **16**(1961), 158.
[Gr 2] ———, J. Mathematical Phys. **3**(1962), 859.
[Gu 1] Gunson, J. and J. G. Taylor, Phys. Rev. **119**(1960), 1121.

[Ha 1] Haag, R., Mat.-Fys. Medd. Danske Vid. Selsk. **29**(1955), no. 12.
[Ha 2] ———, *Les problèmes mathématiques de la théorie quantique des champs*, Centre National de la Recherche Scientifique, Paris, 1959.
[Ha 3] ———, Phys. Rev. **112**(1958), 669.
[Ha 4] ———, Nuovo Cimento Suppl. **14**(1959), 131.
[Ha 5] Haag, R. and B. Schroer, J. Mathematical Phys. **3**(1962), 248.
[Hal 1] Hall, D. and A. S. Wightman, Mat.-Fys. Medd. Danske Vid. Selsk. **31**(1957), no. 5.
[Hei 1] Heisenberg, W. and W. Pauli, Z. Physik **56**(1929), 1.
[Hei 2] ———, Z. Physik **59**(1930). 160.
[Hei 3] Heisenberg, W., Ber. Verh. Sächs. Akad. Wiss. Leipzig Math.-Phys. Kl. **86**(1934), 317.
[Hei 4] ———, Z. Physik **90**(1934), 209.
[Hei 5] ———, Z. Physik **120**(1943), 513, 673.
[Hep 1] Hepp, K., R. Jost, D. Ruelle and O. Steinmann, Helv. Phys. Acta **34**(1961), 542.
[Hep 2] Hepp, K., Helv. Phys. Acta **36**(1963), 355.
[Hep 3] ———, Math. Ann. **152**(1963), 149.
[Hep 4] Hepp, K., Helv. Phys. Acta **37**(1964), 639.

[Jo 1] Jost, R. and H. Lehmann, Nuovo Cimento **5**(1957), 1598.
[Jo 2] Jost, R., Helv. Phys. Acta **30**(1957), 409.
[Jo 3] ———, Helv. Phys. Acta **31**(1958), 263.
[Jo 4] ———, *Lectures on field theory and the many body problem*, E. R. Caianiello, ed., Academic Press, New York, 1961.
[Jo 5] ———, *Theoretical physics in the 20th century*, M. Fierz and V. F. Weisskopf, eds., Interscience, New York, 1960.
[Jo 6] ———, Helv. Phys. Acta **33**(1960), 773.
[Jo 7] Jost, R. and K. Hepp, Helv. Phys. Acta **35**(1962), 34.
[Jo 8] Jost, R., Helv. Phys. Acta **36**(1963), 77.

[Kä 1] Källén, G., Helv. Phys. Acta **25**(1952), 417.
[Kä 2] Källén, G. and A. S. Wightman, Mat.-Fys. Skr. Danske Vid. Selsk. **1**(1958), no. 6.
[Kä 3] Källén, G. and H. Wilhelmsson, Mat.-Fys. Skr. Danske Vid. Selsk. **1**(1959), no. 9.
[Kä 4] Källén, G. and J. C. Toll, Helv. Phys. Acta **33**(1960), 753.
[Kä 5] Källén, G., *Dispersion relations and elementary particles*, C. de Witt and R. Omnès, eds., Hermann, Paris, 1960.

[Kä 6] Källén, G., Nuclear Phys. **25**(1961), 568.
[Ka 1] Kastler, D., Ann. Univ. Sarav. **4**(1955), 206.
[Ka 2] ———, Ann. Univ. Sarav. **5**(1956), 186, 204.
[Kl 1] Klein, O., J. Phys. USSR **9**(1938), 1.
[Kle 1] Kleitman, D., Nuclear Phys. **11**(1959), 459.

[LSZ 1] Lehmann, H., K. Symanzik and W. Zimmermann, Nuovo Cimento **1**(1955), 205.
[LSZ 2] ———, Nuovo Cimento **6**(1957), 319.
[Le 1] Lehmann, H., Nuovo Cimento **10**(1958), 579.
[Le 2] ———, Nuovo Cimento Suppl. **14**(1959), 153.
[Lew 1] Lew, J., Thesis, Princeton University, Princeton, N.J., 1960 (unpublished).
[Li 1] Licht, A. L. and J. C. Toll, Nuovo Cimento **21**(1961), 346.
[Lo 1] Loeffel, J. J., Helv. Phys. Acta **36**(1963), 216.
[Lü 1] Lüders, G., Mat.-Fys. Medd. Danske Vid. Selsk. **28**(1954), no. 5.
[Lü 2] ———, Ann. Physics **2**(1957), 1.
[Lü 3] Lüders, G. and B. Zumino, Phys. Rev. **110**(1958), 1450.
[Lü 4] Lüders, G., Z. Naturforsch. **13a**(1958), 254.
[Lu 1] Luzzatto, G., private communication.

[Maj 1] Majorana, E., Nuovo Cimento **14**(1937), 171.
[Ma 1] Mandelstam, S., Phys. Rev. **112**(1958), 1344.
[Ma 2] ———, Phys. Rev. **115**(1959), 1741.
[Ma 3] ———, Nuovo Cimento **15**(1960), 658.
[Mh 1] Manoharan, A. C., J. Mathematical Phys. **3**(1962), 853.
[Mö 1] Möller, N. H., Nuclear Phys. **35**(1962), 434.

[Noe 1] Noether, E., Nachr. Akad. Wiss. Göttingen Math.-Phys. Kl. (1918), 235.
[Noy 1] Noyes, H. P. and D. N. Edwards, Phys. Rev. **118**(1960), 1409.

[Oe 1] Oehme, R., Phys. Rev. **121**(1961), 1840.

[Pa 1] Pauli, W. Naturwissenschaften **21**(1933), 841.
[Pa 2] Pauli, W. and V. F. Weisskopf, Helv. Phys. Acta **7**(1934), 709.
[Pa 3] Pauli, W., Zeeman Verhandelingen, Haag, Martinus Nijhoff, 1935, p. 31.
[Pa 4] ———, Ann. Inst. Henri Poincaré **6**(1936), 109.
[Pa 5] ———, Ann. Inst. Henri Poincaré **6**(1936), 137.
[Pa 6] ———, Phys. Rev. **58**(1940), 716.
[Pa 7] ———, Rev. Modern Phys. **13**(1941), 203.
[Pa 8] ———, Progr. Theoret. Phys. **5**(1950), 526.
[Pa 9] ———, *Niels Bohr and the development of physics*, W. Pauli, ed., Pergamon London, 1955.
[Pe 1] Petermann, A., Fortschr. Physik **6**(1958), 507.
[Pl 1] Planck, M., Verh. Deutsch. Phys. Ges. **2**(1900), 237.

[Re 1] Reeh, H. and S. Schlieder, Nuovo Cimento **22**(1961), 1051.
[Re 2] ———, Nuovo Cimento **24**(1962), 32.
[Ro 1] Robinson, D. W., Helv. Phys. Acta **35**(1962), 403.
[Ru 1] Ruelle, D., Helv. Phys. Acta **32**(1959), 135.
[Ru 2] ———, Nuovo Cimento **19**(1961), 356.
[Ru 3] ———, Helv. Phys. Acta **34**(1961), 587.
[Ru 4] ———, Helv. Phys. Acta **35**(1962), 147.
[Ru 5] ———, Thèse, Université Libre, Bruxelles, 1959 (unpublished).

[Sm 1] Schmidt, W. and K. Baumann, Nuovo Cimento **4**(1956), 860.
[Sw 1] Schwartz, L., Proc. Internat. Congr. Math. 1950.

[Sw 2] Schwartz, L., Medd. Lunds Mat. Sem. (Suppl.)(1952), 196.
[Sn 1] Schneider, W., private communication.
[Sr 1] Schroer, B., private communication.
[Sch 1] Schwinger, J., Phys. Rev. **82**(1951), 914.
[Se 1] Segal, I. E., Trans. Amer. Math. Soc. **88**(1958), 12.
[Sta 1] Stapp, H. P., Phys. Rev. **125**(1962), 2139.
[Ste 1] Steinmann, O., Helv. Phys. Acta **33**(1960), 257.
[Ste 2] ———, Helv. Phys. Acta **33**(1960), 347.
[Ste 3] ———, Helv. Phys. Acta **36**(1963), 90.
[Ste 4] ———, J. Mathematical Phys. **4**(1963), 583.
[Str 1] Streater, R. F., J. Mathematical Phys. **3**(1962), 256.
[Sy 1] Symanzik, K., Phys. Rev. **105**(1957), 743.
[Sy 2] ———, J. Mathematical Phys. **1**(1960), 249.
[Sy 3] ———, Boulder Lectures, Boulder, Colo., 1960.
[Sy 4] ———, Hercegnovi Lectures, 1961.

[Ta 1] Taylor, J. G., Ann. Physics **5**(1958), 391.
[To 1] Toll, J. C., Phys. Rev. **104**(1956), 1760.

[Uh 1] Uhlmann, A., Ann. Physics. **13**(1961), 453.

[Wei 1] Weisskopf, V. F., Mat.-Fys. Medd. Danske Vid. Selsk. **14**(1936), no. 6.
[Wk 1] Wick, G. C., A. S. Wightman and E. P. Wigner, Phys. Rev. **88**(1952), 101.
[Wig 1] Wigner, E. P., Ann of Math. (2) **40**(1939), 149.
[Wi 1] Wightman, A. S., Phys. Rev. **101**(1956), 860.
[Wi 2] ———, *Les problèmes mathématiques de la théorie quantique des champs*, Centre National de la Recherche Scientifique, Paris, 1959.
[Wi 3] ———, Cours de la Faculté des Sciences de l'Université de Paris, 1957/58.
[Wi 4] ———, Nuovo Cimento Suppl. **14**(1959), 81.
[Wi 5] ———, *Dispersion relations and elementary particles*, C. de Witt and R. Omnès, eds., Hermann, Paris, 1960.
[Wi 6] ——, J. Indian Math. Soc. **24**(1960), 625.
[Wi 7] Wightman, A. S. and S. Schweber, Phys. Rev. **98**(1955), 812.
[Wi 8] Wightman, A. S. and H. Epstein, Ann. Physics **11**(1960), 201.

[Zi 1] Zimmermann, W., Nuovo Cimento **10**(1958), 567.
[Zi 2] ———, Nuovo Cimento **21**(1961), 249.

B. Textbooks

[Ac 1*] Achieser, N. I. und I. M. Glasmann, *Theorie der Operatoren in Hilbertraum*, Akademie Verlag, Berlin, 1954.
[At 1*] Artin, E., *Geometric algebra*, Interscience, New York, 1957.

[Be 1*] Behnke, H. and P. Thullen, Ergebnisse der Math. **3**, Nr. 3(1934), Springer, Berlin, 1934.
[BM 1*] Bochner, S. and T. Martin, *Several complex variables*, Princeton Univ. Press, Princeton, N.J., 1948.
[Bog 1*] Bogoliubov, N. N. and D. V. Shirkov, *Introduction to the theory of quantized fields*, Interscience, New York, 1959.

[CH 1*] Courant, R. and D. Hilbert, *Methods of mathematical physics*, Vol. 1, Interscience, New York, 1953.

[Die 1*] Dieudonné, J., *Foundations of modern analysis*, Academic Press, New York, 1960.

[Dix 1*] Dixmier, J., *Les algèbres d'opérateurs dans l'espace Hilbertien*, Gauthier-Villars, Paris, 1957.

[Fr 1*] Friedrichs, K., *Mathematical aspects of quantum theory of fields*, Interscience, New York, 1953.

[Ge 1*] Gelfand, I. M. and N. Ya. Vilenkin, *Generalized functions*, Vol. 4, Fizmatgiz, Moscow, 1961.

[He 1*] Heitler, W., *Quantum theory of radiation*, 1st ed., Oxford Univ. Press, Oxford, 1936.

[He 2*] ———, *Quantum theory of radiation*, 2nd ed., Oxford Univ. Press, Oxford, 1944.

[Hi 1*] Hilbert, D., *Gesammelte Abhandlungen*, Bd. 3, Springer, Berlin, 1935.

[Kä 1*] Källén, G., *Quantenelektrodynamik*, Handbuch der Physik, Bd. V, 1, Springer, Berlin, 1958.

[Kl 1*] Klein, F., *Nicht-euklidische Geometrie*, Springer, Berlin, 1928.

[Kö 1*] Köthe, G., *Topologische lineare Räume*, Springer, Berlin, 1960.

[La 1*] Landau, L. D. and E. M. Lifshitz, *Mechanics*, Pergamon, London, 1960.

[Ne 1*] Neumark, M. A., *Normierte Algebren*, Deutscher Verlag der Wissenschaften, Berlin, 1959.

[Pa 1*] Pauli, W., *Die allgemeinen Prinzipien der Wellenmechanik*, Handbuch der Physik, Bd. 24, Springer, Berlin, 1933.

[RN 1*] Riesz, F. and B. Sz.-Nagy, *Vorlesungen über Funktionalanalysis*, Deutscher Verlag der Wissenchaften, Berlin, 1956.

[Sw 1*] Schwartz, L., *Théorie des distributions*, Vol. I, Hermann, Paris, 1957.

[Sw 2*] ———, *Théorie des distributions*, Vol. II, Hermann, Paris, 1959.

[Um 1*] Umezawa, H., *Quantum field theory*, North-Holland, Amsterdam, 1956.

[Wae 1*] van der Waerden, B. L., *Die gruppentheoretische Methode in der Quantenmechanik*, Springer, Berlin, 1932.

[We 1*] Wentzel, G., *Einführung in die Quantentheorie der Wellenfelder*, Franz Deuticke, Wien, 1943.

[Wey 1*] Weyl, H., *Theory of groups and quantum mechanics*, Dover, New York.

[Wey 2*] ———, *The classical groups*, Princeton Univ. Press, Princeton, N.J., 1946.

[Wig 1*] Wigner, E. P., *Group theory and its application to the quantum mechanics of atomic spectra*, Academic Press, New York, 1959.